Elector Elektronics (Publishing)
www.elektor-electronics.co.uk

Britsch Library Cataloguing in Publication Data
A catalogue record for this book ia available from the British Library

ISBN: 978 0 905705 68 2

First published in the United Kingdom 2006
Second edition November 2006
Third edition May 2007
Fourth edition November 2008

© Elektor International Media B.V. / Elektor Electronics

Printed in the Netherlands by Wilco, Amersfoort
059011-1/UK

Visual Basic

for

Electronics
Engineering
Applications

Vincent Himpe

Elector Elektronics (Publishing)
www.elektor-electronics.co.uk

The publishers have used their best efforts in ensuring the correctness of the information contained in this book. They do not assume, and herby disclaim, any liability to any party for any loss or damage caused by errors or omissions in this book, whether such errors or omissions result from negligence, accident or any other cause.

Britsch Library Cataloguing in Publication Data
A catalogue record for this book ia available from the British Library

ISBN: 978 0 905705 68 2

First published in the United Kingdom 2006
Second edition November 2006
Third edition May 2007
Fourth edition November 2008

© Elektor International Media B.V. / Elektor Electronics

Printed in the Netherlands by Wilco, Amersfoort
059011-1/UK

Table of contents

About the author

Vincent Himpe was born in Belgium and bitten by the electronics microbe at age 8 when he got a 100-in-1 project box from Radio Shack. After graduating with a degree in Electronics and working as a trainee for Nokia in Finland, he signed up as a clean-room technician for a leading semiconductor manufacturer in Belgium. After developing a number of automation systems, he moved on to the R&D lab as principal lab technologist to support the ASIC R&D community. After spending a couple of years to help build a new R&D lab in North-Carolina, he moved back to Belgium and worked as an application engineer for ADSL and Bluetooth technology.

He recently returned to the United States and is currently living in San Jose – California, heart of Silicon Valley, where he is working on Hard-Disk read/write amplifiers, for a world leading semiconductor manufacturer.

Vincent holds multiple patents on electronic circuits and has written articles and papers published in a number of leading electronics magazines and journals.

His hobbies include, besides electronics and programming, Scuba Diving and underwater Photo and Video.

Introduction

Visual Basic for Electronics Applications

Congratulations, you have decided to embark on an exciting journey: learning one of the easiest to use and most flexible programming languages ever made: Visual Basic.

This is not just another book on programming or Visual Basic. While the Language and programming techniques will be explained in detail, the focus is on its application in electronics. Whether for amateur, professional or engineering applications, the goal of this book is to show you how you can write your own programs using Visual Basic to control various pieces of electronics.

The first half explains in detail the Visual Basic programming environment, the language and programming techniques. As we are programming inside Microsoft Windows, a basic understanding of this windowing and GUI system is somehow required to understand the programming techniques applied in Visual Basic. Extensive coverage of graphical manipulations, ActiveX, multiform projects, classes, object-oriented code is given. Inter-process communications (DDE and **sendkeys**) and inter-machine communications (serial, Ethernet) will be explained in detail. You will also learn to extend the already vast set of functions and objects of Visual Basic with your own, and at the same time tap into the vast library of those embedded inside Windows.

The second half applies the covered elements in detail to controlling various electronics equipment and hardware attached to or inserted into the computer. I will show you how to unleash the power of Visual Basic for application in an experimentation and engineering environment. You will learn how to control instruments over GPIB / RS232, control circuitry over printer ports, serial ports, USB ports, Audio cards and many more. Where necessary the required interface electronics will be explained in detail. I will also show you how to apply the acquired knowledge to real-world systems. Things such as controlling circuitry, emulating protocols and more will be covered. A number of examples combining all the explained material will be given. Finally, I will demonstrate a number of test setups that show the capabilities of a programming system such as Visual Basic.

Now, I know that most programmers get the chills when they hear about programming in BASIC. Some of you might remember the time of the first home computers such as the Commodore and Apple II, and visions of line numbers, **goto**'s and spaghetti code start to doom.

Well, this is no longer the case. All languages are in a continuous state of evolution and so is the Basic language. Basic has matured from a 'Beginners All Purposes Symbolic Instruction Code' to a full-blown object-oriented programming language that does not have to be shy of other languages such as C++ or C#.

With the advent of the NET framework and the upcoming NET 2.0, the engine driving all the programming languages is the same. Whether coding in C++, C#, Java or any other member of the Visual Studio family, the underlying motor is the same.

Besides, Visual Basic is far easier to learn than any of the other languages are, and has the advantages that the knowledge acquired can be used in lots of other programs, too. More and more applications include an embedded version of Visual Basic, called VBA. Any application of the Office family, such as Excel, Word and Access, all include the VBA engine. More and more external vendors also include this engine in their products. Software houses like Oracle, AutoDesk (AutoCAD), Altium (Protel, DXP, Altium Designer PCB / Schematic / Simulation) Mathsoft (MathCAD) and many other professional and engineering programs have embedded the power of Visual Basic in their products. Any windows version beyond 98 has the VbScript language, which is a subset of Visual Basic, inside.

Visual Basic is in the first place a visual programming language. In today's world of graphical user interfaces and windowing environments, this is an absolute necessity. More and more users demand a simple and easy to use interface to the software. Visual Basic enables the programmer to write just this kind of application. The programmer himself however needs not to be deprived of these things. Programming in Visual Basic is really 'visual', during both the development and runtime stage.

You can download all source code for the examples in this book from the website. You can also find the schematics and board layouts for various projects in a separate directory.

The book writing style is a bit different then normal books. Originally, this book started as a collection of notes and slides that were used in a crash-training course to bring electronics engineers up to speed on programming test software for integrated circuits in Visual Basic. Over the years, this course has been given multiple times to a wide audience. Every time the material was refined and augmented, until it came to be what you see in front of you. The training course is normally a three or four-day event that covers most of the programming related material presented in the entire book.

While preparing this book for publication I cleaned out the writing style and added additional material that surfaced since the last rewrite, but still the 'training manual' flow is maintained. The examples are kept simple for a reason. Most programming books construct huge programs during the course of the book. The problem arises when you decide to skip a certain chapter because the contents do not apply to what you need to do, and they are thus shortly of lower interest. Suddenly you end up with code examples you cannot figure out anymore. Not so in this book. The given Examples apply directly to the material presented in the chapter at hand.

During the update, I included a lot of information about the New NET platform. NET is a radical break with the old COM based development environment. NET also introduces the Common Language Runtime: a concept that allows any language belonging to the Visual Studio family to use the same objects and controls. Because of the radical changes in the underlying technology, there is a whole range of hurdles to be taken while upgrading existing COM based code to the NET architecture. Where possible the workarounds are given. In the case where no workaround is possible, the new methods are explained in detail. Since the NET architecture opens up a whole range of new capabilities such as regular expressions, built in network control, operator overloading, new graphics controls, new use interface objects and many more I have also included a dedicated chapter that deals with these new elements.

Also added is detailed information on PCI, PCI express and USB, including schematics and circuitry to make your own peripherals. I had some doubts on whether to remove the chapter in the ISA bus, but ultimately decided to leave it in as the ISA bus lives on as the PC104 form factor computers used in industrial applications. Therefore, I actually updated the ISA chapter to encompass the PC104 interface as well.

The only exception might be the last quarter of the book where real programs are presented to drive simple and complex electronic systems.

I hope you have a pleasant time reading this book and hope you will come to enjoy it as much as I had writing it.

Happy programming,

Vincent Himpe

Conventions used in this book

Normal Text	This is the typeset used for plain text.
keyword	This is a Visual Basic keyword or construction.
Italic	Denotes keystrokes. When this style is between arrows it means you have to hold it down while pressing the next letter. Example: *<ALT> F* means you have to hold the ALT down while pressing F.
Code example	Shows source code that can be run in Visual Basic.

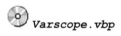 *Varscope.vbp*   Whenever you see this symbol, a sample project is available that explains the presented material in detail.

Chapter 1 : The Visual Basic Background

The use of modern graphical user interface (GUI) based operating systems puts tremendous strain on application programmers. They have to cope with all the stuff that is going on inside the operating system. This calls for a big amount of knowledge that is often hard to understand.

Visual Basic takes a different approach to programming for this kind of GUI systems. It gives you an interface builder where you no longer 'program' but rather draw the interface. Later on you simply attach your code to the interface and you are ready to run. When *Visual Basic,* or *VB* for short, was released, it quickly gained universal acceptance as a windows programming language. It became the first in a series of new programming tools classified as **R**apid **A**pplication **D**evelopment systems, or *RAD* systems for short. It also implemented a programming philosophy called **O**bject **O**riented **P**rogramming or *OOP* for short. Even though the early versions did not implement all features of OOP it was close enough to give a taste of this new programming style to Visual Basic programmers.

Since any programming language under Windows works tightly with the operating system, some things about the operating system need explanation first. Even though, as a normal programmer, in most cases you will not encounter the underlying works, there are a number of important things to know. This background information will come in handy later on, when we start building our own hardware and accessing various hardware ports of the computer.

1.1 : Windows

The windows environment is a graphical oriented environment. This GUI handles any action that occurs here, like a mouse click or a keystroke. Furthermore, the operating system itself can invoke certain actions, too (interrupts, timers, serial communication etc). Whenever anything happens, an **event** is generated. These events can trigger other parts of the operating system or an application running on the system. The target of the event will then take appropriate action and can reflect on what the user sees on the screen.

To inform the underlying code what exactly happened and ask what should be done, an event is generated. You could compare this to an interrupt under a normal operating system.

The object of the action is called a **control**. It literally allows the user to control the environment he is working in. There are a number of standard controls available inside Windows. Any of these can be use inside a Visual Basic program. Furthermore, you can create your own controls or use third party controls.

The way a control looks and behaves, is stored in its **properties.** These can be considered 'variables' that determine the look and feel of the control on the screen. Furthermore, these properties can be changed from within the code.

Every control also has a number of **methods.** These are nothing else than stored subroutines or functions. If you want to resize or move a control on the screen, you can use the MOVE method. The actual code behind this method is buried inside the control and is control specific. For example: moving a square object is not the same as moving a round object, but you can still perform this operation using the move method. The embedded code in the object (the method) will take care that the operation is performed, as it should be.

1.2 : Object Oriented Programming

Windows is also an Object Oriented environment. This means that you will have to apply Object Oriented Programming methodology. Now what exactly is this weird stuff?

Well we have already explained most of it. The first criterion is **encapsulation.** This means that all the information about an object (properties) and the processes performed by the object (methods) are combined inside the definition of the object.

A real world object could be your car. You describe your car by its properties: color, number of doors etc. Each of these is a property of the **object** 'my car'. In Windows, an object could be a button, a textbox or a menu item. Any primitive part of windows is considered an object. These objects live a life of their own. They each have their properties, methods and associated events and they know how to do their stuff. Most of all they are accessible to the VISUAL BASIC programmer.

As for the **methods**, your car does these things in response of certain actions. For instance, you generate the event 'Start Engine' when you turn the ignition key. If you execute the method 'Start Engine', the cars method handler takes over at that time and provides instruction to the underlying system to engage the starter motor, switch on the fuel flow, start ignition and then disengage the starter. You do not have to tell your engine how to start. The method 'Start' of the object 'Engine' knows how to deal with all the low-level stuff.

Now, what is happening in this method, is object related. A diesel engine has a different way of starting than a petrol driven or an electric car. However, since this is encapsulated in the object, we as a user or programmer do not need to worry about that.

The second criterion for OOPS (Object Oriented Programming Style) is **Inheritance.**

It means that one object can be based on other objects. You could define your car as something that has four wheels, an engine, a chassis etc. Now I could define a car that has a retractable rooftop. This new object would inherit all properties of the object 'car' and have one extra property. I could also include a new method to be able to control the retractable rooftop. I do not have to redefine everything for my new car model.

Actually, when I gave the explanation about starting the car, I also hinted at this: The object 'car' holds another object, called 'engine' inside. So actually, inheritance goes a bit further than simply creating derivatives. You can create new objects containing other existing objects.

The last prerequisite is **Polymorphism**. This means that many objects can have the same method, and the appropriate action is taken for the object. For example in your programs, you can print either on the screen or on the printer. Both these objects have a Print method. The difference is that the underlying code will either access the video board or send data to your printer port. Compare this to your engine. No matter whether the car has a petrol, diesel or electric engine, you simply need to call the method 'start engine'. The encapsulated code inside the object takes care of the rest.

1.3 : What can OOP do for you?

The key elements of **OOP** with which you will be working, are re-usable components known as **Controls**. You will build programs with these controls (standard, custom or even your own). These controls have properties that will determine how they look and feel and they will have methods that allow you to perform actions with them. The controls you use, will shield you from many of the tedious tasks of programming.

1.4 : Overview of the definitions:

Throughout this book, I will use several terms pertaining to object oriented programming. It is important to understand these, I order to be able to follow some of the explanations given.

Class	The **class** is the primary building block in an object-oriented environment. Instead of working directly with the data, you manipulate a dataset using the exposed methods belonging to the class. Take the example of a checkbox for instance. All you do is instantiate an 'object' from the class 'checkbox'. By 'checking' it, all you did was assign a Boolean to reflect its state (checked or unchecked). All code pertaining to the graphic manipulations is contained inside the class. As far as you are concerned, this behaves as a Boolean.
Objects	An **object** is the actual element you manipulate. Every object belongs to a **class**, where all the code and data is contained. You can pull (instantiate) as many objects from any class as you like. Each instance will behave as an independent entity. You can instantiate 100 checkbox **objects** from the checkbox class and each can have a different setting for its associated data.
Interface	The **interface** of a class is the collection of parameters (**properties**) and exposed routines (**methods**) to allow the user to manipulate objects.

Implementation	This is the nuts and bolts of the class. The actual code responds to changes of properties and methods and can raise events to make the object to what it is.
Properties	**Properties** are the variables belonging to an object that has been instantiated. For instance, a textbox will have a text property that contains the actual text that is being displayed. There will also be a **Textcolor** property that defines the color in which the text is displayed.
Methods	Each **method** is a block of code belonging to the class that the user of an instantiated object can invoke to perform certain actions. For instance, you can invoke the Paint method of a form. This forces the visual representation to be refreshed. The internal code belonging to the object handles all the aspects of this operation.
Events	An object can raise an **event** to signal the program that something happened to the object. It is up to the programmer to handle the events and decide what to do next. If the user clicks on the instantiated checkbox, the 'click' **event** will be raised. This signals the program that the user has clicked.

1.5 : Visual Basic.NET: A different breed

Visual Basic has been lifted to the next level with the introduction of the **NET** platform. While Visual Basic 5.0 and 6.0, which I will refer to as Visual Basic Classic, already had a pretty complete command set, it did not really implement all elements of object-oriented programming.

If you wanted to do certain things, you found yourself blocked, or had to revert to using complex **API** calls. The same was true for the other languages belonging to the Visual Studio environment. Each had its specifics, and what was easy or possible in one language was not necessarily in another.

The **NET** framework does away with most of these problems by introducing the Common Language Runtime. Any language belonging to the NET family can use all the functionality exposed by this library. Actually, the library is so extensive that it is possible to write entire applications without having to resort to performing complicated stuff like API calls.

Of course, there is a flipside to the medallion. Introducing the CLR turned out not to be so easy, due to certain differences in the way the programming languages work. A number of things we got to know, and took for granted in Visual Basic Classic, had to go. They have been replaced by elements and constructions that are more powerful.

An upgrade wizard was made that can analyze existing 'Classic' Code. Unfortunately, this works only to some extent and you will find you will have to rewrite chunks of code. Most of the time this concerns custom routines you had to write because some functionality was not 'shrink-wrapped' in Visual Basic Classic. There is a very good chance you might find exactly the construct ready made in the CLR.

The NET environment is a much more object oriented environment then Visual Basic Classic. Things that were simple in Visual Basic Classic turn out to take a little but more work in Visual Basic NET, but it is well worth the effort. However, sometimes finding out is not that easy.

I have even heard people make statements like 'They Broke Visual Basic' or 'It is almost as difficult as C'. Actually, none of that is true. Is it different? Yes. Will I need to adapt? Yes. Do I get more capabilities? Most definitely! Visual Basic NET is just the next logical step in the evolution of the Basic programming language.

This book shows code for both Classic and NET. Whenever NET differs substantially an example is given how it relates to Visual Basic Classic. For elements that pertain to NET only, I have tried to give detailed explanation. This should help you cross over and make the learning curve a lot less steep.

Chapter 2 : Exploring the Visual Basic Environment

You might already be eager to start writing code, but let us first have a look at the environment.

2.1 : Starting a Visual Basic project

When you start up the Visual Basic 5.0 or 6.0 programming language integrated development environment (IDE), you are presented the project dialog box.

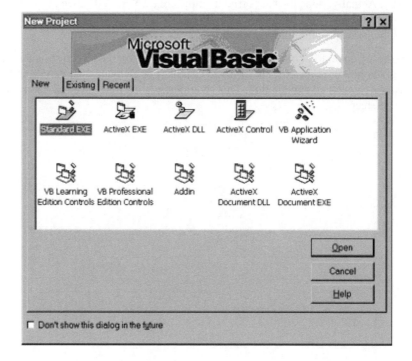

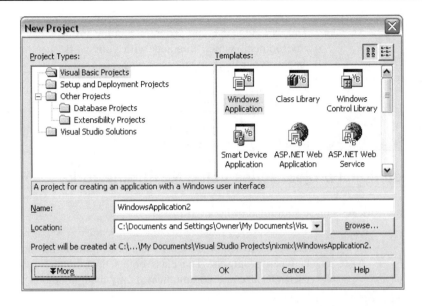

Whereas the NET and 2005 (also called Net 2.0) user interface differs substantially, the same basic project types exist. Of course, a number of additional project type exist that were not found in classic Visual Basic.

2.1.1 : Project styles

The project dialog box lets you choose between different project styles. Even though in the first chapters of this book only the standard EXE style is covered, some other styles will be discussed later on.

Standard Exe	This is the type of project you would use to create a standard Windows based program.
ActiveX exe	This remote automation program performs tasks as part of a program.
ActiveX DLL	This is a remote automation library. It cannot be run stand-alone, but can be called from other applications. An example of such thing could be a database search and retrieval tool.
ActiveX Control	You create this control from scratch, and you can define its properties and methods.
VB application wizard	This choice runs the VISUAL BASIC wizard that builds a skeleton for your program, based on the answers you give to certain questions.

ADD-In	This is a Visual Basic program running inside the Visual Basic environment, which interacts with your work. It allows you to manage your work in an easier way.
ActiveX Document DLL	This creates an application that can run over the internet (you need Microsoft Internet explorer).
ActiveX Document EXE	This creates an application that can run over the internet (you need Microsoft Internet explorer).

2.1.2 : Additional project styles using NET framework

The Net framework adds these additional project types:

Class library	This project will be compiled to a class library and can be shared between programs. The class object does not have a graphical user interface and communicates only using methods, events and properties.
Windows control library	This allows you to create a custom control that you place on a form just like any other control. This replaces the ActiveX controls of Visual Basic 5.0 and 6.0 but it cannot be used on a web form like an ActiveX control could. Use the Web control for that purpose.
Smart Device application	The NET framework allows you to create applications for handheld 'smart' devices such as PocketPC based PDA's and Windows CE based Smart phones. Select this kind of project if you target those platforms.
ASP.NET application	Active Server Pages (ASP) allows smart web pages to be created. In essence, a scripting language, it produces as output HTML and XML documents viewable in a web browser. This project type allows you to create such pages.
ASP.NET service	This is an ASP component that can be called from external applications. Much as a windows service, this runs as a background task on an ASP server.
ASP.NET Mobile Web application	This ASP application can be viewable on smart devices such as PDAs and Smart phones.
Web control Library	This replaces the ActiveX object from Visual Basic Classic (5.0 and 6.0) and can be used on web pages.
Console Application	This console type interface uses command line control instead of running inside the GUI of windows.

Windows Service	A service is a piece of code that continually runs in the background while the computer is running. It does not provide a graphical user interface but it can be accessed from other programs. It is loaded into memory at boot time and can perform operations on the background. Windows itself has many default services like a web server, disk manager and more.

After you have selected the program style, you enter the Visual Basic desktop. This will be your workspace while designing, writing, debugging and compiling your program.

2.2 : The programming environment

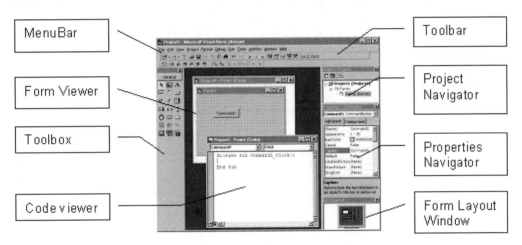

The Visual Basic programming environment is the place where you will perform all your program development. It neatly organizes a number of toolbars and information panels that assist you in creating user interfaces and writing code. It manages and allows you easy access to the entire project.

The Net environment has a similar interface with the same basic functionality but adds a lot more information panels. On-line help is no longer displayed in a separate window such as under VB5.0 or in the MSDN help viewer as under VB6.0 but in its own embedded help window. The entire help system is HTML based and you can even get on-line help.

The user interface offers a tabbed control that lets you flip through the individual views quickly. The new trend is to move away from the old style MDI interface and go to the tabbed control. You can create split views that ease code development.

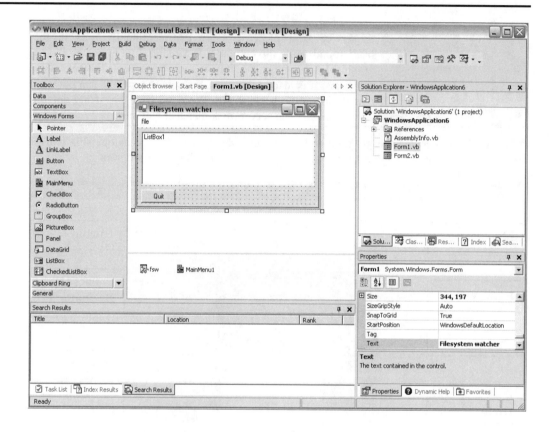

2.2.1 : Using the Menu-bar

The menu-bar provides you with access to all functions that are available in the Visual Basic environment.

As with the menus in any Windows program, you can access the functions using hotkeys. An underlined character in the item's name indicates a hotkey. Hold down the *<ALT>* key and press the underlined character.

2.2.2 : Accessing functions with the Toolbar

The toolbar offers an alternative to the menu-bar. It depicts some functions graphically. When you navigate the mouse over the toolbar, you will see information appear in a small box just below the mouse cursor. This is called ToolTip. This functionality can be embedded in your programs, too!

2.2.3 : The Object Browser (The Toolbox)

This part of the screen shows you which objects are available to use in your program. There are controls that allow you to edit text, show pictures, connect to a database or make selections. Upon creating a new project only the standard Windows objects are available. By right clicking on the panel and selecting Customize you can insert more objects.

2.2.4 : The project navigator

This part of the screen shows you the components that build your project. A program can have more than one window (or *form*), additional modules (a collection of your functions) or related files. This navigator shows you what your program is made of. To jump quickly from one part to another, you can use the navigator.

2.2.5 : The properties navigator or inspector

This allows you to set the properties of the controls on your form. You simply select the control using the mouse (click it) and then edit the properties to the settings of your choice. You can call this window by pressing *<F4>*.

2.2.6 : Form Layout Window

This window gives you an idea of how your program will look at different screen resolutions.

2.2.7 : Form Viewer

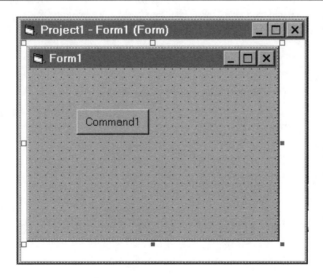

This is the real workplace for creating the user interface. It shows you the window that makes up the user interface. Here you place controls and other objects. To place a control, simply click the desired control in the toolbox and then draw the outline of the control on your form. You can also double-click an object in the object browser and then size it later.

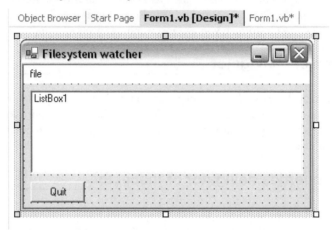

The NET form viewer is a bit different in the sense that it belongs to the tabbed control and no longer is a separate window.

2.2.8 : Code Viewer

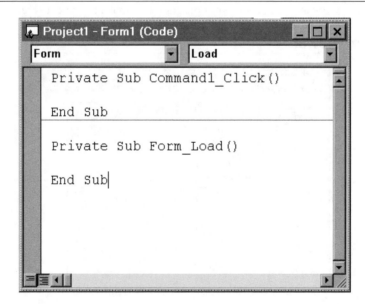

This is the second workplace in your program. Just in the way the form viewer shows the windows that make up your program, this viewer shows the underlying code.

To see the code that is attached to a control, simply double-click the control in the form viewer. The code viewer will open up in the right place to show you the real code behind it. At the top, you can find two selectors. The left list box allows you to select the object you want to modify. The right pull-down list allows you to select the event to which you want to attach code. In the example below the **Form_Load** event will be modified.

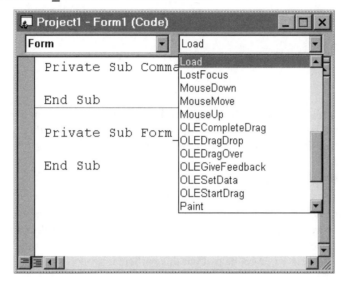

NET retains this capability but adds a very powerful feature: collapsing code. This is a technique borrowed form other programming environments that makes writing and managing code a lot easier. It allows you to partition your code and give each section a meaningful name. A tree-view like interface allows you to 'collapse' sections of code you are not presently working on.

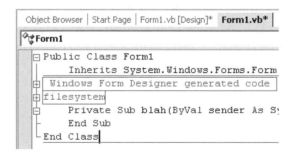

By clicking on the + sign, the tree opens. In a similar fashion: clicking on the – sign collapses a node in the tree.

```
Public Class Form1
      Inherits System.Windows.Forms.Form
   Windows Form Designer generated code
#Region "filesystem"
      Private Sub watcher(ByVal sender As System.Ob
            ListBox1.Items.Add(e.Name & " - " & e.Cha
      End Sub
      Private Sub FileSystemWatcher1_Renamed(ByVal
      End Sub

#End Region
      Private Sub blah(ByVal sender As System.Objec
      End Sub
End Class
```

You can specify your own regions by using the #Region and #End Region construct. Anything between these markers becomes a node in the code tree. You can specify a meaningful name for yourself when defining the beginning of the region.

2.2.9 : The Help system

You can call in the help system whenever you want. Simply select the item you want help about and press F1. This works in every place of the environment. You can select a control and press F1 for help on the control. On the other hand, you can select a control, then select one of the properties, and then press F1 to get help about this particular property.

Note	While in version 5.0 the help system was built into the development environment, subsequent version (6.0 / NET / 2005) require you to install the MSDN library in order to access the help.

Another possibility is to highlight a word inside the code window and press F1: if it is a basic keyword, you will get more information than you bargain for.

Furthermore, the code editor has real-time Help. While you are typing code, the system will show you your options for continuing your line of code. It will correct most of the syntax errors for you. Simple typing errors, such as missing quotes at the end of s string, will automatically be corrected for you.

Chapter 3 : The Basic Objects and Controls

At the core of a Windows programs you will always find objects and Controls. A control is a type of object that is visible on the user interface.

3.1 : The Form

The first object you have in almost every program, is a *form*. This is the workspace for your entire program. Every control in your program needs to be placed on some form. In addition, this is the real thing that gets started. You can add forms at will by using the Project- Add form menu.
Your program has one and only one main form. This form will be started first. You can select this in the project setup parameters (Project / project properties)

Just like any other object, the form has *properties* and *events*. The properties can be set, using the properties navigator or programmatically. The most important property of any object is its name. This name is the unique designator used to refer to a particular object from within your code. All references to the objects properties and/or events will be made by this name. If you name your form *'MyForm'* then you can refer to it as *MyForm*. Suppose you want to change the property *caption* from code, then you simply type:

```
MyForm.caption ="hello"
```

The click event will then be known as *MyForm_Click ()*. All other events can be reached in a similar way.

Note	When you double-click a control, the code viewer will show you the default event for the control. You have to use the event browser on top of the code viewer to select the event you want to edit.

One of the events generated by a form is *Load*. This event is generated whenever your form is loaded the first time. In case of the main form, this is at the start of a program. This procedure is the right place to load user settings etc. Its counterpart, the *Form_Unload* event, is activated when a form is unloaded from memory.

3.2 : The Controls

When your form has been given a name and you have set the properties to your taste, then you can start adding controls to it. To do this, simply click one of the controls and then draw the outline of it on your form. Just like with the *Form* you can give your control a name. Let us call it *MyButton*.

From now on, you can access the control from code as *MyButton*.

Visual Basic is a case-insensitive language. This means that **MyButton** is the same as **mybutton** or **MyBuTtOn**. It case does not matter.

To this new object **MyButton** you could attach code for the **Click** event. Whenever you click that button, this piece of code will be executed. You could for instance change its **Caption** property

```
Sub MyButton_Click ()
    MyButton.Caption = "You clicked me! "
End Sub
```

The most basic program of them all could be created as follows:

Start a new project by going to the File menu and selecting New Project. On the dialog window that pops up, select **Standard executable**. A new project will be created with one form and no code attached. Now grab a label and a button from the toolbox and put them on the form.

Change the name of the button to **ClickMe**. You can do this by highlighting the button in the design view and then mouse over to the properties tab. Where it says 'name', name you enter the name of the object.

By default, the Visual Basic environment names newly instantiated objects with a default name and sequence number. While it is perfectly OK to use these, it is easier to give them a sensible name. This will make it easier on you when coding the guts of the application. A good and consistent way to do this is by preceding the object name with the object type. For example, a button called **btn_MyButton** or a label called **lbl_MyLabel**. This makes it easier when browsing through your code to keep track of what kind of objects the code refers to.

In a similar way, you rename the label to '**Hello**'. Also change the '**caption**' property of the label to empty ('').

The properties set in the property window are the defaults with which the program will start. Of course, any code you write, can override these on the fly.

To change any of the properties, simply click it and you can then either select from a pull-down menu, or type in your text.

Also, change the caption of the button to '**Say Hi**'.

In order to attach some code to an object, simply double-click the object and the code editor will open in the correct subroutine. Let us double-click the button we have just put on the form and attach the following code:

```
Sub ClickMe_Click ()
    Hello.Caption = "Hello World"
End Sub
```

The subroutine definition is automatically put in place for you, together with all relevant arguments the particular event requires. The objects default action is highlighted. We will later on explore how to attach code to various elements of an object. For now, we will just use the default '*CLICK*' event for the button.

The code above will execute whenever the button *ClickMe* is clicked on with the mouse. All the code does is modifying the caption property of the object called '*Hello*', which is the label we put on our form earlier.

By hitting [F5], you can run your first program. If you click on the button, it will display the famous 'Hello World' in the label.

And there you have it. With physically typing one line of code (*Hello.Caption =*"*Hello World*", all the rest was generated by the Visual Basic environment) you have created you first object oriented, event driven, and GUI based windows program. You have written an *event handler* (*Clickme_click*), and controlled *properties* of *objects*.

Moreover, all of this with one line of code! How's that for Rapid Application development.

Of course, you can do the above also with other programming languages. However, it will cost you a great deal more effort to reach the same result.

3.3 : The Standard controls inside Visual Basic 5.0 and 6.0

Microsoft Windows provides a set of universal controls belonging to the operating system. These are always accessible and do not require additional libraries. Any program written in any language under the Windows GUI can use these controls. Additional controls are available but these are contained in separate control libraries that need to be loaded. We will deal with that a bit later. For now, let us have a look at the standard controls.

Icon	Name	Function
	Picture Box	This acts as a drawing canvas allowing you to display graphics and draw lines and other graphical elements on it.
A	Label	This acts as a container for text on a form. The text is not user editable. The Label is typically used to 'label' other controls, i.e. explain to a user behind the screen what the objects next to them are supposed to contain.
ab|	Textbox	Allows you to display and edit text, numbers and dates. The object can handle multiple lines.

	Frame	The frame provides a method for grouping other controls. Besides acting as a visual grouping, certain other controls such as radio-buttons placed onto a frame can interact with each other.
	Command Button	Provides a means to activate program functions.
	Check Box	Displays or allows input of Boolean choices such as Yes -No, True - False or On – Off.
	Option or Radio Button	Displays and allows a choice among multiple items. These controls can be interacting with each other as to assure that only one of them is selected. Interaction is bound to similar objects belonging to the same 'parent'.
	Combo box	Allows the user to select an entry from a list or enter a new value into a list.
	List Box	The list box allows the user to select an entry from a given list.
	Horizontal scrollbar	This allows the user to input numerical information. This is in essence a numerical value controlled by a slider bar.
	Vertical scrollbar	Allows the user to input numerical information similar to the horizontal scrollbar, except this one uses slides vertically.
	Timer	This control provides a timed event. This can be used to fire actions on a timed basis.
	Drive List box	Displays and allows a user to choose from available disk drives in the computer.
	Directory List Box	Displays and allows a user to choose from available directories on the computer.
	File List Box	Displays and allows a user to choose from the available files in the computer.
	Shape	Displays geometric shapes on the form.
	Line	Displays line on the form.
	Image	Displays graphic images.
	Data Control	Provides a link to database files.
	OLE Control	Provides a link to OLE servers (ActiveX).

The above sets are the controls made available by windows. Apart from these controls, there are many other, additional, controls that you can plug into the system. Some of these come shipped standard with Windows, some come together with the Visual Basic language. One set of interesting controls is the **CommonDialog** collection.

This control allows many common tasks to be performed by the system. Things like printer selection, color selection, file dialog boxes and other commonly used selector windows reside inside this control. You do not have to write code each time you want to give the user a file dialog box. You simply call in this control and you are done.

Another interesting set is the Windows Common controls. These include the new GUI style controls. These controls work only in the new GUI on WIN32 (Win95 and NT4.0 and up).

3.4 : Common Controls from COMCTRL in VB 5.0 and 6.0

Icon	Name	Function
	UP-Down Control	This control 'glues' itself to another control. It allows you to changes numerical values up and down.
	Animation	This allows you to specify an animation sequence, such as the flying paper when file copy is in progress.
	Slider	This allows the user to specify a numerical value. This belongs to the standard controls in NET under the name **Trackbar**.
	Listview	This looks like a file list-box.
	Treelist	This displays and indexed list like in the windows explorer.
	Imagelist	This allows you to specify a list of images. This can be used to make animations. This belongs to the standard controls in NET.
	Progressbar	This can be used as a progress indicator. This belongs to the standard controls in NET.
	Statusbar	This control belongs to the common control collection and can be used to make snazzy status bars.
	Toolbar	Creating toolbars is a snap. Looks like the menu editor.
	Tabstrip	The Tabstrip allows you to make multi-panel forms. This belongs to the standard controls in NET.

To insert these controls, and others, you can click on the control toolbox with the right mouse button. Then select Customize Toolbar. Here you will see all available controls on your system. Simple select the ones you find interesting and you are off. The library that holds the Common Controls is called Comdlg.dll. Like all components of Windows, it is subject to revisions. You have to keep this in mind when you distribute your program to an end-use. Make sure he has the same as or a later version than yours. You can do this by creating a so-called distribution-pack. (This will be explained later).

3.5 : Common Dialog Control from CMDLG in VB 5.0 and 6.0

Icon	Name	Function
	CommDlg control	Allows you to access commonly used dialogs directly without having to write code.

This control gives you a set of commonly used forms. It takes away the problem of having to reinvent the wheel all the time. Almost every program needs a file selector anyhow. This control accesses the standard windows methods of selecting a filer, printer, color etc.

NET **2005**	With the introduction of windows XP, the GUI has gotten a cleaned up interface. It is not an entire new interface; it just got a lick of paint here and there. Starting with version 6.0 of the Common controls, both the old style and new style are available. Users of Visual Basic 2005 are using the new version by default, whereas Visual Basic6.0 and NET need to explicit switch. Later on we will see how this is done. Note that this is not possible with Visual Basic 5.0, as it cannot handle the version 6.0 of the common control.

3.6 : Additional Controls only available in the NET framework

The Net framework as done away with a whole range of external libraries and embedded their functionality directly in the framework. Especially the Data controls, Common controls and common dialog control are no longer required as they are per default inside the net framework. The advantage is that there is no longer confusion possible between runtime versions of these often-used controls.

At the same time, a number of new XP style controls have been added that assist you in making dynamic forms.

Icon	Name	Description
A	LinkLabel	This is expands the capabilities of a standard label by allowing it to create a hyperlink. Just like a link found on a webpage you can set a target and the link will change color once it has been 'visited'.
	MainMenu	This object replaces the old style menu editor as found in Visual Basic 5.0 and 6.0.
	Panel	The panel acts like a GroupBox (what used to be a frame in Visual Basic 5.0 and 6.0) with the advantage that it can have scrollbars. This allows you to create scrolling surfaces to put

		other controls on. Besides that, the visual look is different from the regular GroupBox as well.
[XY]	GroupBox	This replaces the frame that was existing in Visual Basic 5.0 and 6.0.
	DataGrid	The DataGrid allows you to create a browser style representation of ADO.NET data. This is primarily used to access and interact with Ado.NET databases.
	Checkedlistbox	This behaves like a normal list box except that every item has a checkbox in front. This allows easier selection of multiple items in a list. You might want to use this style to lean closer to the XP style user interface format.
	Listview	Listview allows you to display far more complex data than is possible with a regular list box. You can have multiple columns; apply icons to every entry and so on.
	Treeview	This is the companion to the Listview control. It allows you to display a list as a hierarchical 'tree', very much like the folder browser works in windows.
	Tab control	This replaces the tab strip control as found in the COMCTRL library from Visual Basic 5.0 and 6.0.
	Datetimepicker	The Datetimepicker is used to provide simple date and time selection to the user. It offers a standardized interface. The Datetimepicker shows one month at a time. It provides a drop down MonthCalender.
	MonthCalender	The MonthCalender, while being also used by the Datetimepicker, can also be used as a standalone control. You can specify the number of months to show and a whole range of parameters to control very tightly how it interacts with the user.
+‖+	Splitter	The splitter allows you to create resizable subdivisions. Very much like the way windows explorer lets you browse your hard disk in 2 resizable panels. All you do is, set this control in between the controls that need to have the 'resizable' border and tell the surrounding controls that they have to track the splitter. The rest is handled automatically.
	Domainupdown	This is an up-down style scroll box that allows you to select one out of a list of strings.
	Numericupdown	This is an up-down style scroll box that allows you to select one out of a list of numbers.

	Trackbar	This replaces the slider control that exists in the common control library under VB5.0 and 6.0.
	Progressbar	This is now a standard part of the NET framework and no longer requires an external object library.
	Rich text box	The Richtextbox allows you to display and edit RTF based text. It has more editing capabilities than the standard textbox, and allows for multiple fonts, colors and other elements.
	Imagelist	This is now a standard part of the NET framework and no longer requires an external object library.
	Help provider	The help provider controls the context-sensitive help provided by your program, such as tool tips and pop-up help. You need to add this control in order to provide this functionality.
	Tooltip	This object handles the Tooltip display. Under the NET framework, individual controls no longer have a Tooltip property. Instead, the Tooltip object handles the tool tips for all controls belonging to the same form where the Tooltip control is placed.
	Contextmenu	The Contextmenu control allows you to create a popup menu for a specific object, when a right-click event is fired on the object. Very much like you get a pop-up menu on a textbox if you right click it, you can use this Contextmenu to provide additional options for other aspects of the user interface.
	Toolbar	This is now a standard part of the NET framework and no longer requires an external object library.
	Statusbar	This is now a standard part of the NET framework and no longer requires an external object library.
	Notify icon	This allows you to add an icon to the System tray. This is typically used for processes that have no real user interface such as services running in the background, e.g. virus scanners or volume or screen resolution controls.
	Openfile dialog	These controls used to be un the *CommonDialog* object in Visual Basic 5.0 and 6.0. They are now a default part of the NET environment.
	Savefile dialog	These controls used to be un the CommonDialog object in Visual Basic 5.0 and 6.0. They are now a default part of the NET environment.

	Folder browser dialog	This gives an interactive folder browser similar to what was found in the CommonDialog object (CommDlg) under Visual Basic 5.0 and 6.0, except that it resides inside the NET framework and does not require an external object library to be loaded.
	Font dialog	This allows the user to select a font in a similar way to what was found in the CommonDialog object (CommDlg) under Visual Basic 5.0 and 6.0, except that it resides inside the NET framework and does not require an external object library to be loaded.
	Color dialog	This allows the user to pick one of the available system colors. Similar to what was found in the CommonDialog object (CommDlg) under Visual Basic 5.0 and 6.0, except that it resides inside the NET framework and does not require an external object library to be loaded.
	Print dialog	This allows easy selection of a target printer for printing output. Similar to what was found in the CommonDialog object (CommDlg) under Visual Basic 5.0 and 6.0, except that it resides inside the NET framework and does not require an external object library to be loaded.
	Print preview dialog	Visual Basic NET adds a standardized print preview. Anything written to the printer object can be rendered visible before the actual output is sent to the printer.
	Error provider	This object acts as a problem notifier to the user. For instance, when filling out a form you can have this object pop up next to a field that contains malformed or incomplete data. When you mouse-over the object, a help text can be displayed in a balloon.
	Printdocument	This object acts as the canvas where all printing operations take place. You manipulate the methods and properties to create printer output. This output can subsequently be sent to the print preview or to an actual printer device.
	Pagesetupdialog	This shows a standardized page setup control used in setting up the printer.

NET 2005	In NET, the File list box and Drive list box are no longer available but they have been replaced by other controls that offer far more flexibility in dealing with files.

3.7 : Serial Communication Control MSCOMM

This control allows you to perform serial communications. This control is simply put on a form and given a name. Using the properties, you can select things like baud rate and settings of the serial port.

The control is invisible during runtime. You can have up to 16 of these Comm. controls on the form. The reason is the hard limit of the controls' capabilities. It cannot handle more than 16 ports at a time. This is a so-called OCX control. It is a wrapper, around a collection of commands belonging to Windows, which makes the programmer's life easier.

NET	The NET framework has no built-in support for serial port communication. This problem is fixed in the NET 2.0 framework. Fortunately, the serial port can be accessed using API calls. It is also possible to use the MSCOMM control in de NET environment but this requires you to have a valid license of Visual Basic 6.0 installed on your development machine as well.

2005	Visual Basic NET and 2005 no longer support this control but expose the serial port as a class library that can be called directly without the need for this wrapper. It requires writing a bit more code but it speeds up the program. The reason for this is that all programming languages in NET use the same underlying engine: the so-called Common Runtime Library. This functionality is standard in NET 1.1 and above.

Icon	Name	Function
📞	Comm. control	Allows you to perform serial communication.

3.8 : Menu's

The menu on a form is a control just like any other, except that it does not appear on the Control browser. The reason is that the menu is actually part of the form. You cannot have more than one menu on a form.

To create or edit a menu, you have to start the menu editor. Tools - Menu editor or click on the Menu editor icon of the toolbar.

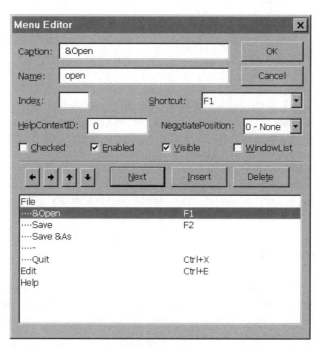

You start by typing the caption to appear on the menu bar. In the above case *&Open* is typed. The ampersand (&) means that the character following should be displayed as underlined. This will be the hotkey for the Open command. It also has the <F1> key assigned to it (Shortcut).

The next thing you have to do is give the item a name. In the shown example it is simply 'open'.

Any references to this menu item will be made by this name. So if I would like to have a checkmark appear before it, I would execute *open.checked = true*.

To make multi-level menus you simply use the arrow buttons on the menu editor. You can move items using up down or shift them to a different level using left right.

Note	To make a divider-line appear you have to specify a minus sign as the name for the entry. This kind of item cannot be activated, and loses all other properties.

When you have finished editing, simply click Close. The menu editor then compiles your menu and puts all controls in place on your form. Since every entry in your menu is actually a small control, you can change certain properties of these entries. You can, for instance, change the checked or enabled property. In case of an error (you forgot to give a menu item a name or the syntax is incorrect), you will not be able to close this window. You must first correct the errors before you can continue.

With checked a small checkmark could be made to appear before the menu item. You can use this to show the user which items he has selected. With the **enabled** property, you can disable or enable certain menu options.

NET 2005	Stating with the NET framework there is no menu 'object' anymore. Older versions of Visual Basic were not really capable of using the menu system as it is exposed by windows. A translation layer was used that exposed most but not all capabilities. That is the reason the Menu wizard has always resided on the programming environment rather than be available as a real control. In NET, the menu is a real control just as any other control like a textbox or button. The actual menuing system of a form is very powerful but a rather complex entity. NET has dealt with this problem by introducing a new way to tackle this.

3.8.1 : Net Menu editor

Editing the menu in NET differs from editing in the 'classic' Visual Basic environments. There is no longer the requirement of having a separate control panel to build the menu. Just like with any other control the entire menu is now contained in an object you simply drag onto the form.

Editing is interactive, and happens in place. A default blank menu entry is made that simply contains the text 'type' here.

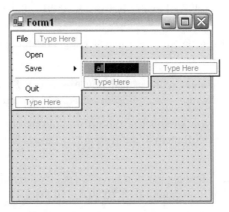

To add entries into the menu simply start click with the mouse where it says 'Type here' and start typing. Just like in Visual Basic Classic you can add divider lines by typing a single dash '-' and you can add an underscored hotkey by preceding the letter of your choice with an ampersand (&) character.

For every entry you create, you will get a 'type here' box below and to the right. In order to make a nested menu, simply type in the field right of what has to become the top level. In order to remove a menu item simply right click it and select 'delete'.

You can use the property control panel to set the names of the menu items but there is an easier way. Right-click on the menu and select **Edit Names**. The view will change and show the names of the attached event handlers next to the menu text. You can now change the names of the handlers. To return to normal editing right click again and deselect 'Edit names'.

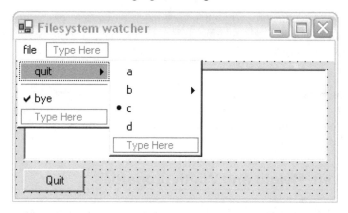

It is possible to add checkmarks to a menu item just like in Visual Basic Classic by setting the **Checked** property of a particular menu item to **true**. What is completely new in NET is that you can make Radiobutton style checkboxes. Set the **RadioCheck** property of the menu items to true. Menu items existing on the same menu level will automatically work together if their **RadioCheck** is set to **true**. A menu entry that has its **checked** or **RadioCheck** property set to **true** cannot have submenus.

| Note | There is a bug in the menu editor of NET 2003. The editor will actually allow you to create submenus of menu entries that have their **RadioCheck** property set to true and have set their checked property to false. Should you change the checked property from within code, then a runtime error will be the result. |

3.9 : Properties in detail

Every control has 'properties' that accurately define how it looks and feels. It would lead us too far to explain all of them. The detailed help system inside Visual Basic is far more useful to explore them. However, some basic properties need to be known. These properties exist and about 90 percent of all available controls.

3.9.1 : Name property

This is the single most important property a control can have. It does define the symbolic name through which you will manipulate this particular object. You should set this property as soon as possible and before you start writing any code for the object. Each instantiated object (an object that was placed on a form) gets a default name. As soon as you start writing code, the

Visual Basic environment will generate the correct subroutine definition for you to attach code to. Once these are generated, it is not so easy to change the name of an object. While it can be done, it will require you to edit the subroutine definition manually.

Note	If you change this property when code has been written for a control, you will have to update all your code relating to it manually! So as soon as you place an object, change this property to a, for you, meaningful name.

NET 2005	The problem that existed in Visual Basic Classic has been solved. You can now safely change the names of objects. The code editor will automatically rewrite the code to reflect the changes. Part of this capability comes from the new way code is attached to events.

3.9.2 : Top, Left, Height and Width properties

These properties define the location of the control in relation to its parent. The parent is the 'container' the object is placed on. Only forms and Panels can act as parents for other objects. When you move the control in the form editor, you will see that they are changed. You can also adjust them manually to create neatly aligned controls, or you can change them from within your program at runtime to make objects move on the screen.

3.9.3 : Backcolor, ForeColor and Textcolor properties

With these properties, you can modify how the control looks on the screen. You can set specific colors using the color selector or you can use the DOS based colors. Under DOS, you had 16 colors available. You can still use these numbers to specify a color. To convert these numbers to the Windows coloring scheme, there is a function called *QBcolor*.

When designing forms it is a very bad idea to freeze colors. The windows design guide describes that you should use the system colors instead of forcing your own. This can be done very easily. If you look at the color selector on the properties bar, you will see that there are two panels. One is holding a color chart. The other is listing variables that refer to the system colors. You should use these variables instead. Whenever your program starts, it will retrieve the system colors and use these for your program. A set of predefined variables is available that allows you to specify colors with textual names.

NET 2005	The *QBcolor* command has been removed in NET and 2005 and replaced with a class describing a standard color set. The colors can be accessed through the *System.Drawing.Color* collection. More about this will be explained in the chapter on graphics.

3.9.4 : Caption and Text

The settings of these variables control what is displayed on the object. In general, **Caption** is used for a static text display. This means the text is not changing a lot and the user does not have to edit the text. **Text** is a dynamic control. This means the user can change it, edit it., whatever he could do with a text.

Most controls will thus have a **Caption**. Only **Textbox** and **Combobox** have a **Text** property (there are others but they are not part of the standard windows control set).

NET **2005**	The **Caption** property has been replaced by the **Text** property in these versions of the Visual Basic environment. This was done to remove confusion on when to use what property.

3.9.5 : Enabled and Visible

These properties define the active state of the control. The **enabled** property defines if the control will respond to events. If you set this property to **false** the object is detached from the message stream and it will no longer react to user events. If you set the **visible** property to **invisible** the object just disappears from the screen. It is not detached from the message queue. The **visible** property only takes effect at runtime. During design time, all controls are visible.

3.9.6 : Index

This specifies the objects place in a control array. If empty, the control does not belong to an array. Otherwise, it determines the position in the array. We will deal with control arrays a bit later on. Suffice it for now to say that a control array is a group of identical objects calling the same code but passing an argument defining which one amongst them is the caller. This feature allows for easy selection of options, and minimizes the amount of code that needs to be written to deal with groups of objects.

3.9.7 : Tabindex

This is also an index in an array but it determines the order in which controls are accessed. If you press the tab button, you can switch from control to control. This is useful for users that do not have a mouse. The list is scanned in ascending order.

3.9.8 : TooltipText

This handy property allows you to enter a few words of explanation about a control. During runtime whenever the user moves the mouse over a control and leaves it there for a few seconds this text will be displayed just below the mouse cursor. It gives instant help in your programs.

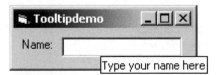

NET

2005

The *ToolTip* property in the NET framework is replaced by a Tooltip class. When instantiated as an object form this class the *Tooltip* control taps into the event handlers for the current form. The advantage is that all information can be stored in one location instead of becoming scattered. Furthermore, the information can be quickly loaded from an external resource files. This would allow easy customization for a multi-language user interface. The new Tooltip object also allows complete control over duration, timeouts, style, multiple lines and even the look of the Tooltip balloon when displayed on the screen.

Chapter 4 : Events and Methods

As explained before, events are the driving power behind the OOP / GUI programming style. Whenever something happens, for instance the user clicks with the mouse, hits a key or a character comes in over the serial port, an event is generated.

Now the above examples are only a small part of the possible events. Every tiny bit of action generates events. Even the mere fact that you move the mouse generates a stream of events.

Hitting a key alone generates three events. *KeyDown*, *KeyUp* and *KeyPress*

A simple thing like clicking the mouse can generate four events: *MouseUp*, *MouseDown*, `Click` and `DoubleClick`. While clicking you could have moved the mouse so that a stream of *MouseMove* events could have occurred.

The Windows operating systems is one big event scheduler and dispatcher. The event dispatcher collects all events from all possible sources, looks at their assigned priority and decides when to call the assigned event handler.

4.1 : Tapping into Events

You can tap into any of these events by using the properties browser in the code editor.

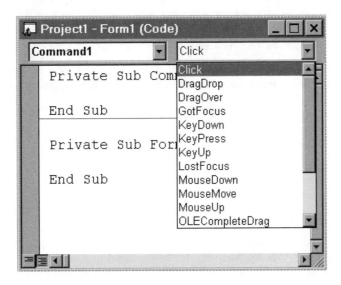

Every control has its own set of events that it can generate. Fortunately, for most of the programming you need to interact with only a limited number of possible events. It is not until you start to do more complicated work that you will need the other events. Actually when you edit code using the method of double-clicking an object, the code editor will show only the most used event. The others have to be accessed using the event browser of the Code editor (see picture above).

4.1.1 : Click (Most controls)

This is probably the most used event. Whenever the user clicks an object, this event is fired. This is the place you will attach the real code of your program. As the user of a GUI based systems typically points at and clicks on objects, this is the most commonly used event for any graphical object.

4.1.2 : DblClick (Most controls)

The same as the **Click** event but it is fired only when the user double-clicks. Important: double-clicking does not fire the **Click** event. The Windows GUI is smart enough to fire only the most appropriate event for the action the user performed.

4.1.3 : KeyPress (Most controls)

Whenever you hit a key on the keyboard, this event is fired. Only the object that has the current focus will be affected. You can tell which graphical object has the current focus by looking at it. For a textbox or other entry control either the cursor will be there or it will be highlighted (Combo box, listbox, Radiobutton, etc). Normal buttons have a slightly heavier outline or other visual aspect to them once they receive the focus.

It is useful in combination with textboxes to make masking. Suppose you want the use to enter a number only. You could attach the following code to the **KeyPress** event of the textbox

```
Private Sub Text1_KeyPress (KeyAscii As Integer)
        Select Case Chr$(KeyAscii)
        Case "0" To "9"
            Text1.Text = Text1.Text + Chr$(KeyAscii)
        Case Else
        End Select
    End Sub
```

The **KeyPress** returns the ASCII value of the key that was hit. Therefore, if we detect that it lies between zero and nine (thus being a valid number) we allow it to go into the textbox. Normally whenever a key is hit when the textbox control has the focus, the windows event scheduler will receive a **KeyPress** event. The scheduler passes this on to the handling code inside the receiving object. However, you can modify this behavior by writing your own event handler as in the case above. Normally the event would be passed to the code inside the textbox object. Since here we wrote our own handler, this is no longer the case. We re-directed an event in order to handle it ourselves.

 Whenever you attach code to any of the **KeyPress** events, the object will not handle the keyboard input for you. You are then responsible for taking appropriate action.

4.1.4 : MouseMove (Most controls)

Whenever the user moves the mouse, the object under the mouse will fire the **MouseMove** event. You can use this event to retrieve the coordinates of the mouse. This can be useful if you want to make a small drawing program.

4.1.5 : Activate (Form)

Only a Form generates these events. Whenever the user moves the focus to a form, it will fire this event. Suppose you have a program with four forms. You can only have one form active at a time. The form then becomes the new active form will fire this event. You can use this to update status bars, or to create context sensitive help.

4.1.6 : Deactivate (Form)

This command is similar to the above. Whenever a form gets the focus, another one must lose it. The form that loses focus is generating the **Deactivate** event.

4.1.7 : Load (Form)

This is probably the most useful form-related event. Together with the **unload** event. If you are using local variable or need to load configuration or INI files, this is the place to do it.

Whenever a form gets loaded the first time, it fires this event. Since in a typical application a form only gets loaded once, during the start of the program, you can use this event to attach your startup code.

4.1.8 : Unload (Form)

Similar to the **Load** event, the **unload** event gets fired when a form is destroyed (unloaded). Since this only happens during program termination, you can use this event to store user preferences, or form size and position into an INI file, the registry or whatever.

This is the place where you put your program's bailout code.

4.1.9 : Change (Textbox)

The *change* event is fired whenever the contents of the textbox change. Not that this also happens if you change the textbox contents from your own program code. You can use this to cascade commands.

4.1.10 : Calling events

You can tap into many more events. You can even generate your own events from within code! Since an event handler is nothing else than a subroutine, you can call them from another part of your code.

Note

By default, events are proprietary to the form where the owning object lives. You cannot call them from other forms, except if you declare the subroutine that handles the event as *public*. However, declaring such an event handler public should only be done in 'modules' and even then it is still considered bad programming practice. It can lead to very strange program behavior. A better technique is to specify in detail where a subroutine is located. This is done by specifying the entire event tree

Example: *form1.button1_click* refers to a button called Button1 residing on form1. You could have made button1_click a public subroutine but then what happens if 2 forms happen to have an object called button1? How will you distinguish? It is better to be prepared for code re-use and provide the full path to an object. It make your life easier later but also makes the program slightly faster as the ambiguity is gone and the scheduler does not need to figure out where a certain event handler is located.

Suppose the following: You have a couple of buttons on a toolbar that allow you to Edit cut copy and paste text.

On your edit menu you have the same functions: Cut, Copy and Paste. Now the question is, are you going to write the cut copy and Paste code twice? I think not. The events generated by the toolbar buttons will simply pass control to the events activated by clicking on the menu bar.

```
Sub Cut_Click ()
    ' Cut text from textbox code ...
End sub

Sub ToolbarCut_click ()
    Call Cut_click ()
End sub
```

The first subroutine is the event handler for the Menu bar. The second Event handler is attached to the button on the toolbar. Whenever you click the button on the toolbar, it passes control to the event handler on the Menu bar. Done! No additional code required. In this case, one event simply fires another event and leaves it up to that one to perform the appropriate action.

The only pitfall in this is that you have to make sure your event handlers are not calling each other. This will create a recursive event and blow the event stack sky-high. Later versions of windows (2000 / XP) have a detection mechanism in place that prevents this from happening. However, older version can have trouble. Fortunately, the Visual Basic compiler checks for this behavior as well and will try to prevent it from happening.

This programming technique is quick and dirty. It is better to write an altogether different routine to handle a certain task and then call that routine from both event handlers.

For the case above, the following is a better example.

```
Sub perform_cut_operation()
End Sub

Sub Cut_Click ()
    Perform_cut_operation
End sub

Sub ToolbarCut_click ()
    Perform_cut_operation
End sub
```

4.2 : Methods

So far, we have talked about objects, their properties and the events they can generate. Now, an object has one last thing that is called *Methods*.

The easiest way to understand them is to think of them as built-in procedures. Let us take the 'Move' method. Almost any object supports it. Suppose you want to move a button. You could of course change the properties *Top* and *Left*, but that takes too much work (you have to calculate the absolute movement from the current and the new coordinate). Well, you can use the *Move* method.

```
Object.move (x, y)
```

This will move the object to the new coordinates. Now the underlying code for a button is not the same for let us say a textbox. This is the strength of Methods. They have the same name, work on nearly all objects but are completely different internally.

A typical other method is the *Print* command. In normal Basic, *Print* is a keyword while in Visual Basic it is a method. Why, you might ask? Well, simple: you can pick an object and print to it. As you can print to the form, you can also print to a button or a graphics box or even to the Printer object!

The internal workings are completely different, yet the action has the same result. Except that, when printing to the form, it ends up on the screen, and when printing to a printer, it ends up on paper.

Now that we have discussed the nuts and bolts of the Visual Basic programming language and the environment it works with, it is about time we start building a program. The next few chapters will show you how to build a user interface, how to attach code and how to get it up and running.

Later in this book, more examples will be given to detail a bit on the most used features inside the programming language. First, something needs to be told about the language itself.

Chapter 5 : The Visual Basic Language

Before we can start writing code, we should know a little about the driving force behind all of this: the Basic language. Originally conceived by Kemeny and Kurz in 1968 this language has often been regarded to as 'not useful for anyone beyond first grade'.

To be sure, Basic tended to lead to sloppy code, and the first interpreters were terribly slow, but today's compilers can unleash the power of the machine. For technical environments Basic is still the Number One language. Many research departments from outstanding universities solely depend on it to build the 'quick and dirty' problem solver they needed 3 weeks ago.

Since the compiler has to generate code which deals with whatever the programmer is cooking up, the resulting code will always be slower then a very low level language like 'C' and Assembler, or more structured language like Pascal.

However, all good programming languages are in a continuous state of evolution, and so is Basic. Major improvements have been made over time. The language borrowed constructs and concepts from other languages, subroutines and functions have become available, line numbers disappeared. With the advent of the GUI system and concepts such as Object Oriented Programming, the Basic language was up for an update. That is where Visual Basic started.

The initial versions (1 to 3) were targeted for Windows 3.0 and 3.11 and implemented a whole range of elements from the Object oriented programming model. Technical difficulties and a radical difference in programming philosophy between Basic and other languages made it virtually impossible to implement the full concept.

Visual Basic 4.0 attempted a first shot at implementing OOP properly and succeeded in bringing more functionality, albeit not all of it. This was also the first version that could create applications for 32-bit windows (Windows 95).

As from Version 5.0 on, the Visual Basic compiler uses the same underlying technology as the Visual C++ compiler from Microsoft. This means that the code generation process is used for both. Because of the inherent difference between C++ and Basic, certain additional runtime libraries are required for Visual Basic generated code. This makes the code still a bit slower as certain tings need to be 'wrapped' before they can be handled by the C compiler. The advantage is that the full OOP framework becomes available.

The NET and 2005 version do away with this altogether. The strong point of the NET framework is the **Common Runtime Library**. Any program written in a compiler that uses the NET framework will behave in the same way. Unfortunately, this meant that for Visual Basic some liberties needed to be taken away as they could not be unified into other languages.

The true power of Basic lies in the possibility to develop a program in virtually no time. A Basic program will be running and starting to do something while in other languages you are still deciding what variable type to use, checking out which library you need or putting punctuation and compiler directives into place.

A programming language is very similar to a human language. Before you can learn it, you need to know the vocabulary (instruction set) and grammar (syntax). This will allow you to construct sentences (lines of code). The contents of the text written in a language (the algorithm) is a different matter however. This is only acquired by practising. Just as you can express something in different ways, you can solve problems programmatically in different ways.

Computer languages differ a bit from the human languages. They are much more organized. They need for instance ways to describe the data. They also need to put a logical flow to things and, most of all, they need to explain in far greater detail to the computer what he needs to do. Computers do not make assumptions or fall back on their gathered knowledge. They simply execute what you tell them to.

As computers typically move information around, this information needs to be stored somewhere. So let us take a look at how we manipulate data.

5.1 : Variables

A computer language uses variables to store data. They are a symbolic name used by the programmer to refer to data stored somewhere in memory. The compiler will allocate the necessary storage space and map it into the computers memory. Data comes in all sorts of colors and flavors. You can have numbers, letters, strings etc... Therefore, it is logical that there are different ways to store data. In most programming languages, you have to explain to the compiler what kind of data to store. In Visual Basic, you DO NOT have to!

There is only one variable type. In other languages, you need to specify what kind of information to expect: integer numbers, floating point numbers, strings of bytes or other types. In Visual Basic, there is just storage space. What do you want to store? That does not really matter. How big is it? That is of no importance either.

Visual Basic introduced the concept of a *Variant*. (NET and 2005 no longer support this)

A variant is a universal storage space. It is virtually unlimited in size (16.777.216 bytes max) and can hold everything ranging from strings, numbers, pictures and even other objects.

You even do not need to define it. Just use any name you want. In Basic, it is the compiler's job to figure out how to store and retrieve your data. The compiler will even generate the correct code to change the exact data type depending on the operations you perform.

However, in the course of time, the users of Basic found out that if you were not careful enough, you would end up with messy code that can be very buggy. Therefore, Visual Basic allows you to force yourself to program in a clean fashion. You can use the *Option Explicit* command in the top of a module. Then you need to declare the variables and *typecast* them. This gives also some speed improvement since now the compiler can generate much more optimized code. In addition, you will have more storage space. When a variable is typecast, then only the necessary amount of memory is allocated. A variant always uses at least 16 bytes of memory, even if it is empty.

NET 2005	Because of the requirement that programs use the Common Language Runtime, certain variable types have gotten a new definition in NET and subsequent version of Visual Basic. A number of the 'old' types have been resized in terms of memory allocation while others have been removed altogether because they proved they could not be unified with the CLR.

5.1.1 : Available Data Types in Visual Basic

Type	Character	Memory Requirement	Range of Values	Stores
Integer	%	2 byte	-32.768 to 32.767	Whole numbers
Long	&	4 byte	Approx 2 billion	Whole numbers
Single	!	4 byte	-1e-45 to 3e38	Decimal numbers
Double		8 byte	-5e-324 to 1.8e308	Decimal numbers
Currency		8 byte	-9e14 to +9e14	Numbers with up to 15 digits left and 4 digits right of the decimal
String	$	1 byte + 1 byte per character	Up to 65000 characters for fixed length and up to 2 billion for dynamic strings	Text information. Fixed lengths strings can be created by specifying a length. Example: dim a as string *100
Byte	None	1 byte	0 to 255	Whole numbers
Boolean	None	2 bytes	True or False	Logical values
Date	None	8 bytes	1/1/100 to 12/31/9999	Date and time information
Object	None	4 bytes	Not applicable	Pictures and OLE objects
Variant	None	16 bytes + 1 byte per character	Not applicable	A variant can store any of the above data types.

In Visual Basic NET and Visual Basic 2005, a number of changes had to be made in order to align Visual Basic with the Common runtime library requirement. The biggest impact is the removal of the Variant data type. Fortunately, the CLR has a similar data type called 'Object' that can take its place. So moving variant handling code to NET is worst case a matter of changing a couple of definitions. The specifics are explained in the next topic.

Typecasting a variable can be done in two ways. You either declare a variable explicit or use the typecasting character (implicit).

```
a$ ="test"    'implicit declaration

Dim a as string
a ="test"     'explicit declaration
```

The net result is the same. By ending the name of a variable by the typecast character, you force its type. In the second case you declare them using the **As** keyword. They both have their advantages and disadvantages. It is up to you which one you use.

If you decide to go for the explicit method, then you have to use the **As** keyword

```
Dim account As Currency
Dim a As Byte
Dim power As Boolean
```

There is a minor difference between implicit and explicit declaration. When using implicit declaration you add the type declaration character at the end of the variable name. This means that from now on you must reference the variable including the type character. Explicit declaration avoids this, but then you cannot immediately see what the type of the variable is. You have to look it up in the declaration clause of the variable. It is up to you what you want to use.

NET

2005

You can initialize variables directly to a default value by using the = sign followed by the initial value for the variable. For example: **Dim x as integer =100** or **Dim My_String as string = "hello world"**. This saves some typing later on and actually makes execution faster as well since a number of data move operations are omitted.

Note

A variable name must start with a letter; the name cannot contain a period and can be no longer than 255 characters.

5.1.2 : Data types in NET

Below is the table of data types as it is in effect in the NET platform. You will see that certain data types no longer exist, some have changed the amount of storage required and new ones have been added.

The integer and long data types in pre NET Visual Basic are 16 and 32 bit respectively. In light of the NET framework, these have been upgraded to 32 bit for an integer and 64 bit for a *Long*. For 16-bit data types, a new data type, the *Short*, has been introduced.

The currency data type has been abandoned and replaced by the **Decimal** typecast. This stores numbers as a 96-bit integer with a moving decimal point.

The **Date** type, typically used to perform calculations on date/time has been internally re-arranged and has become a 64-bit number. For existing code that treats dates as the old 'double' data type, a wrapper is available in the form of the **ToOADate** and **FromOADate** functions. These allow you to re-use old code without major re-writes.

Fixed length data strings are no longer available. The old style of declaring a string as fixed size by specifying the length is no longer supported. Fortunately, a wrapper is available in the form of a class. It can be found in the **VisualBasic.compatibility** namespace (more on namespaces later on in this book).

Custom Types are a flexible means of creating custom data structures. The NET framework pushes this even further and introduces the **Structure**, to abandon the **Type**. Only minor changes are necessary in the definition to re-use the code.

Type	Memory Requirement	Range of Values	Stores
Integer	4 byte	-2,147,483,648 to 2,147,483,647	This stores whole numbers. This is doubled in size compared to Visual Basic Classic
Long	8 byte	-9,223,372,036,854,775,808 to ,223,372,036,854,775,807	This stores whole numbers. This is doubled in size compared to Visual Basic Classic
Single	4 byte	-1e-45 to 3e38	Decimal numbers
Double	8 byte	-5e-324 to 1.8e308	Decimal numbers
Decimal	16 bytes	Incredibly large numbers (29 digits) to extremely small (28 decimal places)	Replaces the Currency data type of Visual Basic Classic
String	Depends on implementation	A string can hold up to 2 billion Unicode characters.	A strong holds a sequence of bytes, such as text information. Fixed lengths strings can be created by specifying a length. Example: dim a as string *100
Byte	1 byte	0 to 255	Whole numbers

Boolean	2 bytes	True or False	Logical values
Date	8 bytes	1/1/100 to 12/31/9999	Date and time information
Object	4 bytes	Not applicable	Pictures and OLE objects
Char	2 bytes	0 to 65535	
Short	2 bytes	-32,768 to 32,767	
Object	4 bytes	Depending on what is stored in it.	Any type can be stored in this data type. It consists of a pointer to the location where the real information is stored.

When dealing with runtime created objects, you needed to use the *Set* keyword to assign the object to a variable name. The NET CLR unifies this by removing the *Set* keyword and using the = sign instead. This reason is that a non-typecast variable is an object by default so no special keyword is needed anymore.

NET **2005**	Variable scope has been extended and modified. While retaining the top-down scope approach additional levels have been added. More details later on.
	Variables can be initialized at definition time. You no longer have to write code later on to initialize the m to a certain value. For example Dim x as integer = 10 replaces the old style of writing Dim X as integer: x=10

5.2 : Arrays

Suppose you need to have more than one variable with the same name, for instance a table or an array. It would make programming easier if we could use an index to refer to a set of variables. That is exactly what arrays are intended for. Arrays can be created for any kind of variable. You can even create arrays for objects (more on this later). Contrary to regular variables, you need to declare them. Regular variables you can use on the fly. However, you do not need to typecast them.

5.2.1 : DIM

An array is declared used the *DIM* keyword just like a regular variable

```
Dim myarray(5)
Dim twodimensions(5,6)
Dim ThreeD(5,10,100) as integer
```

The above examples are declarations for a number of arrays. The first two are not typecast (no explicit type for them is declared). The last one is typecast as integer. When using big arrays, it is useful to typecast them. Since arrays typically contains many variables (the multiplication of all dimensions: example a (5, 10, 10) contains 5*10*10 = 500 elements) it is wishful to typecast them. Doing so will preserve a lot of memory.

If they are not typecast, then they are assumed as Variant (which takes 16 byte per item if empty). You can declare arrays of up to 255 dimensions. Do not try to visualize how this would look, you can't. In fact nobody ever does this (except maybe some mathematicians or physicists).

NET

2005

Non-typecast arrays are per default of the Object type.

Just as with single variables, you can specify the initial contents of an array as well. Visual Basic automatically sizes the array correctly. The list of data has to be contained in {} brackets.

Example:
```
Dim x() as string = {"John", " Sally ", "Ann", "Chris"}
```
Or
```
Dim y() as integer = {10, 44, 107, 2, 12}
```

An array is by default Zero-Based. This means that if you declare an array of five elements, you have access to elements 0 to 4. Suppose you want to store the years between 1900 and 2000. To conserve space you could declare an array that stores only the last two digits. (DO NOT do this! The Y2K problem was caused by exactly this sort of shortsightedness). After all, if you declare an array of 2000 elements you will waste the first 1900 of them. Well, Visual Basic allows you to change this base.

```
Dim years (1900 to 2000)
```

The above will declare an array with 100 elements. The first element will have and index of 1900 and the last will be 2000.

```
Dim MyMatrix(1 To 5, 4 To 9, -3 To 5) As Double
```

This will create an array with specified bounds.

Arrays created in this manner are called **Static** arrays. You lock the amount of memory at coding time. Equally, you can create dynamic arrays

```
Dim myArray()
```

Later in the code, you can re-dimension your array with the **REDIM** command

Since the option base is no longer programmable in the NET framework, the previous examples will not work. Dim years (1900 to 2000) will produce an error and will have to be rewritten as Dim years (2000). This does no longer waste space. Since all arrays are internally stored as a dynamic structure the elements containing no data occupy no space in memory (actually the contain the NULL value)

NET 2005

In addition, NET loses the ability to use negative values as array indexes. This might require some code rewriting should you upgrade existing code containing such constructs to the NET platform.

5.2.2 : ReDim.

The *ReDim* statement is used to set or change the size of a dynamic array that has already been declared using a *Private*, *Public* or *Dim* statement. When defining the original array no dimensions were given and they will now be set using the *redim* command

You can use the *ReDim* statement as often as you want to modify the number of elements, and possibly dimensions, in an array. The one thing you cannot do is change the data type of the array, unless the array was originally defined as being stored inside a Variant and you do not use the *Preserve* keyword

If you want to retain the contents of the array by using the *Preserve* keyword, you can modify only the last dimension. The number of dimensions cannot be changed since there is no way to resolve where the data should end up.

```
ReDim X (10, 10, 10)
' other code goes here
ReDim Preserve X (10, 10, 15)
```

The use of *Preserve* limits you to changing the upper boundary and attempting to change the lower bound causes an error.

If you resize the array to be smaller than originally defined the data in the removed elements is be lost. When a variable is initialized, it defaults to either zero for a numeric variable, an empty sting "" for a variable-length string, or all zeroes for a fixed length string. Variables of the Variant type are set to 'Empty'. All elements of user-defined types are initialized as if they were separate variables. A variable that is typecast as an object, is pointing nowhere, and needs to be assigned to an object using the *Set* statement before it can be used. Until that time is set to 'Nothing', which indicates that it does not point to any specific instance of an object.

NET 2005

In NET and 2005, non-initialized space contains the NULL as opposed to 'empty' in VB5 / VB6.

When you are writing procedures or functions that have to accept data in arrays, it is always wise to query the array for its bounds. There are commands **Ubound** and **Lbound** that allow you to do just that.

5.2.3 : Ubound

This function returns a Long containing the highest available location for the indicated dimension of an array.

Ubound (array name [, dimension])

Array name	The name of the array.
Dimension	An optional variant or long data type. This is a whole number indicating which dimension's upper bound is requested. If no dimension is specified the default value of 1 is used.

The **Ubound** function works in conjunction with the **Lbound** function to determine the boundaries of an array. You can use the companion function to **Ubound**, **Lbound**, to find the lower limit of an array dimension.

Ubound returns the following values for an array with these dimensions:

```
Dim A (1 To 10, -2 To 3)
```

Ubound(A, 1)	10
Ubound(A, 2)	3

5.2.4 : Lbound

This companion function to **Ubound** returns a Long containing the lowest available array location for the given dimension of an array.

Lbound (array name [, dimension])

Array name	The Name of the array variable.
Dimension	An optional variant or long data type. This indicates which dimension's lower bound is returned. Just like with **Ubound**, if the dimension is not given a default of 1 is used.

Lbound returns the values in the following table for an array with the following dimensions:

```
Dim A (1 To 10, -2 To 3)
```

Lbound(A, 1)	1
Lbound(A, 2)	-2

The default lower bound for a dimension is determined by the setting of the **Option Base** statement. If the option base is specified to be Zero then the lower bound is zero by default. If **Option base** is set to 1 then the default **Lbound** value will be 1.

If you create an array using the 'To' clause in a **Dim**, **Private**, **Public**, **ReDim**, or **Static** statement, then you can have any integer value as a lower bound.

NET **2005**	As NET no longer has based arrays, the **Lbound** instruction is retained for compatibility reasons but it will always return 0.

5.2.5 : Array

The Array command is used to create an array and store it in a variable of the Variant Type. The basic syntax is as follows:

Array (argument list)

The argument list is a comma-delimited list of values to be assigned to the elements of the array. If no arguments are given, the newly created array will have a length of zero.

```
Dim A As Variant
A = Array(5,10,15)
B = A(2)
' b now contains the value 10
```

Note	Any Variant can contain an array, even if it was not specifically declared using the Array command. A Variant can store an array of almost any type. The exceptions are fixed-length strings and user-defined types. The functions to access the contents of an array stored in a variant remains the same as for any other array.

The example below shows how to store an array of strings in a Variant:

```
Option Base 1
Dim My_Weekdays, My_Day
My_Weekdays = Array ("Monday", "Tuesday", "Wednesday", "Thursday", _
                     "Friday", "Saturday", "Sunday")

My_Day = My_Weekdays (2)    ' MyDay contains "Tuesday".
My_Day = My_Weekdays (4)    ' MyDay contains "Thursday".
```

5.2.6 : Arrays and the NET framework

Visual Basic NET adds a class dealing with arrays. As explained before, variables are all considered objects under the NET framework. Thus, a variable can have a method attached to it, derived form the class it belongs to. Since an array is a variable holding a collection of information, this model can be applied here too. We will see this working style applied throughout the NET framework. Later on, when we start dealing with strings (which can also be considered as a sort of array), the same idea will come back.

The array Handling has been changes from older Visual Basic versions as well. In VB5 and VB6, you could specify a base for your array. This functionality is gone in NET.

In Visual Basic NET, all arrays are dynamic, meaning they can be resized on the fly. You might want to check your code for redundant usage of the **ReDim** statement. As it does not cause any harm, you can gain some speed.

5.2.7 : Sort operation (NET only)

The array class has a sort method. This method allows you to sort an array quickly. The drawback is that the sort method can only handle one-dimensional arrays.

```
Dim my_array() as string = { "Joe", "Brian", "Ron", "Pedro", "Cal", _
                             "Bill", "Mike"}
Array.sort(my_array)
Debug.print my_array(0)  ' prints 'Bill'
Debug.print my_array(1)  ' prints 'Cal'
```

Note that the above code only works in the NET environment. It is possible to sort multiple arrays based on the first one in the list. Suppose you have an array containing the family names and an array of given names. If you want to sort according to family name, simply pass the two arrays starting with the given name array. This array will be sorted and the manipulations on the indexes are propagated to all other specified arrays. The other arrays are NOT sorted; their order is rearranged according to the sorting in the first array. This will thus keep data together.

```
Dim family_names() as string = { "Williams", Swanson", "Schirmer" }
Dim given_names () as string = { "Mike", "Cal", "Bill" }

Array.sort(family_names, given_names)

' the result after the sort will be
' Shirmer, Swanson, Williams
' Bill   , Cal    , Mike
'
```

5.2.8 : Binarysearch (NET only).

This method can be used to retrieve the index of a piece of data in an array.

```
Dim my_array() as string = { "Joe", "Brian", "Ron", "Pedro", "Cal", _
                             "Bill", "Mike"}
X= Array.binarysearch(my_array, "Bill")
```

The above example will return the value 5 in x.

If the requested data is not found, a negative value will be returned. It is imperative that the data type of the array, and the data type of the information to be found, is of the same kind. Do not try to find a variable of the *Date* type in an array of strings.

5.3 : Types

An array can be regarded as a simple database. If you require storing data in a database-like way, you can create your own data types.

Type is used at a top level or module level to define your own data type containing multiple elements.

```
[Private | Public] Type varname
                 elementname ([subscripts]) As type
                 [elementname ([subscripts]) As type]
                 ...

End Type
```

Public	An optional parameter to declare a user-defined type that is available throughout the entire project.
Private	An optional parameter to declare a user-defined type that is available only within the module where it is declared.
Varname	The name of the user-defined type.
Elementname	The name of an element belonging to the user-defined type. Element names follow the standard variable name conventions with the exception that keywords can be used as well. In case an array element is defined, you can specify dimensions as well. Standard array definition conventions apply.
Type	The data type of the element. As usual this can be either a Byte, Boolean, Integer, Long, Currency, Single, Double, Date, String, Object, Variant or even another user-defined type.

You can only declare a new *Type* at module level, not inside a subroutine. Once defined, the user-defined type is accessible throughout the scope set forth in its definition. Use *Dim,* **in combination with** *Private, Public, ReDim,* or *Static* to declare a variable of your self-defined type.

When you declare an array inside a user-defined type, you must hard-code the dimensions, by either numbers or constants. Note that the **Option Base** statement also has an impact on the lower bound for arrays inside user-defined types.

```
Type Employee ' Create user-defined type.
      Badge_ID As Integer
      Name As String * 20
      Address As String * 60
      Phone As Long
End Type

Dim My_employees(999) as employee

Sub Create_a_Record()
      My_employees(42).Name = "Arthur Dent" ' Assign a value to an
      element.
End Sub
```

This example uses the **Type** statement to define a user-defined data type. The **Type** statement is used at the module level only.

NET **2005**	NET no longer supports the **TYPE** construct. The more powerful **Structure** is preferred but it involves writing a bunch more information since a **structure** is basically a class with very specific rules. You can also define a class altogether to store information.

In order to be honest with you: You can perfectly create your own database system using custom Types, but there are ways that are far more powerful at your disposition. Visual Basic has direct access to ODBC objects (Open Database Control). This allows you to create and manipulate data far more efficiently than by coding everything yourself. For simple things, it might be useful and faster not to use this heavy database engine. It is up to you to decide on this.

5.4 : Constants

Storing often-used numbers in a variable makes programming easier. Furthermore, it makes modifying and reading the program a lot easier afterwards. However, it has two drawbacks: it eats memory and the number could be modified by mistake, rendering the program to produce erroneous results. Therefore, the concept of a constant has been defined. A constant is a placeholder for information. The only difference is that it has no memory allocation during runtime. During compilation, Visual Basic will replace all instances of the constant name with its contents.

Just like variables you can have **Public (Global)** or **Private** Constants. Constants are declared with the **CONST** keyword

```
const version$ = "Version 1.0"
```

```
        const pi = 3.1415927
```

You can store anything in a constant. Since it has no real substance you do not have to specify the type. However, you have to take care when using them.

With the above constants, this would yield an error:

```
        result = pi * version   ' multiply a number with a string??
        version = 12      ' error: you cannot change a constant
```

5.5 : Enumerations

Enumerated lists, or enumerations for short, are a new construction in Visual Basic that did not exist before. Enumerations provide an easy way to deal with often-used groups of constants.

Suppose you have a variable 'DayOfTheWeek'. Suppose DayOfTheWeek is set to 3: does this mean Wednesday or Tuesday? It all depends if the week starts on Monday or on Sunday. Instead of setting *DayOfTheWeek=3* you could define a bunch of constants to specify day names, for Example: *Const Monday=1, Tuesday=2, Wednesday=3* and so on.

Nevertheless, I could still write *DayOfTheWeek = Green. Or DayOfTheWeek =9* since nothing forces me to use these constants.

This is where enumerated lists come in handy. By defining an enumerated list and declaring a variable of that enumerated type, you can only select items from the list. The actual numerical value assigned to the element is no longer of impotence as it is passed by its reference and will thus always be correct.

Example:

```
        Enum weekday
            Monday = 1
            Tuesday = 2
            Wednesday = 3
            Thursday = 4
            Friday = 5
            Saturday = 6
            Sunday = 9 ' note the deliberate mistake here
        End Enum.
        Dim DayOfTheweek as weekday
        DayOfTheWeek = Monday
        Dayoftheweek = Sunday
        If Dayoftheweek = Sunday then msgbox "It is Sunday !"
```

You might say that Sunday is not the ninth day of the week but that does not matter anymore since we are going to use the symbolic names anyway. The if-then-else clause is going to evaluate anyway.

As you are typing code, the editor will pop up the enumerated list automatically. The list will be sorted. So in the above case, the names look out of order but they are alphabetized.

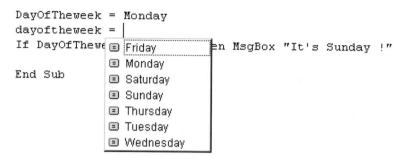

```
DayOfTheweek = Monday
dayoftheweek = |
If DayOfThewe ☐ Friday          en MsgBox "It's Sunday !"
               ☐ Monday
End Sub        ☐ Saturday
               ☐ Sunday
               ☐ Thursday
               ☐ Tuesday
               ☐ Wednesday
```

Unfortunately, in Visual Basic Classic it is still possible to circumvent this system by simply writing DayOfTheWeek = 7 .

Visual Basic NET has an option flag to enforce the usage of the enumerated lists. By specifying **Option Strict** the enumerated list is enforced whenever an enumerated variable is encountered. If you do not pass the references used in the list, a compile error will occur.

5.6 : Collections

A collection is a new method of storing information that was introduced in NET. A collection is a class that stores a list of items. You can store any variable or object inside a collection.

Te define a new collection simply instantiate an object of the Collection class

```
        Dim my_collection as new collection()
```

Elements are stored in the collection by using the Add method, or removed using the Remove method. In order to easily retrieve information from the collection, you can specify a 'key'. This additional string gives each element a name by which it can be referenced.

Example:

```
        My_collection.add ("name1","Bill")
        My_collection.add ("phone1","123-456789")
        My_collection.add ("name2","Cal")
        My_collection.add ("phone2","321-654987")

        Dim x as string
        X = my_collection("name1")
        ' x will contain the string 'Bill'
```

5.6.1.1 : Adding information to the collection

The information is accessed by specifying the 'key'. You can think of this as a search parameter. It is also possible to specify the order in which elements are to be added. If nothing is specified, it is added to the end of the list, or you can specify a 'before' or 'after' key.

Example:

```
        My_collection.Add("Location1", "Raleigh", "Phone1")
```

This will insert the information 'Raleigh' under keyword 'location1' just before the element with key 'Phone1'.

The list will thus look like this:
```
Bill
Raleigh
123-456789
Cal
321-654987
```

It I also possible to store information after the search key by specifying it as the fourth parameter in the Add method.

Example:

```
        My_collection.Add("Location1", "Raleigh", , "name1")
        ' note the extra comma here  -------------|
```

5.6.1.2 : Removing elements

In order to remove an element, simply invoke the Remove method and pass it the key under which it is stored.

Example:

```
        My_collection.remove ("Cal")
```

Finally, you can retrieve the number of elements in a collection by reading the Count property.

Example:

```
        Messagebox.show ("there are" & my_collection.count &"items")
```

Because of the way a collection stores information, it uses up far more memory than a regular array. It should therefore be used only when the data changes a lot in content.

5.7 : Scope of Variables

 Vartype.vbp   There is a tutorial program available that explains the constructs, explained in this topic in further detail.

When you define a variable (i.e. declare it using DIM or simply start using a new variable name), it only exists locally on the level it was first used or defined.

An example:

```
Sub Button1_click()
      Dim a as Integer
End Sub

Sub Button2_click()
      Dim a as Long
End Sub
```

In the above examples, both variables **A** are independent variables. They have nothing to do with each other. When you exit a subroutine, all variables are destroyed. When you allocate them the first time, then they are created and reset. The contents are set to zero for numbers or 'nothing' for strings. Keep in mind that the NET framework uses a different approach and even lets you specify a default value.

Sometimes you might want a variable to be accessible form outside of your procedures, or even project wide.

This can be done. There are four ways to modify the 'scope' of a variable: Static, Private, Public and Global.

An important thing to note about variables is that they 'live' inside the chunk of code where they are defined. As soon as that chunk of code is no longer accessible, the variable ceases to exist. A variable defined in a subroutine ceases to exist upon exit of the routine, just as a variable defined in a form ceases to exist upon destroying or 'unloading' the form from memory. The contents of the variable are lost, and each time the block of code containing the definition is executed, the variable is recreated and re-initialized. Fortunately, a modifier exists to override this behavior in certain cases.

5.7.1 : Public / Global

A public variable is accessible throughout the module that contains its definition, and it can be used from any lower level. In essence, it is exposed to lower levels directly, while higher scope levels can use it by using a full reference to it.

For example:

```
Public x as integer
Sub button1_click ()
Debug.print x
End sub
Sub button2_click ()
X=x+1
End sub
```

Whenever **button2** is clicked, the value of **x** will be incremented. Clicking **buton2** will access the variable **x** and print its contents.

The above code al resides on the same form, so relaxed referencing can be used. Suppose the program consist of two forms both with a button.

```
Form1:
Public x as integer
Sub button1_click ()
Debug.print x
End sub

Form2:
Sub button2_click ()
Form1.X = form1.x+1
End sub
```

In this case, the reference was given by specifying the module where the variable resided. Since the variable was exposed using the *Public* modifier we could actually access it.

A *Global* variable is directly accessible, without using full referencing, from anywhere in the project. Windows itself contains a whole set of Global variables. Items such as system colors, system pathnames etc. are all accessible globally throughout the system. Note that some of these are read only.

Global variables should be used sparingly as they typically can be modified by any part of the program. A small bug in a module somewhere could change a global, resulting in possible unwanted behavior.

Global variables can only be defined at module level. They have to reside inside a module of your program. They cannot belong to a form.

5.7.2 : Private

A private variable is a variable that only exists in the current portion of code. Only routines belonging to the same form or module as the one where the variable has been declared can access it. By default, ALL variables defined without a scope modifier are private and thus can only be accessed from lower scope levels in the code.

5.7.3 : Static

This variable can only exist inside the function or procedure where it has been declared. It behaves just like a normal variable, but it will not be destroyed upon exit of the procedure. Remark that nobody outside the procedure that contains the declaration of the static variable, can access it.

```
Function countup ()
    Static x As Integer
    countup = x
    x = x + 1
End Function
```

If you would declare 'x' as a normal type then the function would always return zero. Every time you call the function, a storage space for 'x' is allocated, set to zero and upon exit, the storage space is freed. By declaring the variable as *Static* it only is created the first time you call the function. The next time you call the function then the variable x still exists, and its content is unaltered.

5.8 : Scope levels

 *Varscope.vbp*

There is a tutorial program available that explains the constructs explained in this topic.

Besides the *static, public,global* and other types, variables can be bound to the code module they live in. A Module is a physical file that contains code. Forms, BAS files etc. are all modules. A program is created from one or more of these.

Consider the following piece of code:

```
    Dim x as integer

Sub form1_load()
    Dim y as integer
    Y = 2
    X = 5
    Call addup
    Debug.print y,x
End sub

Sub addup()
    Debug.print x+y
End sub
```

When this program is run, it will always return 5. Why? Well simple: the variable X is defined at a higher scope level. This means it is accessible from anywhere from the same level or the levels below. As long as you do not re-declare it on a lower level, you can use it. The variable Y is created inside the form1_load subroutine. This means it is only accessible from within this level. As control is transferred from one routine to another, the scope level changes and *y* is not accessible for the *'addup'* subroutine. As the subroutine *form1_load* is not terminated yet, the variable is still available. Upon re-entry (after the *addup* routine has reached its end it will return control to its caller, in this case the form1_load subroutine.) the variable y still exists. Hence, the *debug.print* will show its contents. Once the *form1_load* routine reaches the end then the variable Y is destroyed.

Referencing an in-existing variable will create it and set it to the default value for its type, as this is the standard behavior for Visual Basic. You do not need to declare variables. They are created automatically upon their first use.

Therefore, the net result of *X+Y* is 5 + 0 = 5.

The scope levels can be explained graphically as follows

Highest level			Lowest level
Project level Modules and imported variables from the operating system			
	Forms and modules		
		Instantiated Object properties and Subroutine variables	
			Object properties

By default a lower level can access variables defined in a higher level, if they have not explicitly have been made **Private**.

A higher level cannot access variables of a lower level unless they have been made Public, and even then, they need to be accessed by specifying the complete reference.

Inside a level, variables are accessible directly. Keep in mind that two subroutines cannot see each other's variables, even though they reside on the same level. They are two separate entities and thus need to pas information using arguments to each other.

NET

2005

The NET framework adds even one more level of scope. It is now possible to declare variables inside loop constructs. These variables are only accessible on the level they were declared and the levels below, unless overridden by a redefinition

Example

```
Sub dosomething()
    Dim x as integer
    Dim y as integer

    For x = 1 to 10
        Dim p as integer
        For y = 1 to 10
            z = z+1
            P = p+1
        Next y
        Debug.print z,p ' this will print twice he same number
    Next x
    Debug.print z,p 'this will print the last value of z
                    ' followed by a zero since p is out
                    ' of scope here.
End sub
```

The variable p only exists on the level of the '**for x**... **next x**' loop and the levels below. Once the '**for x**... **next x**' has terminated the variable **p** is destroyed.

Accessing it outside the loop, instantiates a new variable *p* that is per default zero.

The advantage of this construction is that you can create temporary variables with extreme short lives. When manipulating large amounts of data this reduces the amount of memory required as the no longer needed variables can be destroyed thus freeing system memory much quicker.

5.9 : Subroutines and Functions

There is a tutorial program available that explains the constructs, explained in this topic, by way of example.

While programming you might have developed chunks of code or algorithms that are interesting to keep and that can be used in different portions of your programs, or even in different programs altogether. Instead of writing the code every time you need I, you can organize chunks of code in subroutines or functions.

You might also decide to create a class or custom object as these objects have even more capabilities. We will deal with those object-oriented constructs later on.

Let us first take a look at the classic subroutines and functions. There is also a chapter on 'Advanced Subroutines and Functions' later in this book. This pertains specifically to the capabilities of the NET framework. Here we will deal just with the basic construct as was found in Visual Basic Classic (5.0 and 6.0)

5.9.1 : Subroutines

The simplest form of a partition of code is a subroutine. It is a portion of code that performs a certain action based on the inputs you feed it. It does not return any resulting output to the calling process.

```
Sub DrawLine (x1,y1,x2,y2)
End Sub
```

The procedure can work with the passed information and does something without returning an answer.

To invoke the subroutine you would write

```
drawline 1,2,3,4
Call drawline(1,2,3,4)
```

Alternatively, in the NET environment:

```
drawline (0,1,2,3)
call drawline(0,1,2,3)
```

Note	A detailed explanation on the differences between passing a variable *ByVal* or *ByRef* is explained in the chapter 'On passing parameters to functions and procedures' later on in this book.

NET 2005	NET will automatically put round brackets around the variable list and add the *ByVal* modifier to specify exactly how the variable is passed. This was done to make the syntax more conform and avoid confusion.

5.9.2 : Functions

A function is similar to a procedure but it does return a value to the calling process.

```
Function Add (alb)
      Add = a + b
  End Function
```

The programming environment will automatically provide syntax help for any procedures or functions in your program. It shows you while typing what a certain procedure expects from you now. While declaring a procedure or function, you can typecast the variables that need to be passed to them, or are returned from them.

```
Function addup (a as integer, b as integer) as integer
    c = a + b
    return c
End function
```

Note	As an alternative method of returning information, you can just assign it to the function name.
	
	The above example would then be:
	``
	Function addup (a as integer, b as integer) as integer
	    c = a + b
	    addup = c
	End function
	``

You can call a function without having to collect the result. You simply call it as you would call a subroutine:

```
Addup 2,1
Call addup (1,2)
```

Alternatively, in the NET environment:

```
Addup(1,2)
Call addup(1,2)
```

But then again, what is the point in not retrieving the return value? You might as well have written the block of code as a Subroutine.

In the above example would call the function but not collect the return value. If I wanted the result of the function, I would call it like a function:

```
X = addup (1,2) ' x will contain 3
```

After the function has executed the result will be stored in the variable I assigned to it, in this case x. A function can only return one result of a given data type.

If you need to return an array or several variables there is a workaround. You can pass these variables **ByRef**. This allows the function to actually modify the passed variables. This is explained in the chapter 'On passing parameters to functions and procedures' later on in this book. If a variable is passed by reference the function can modify its contents as opposed to **ByVal** passing in which case a copy is passed and the variables contents cannot be changed, only the contents of the copy can be changed.

Note	Just as with Subroutines, you can pass variables **ByVal** or **ByRef**.

5.10 : Scope of procedures

 **proscope.vbp**   There is a tutorial program available that explains the constructs, explained in this topic, by example.

Just like variables, subroutines or functions also obey to a certain scope. You can force this scope using the Public or Private modifiers. They cannot be made Static.

By default, you can call any routine as long as it lives inside the same module. It is of no importance whether they are public or private. This scenario changes when you go to multi-module programs (multiple forms and or included files). The privately declared procedures are invisible to other modules. The public ones are visible. This means that you can have two modules called '**addup**' in two different modules without any problem.

5.11 : Numerical Operators

Visual Basic supports the basic numerical operators. The conversion from one base to another is done automatically for you. The resulting number is stored into the format of the variable used to hold the result. If you use a variant, then the number is automatically stored in the most precise format.

The order of execution obeys to the mathematical rules. You can force an execution order by placing calculations between round brackets ( ). Typically, it is good programming practice to always write brackets. After all, errors are quickly made to mathematical rules. This even gets worse when applying logical operators. After all, can you tell what this evaluates to?

```
X= 5*y-7 or int (sin z)-14 /12 '???
```

If you rewrite this, using brackets, to:

```
X= (((5*4)-7) or (int (sin z)-14)) / 12
```

It gets a lot clearer and you are sure this will be executed exactly as you wrote it. Below is a list of available mathematical operators.

Operator	Name	Function
+ - * /		Basic math operators
^	Exponent	Takes a number to the given exponent
Int	Integer	This method strips off any digits after the decimal. It does not perform rounding!
Abs	Absolute value	Removes any sign from a number
Sgn	Sign	This extracts the sign from a number. 1 for positive -1 for negative and 0 for zero.
Exp	Antilog	Returns a number specifying e raised to a power
Sin	Sine	Std trig calculation Uses RADIANS!
Cos	Cosine	Std trig calculation Uses RADIANS!
Tan	Tangent	Std trig calculation Uses RADIANS!
Atn	Arctangent	Std trig calculation Uses RADIANS!
Log	Logarithm	Natural logarithm (e based 2.718282)
Rnd	Random	Generates a random positive number between 0 and 1
Sqr	Square root	Takes the square root of a number
Mod	modulus	Returns the remainder after an integer division
\	Integer division	Returns as a result the integer number of times the divider fits in the divisor. Example:

$$5 / 2 = 2.5 \text{ but } 5 \setminus 2 = 2$$

$$13 \ /2 = 6.5 \text{ and } 13 \setminus 2 = 6$$

The other operators can be derived from these. The Visual Basic help system has a complete list of things like Sin-1, cos-1, Sin Hyp etc.

Note The built in Log function returns the natural logarithm. On handheld calculators, this is the Ln function. The Log function on a handheld is the Base 10 Log. There is no default function in visual basic to calculate this. However, this is easily written as follows:

```
Public function log10(value)
    Log10 = log(value)/log(10)
End sub
```

5.12 : Base conversion

Sometimes you might feel the need to use hexadecimal or octal numbers. Visual Basic supports these bases as well. To specify such a number you add &h or &o in front to specify that a hex or octal number is following.

```
X = &h3BC ' assigns hexadecimal 3BC to x
Y = &o701 ' assigns octal 701 to y.
```

Note Visual Basic does not support the binary base! However, the VISION system present later in this book contains Visual Basic code to add this base you have access to this number format, as it makes bit manipulations a lot easier.

Note 2 Converting strings to numbers and back is also considered base conversion. This is explained later on in the string manipulation chapter. The same rules apply. You can also put *&h* or *&o* in your strings.

5.13 : Logical Operators

Apart from the standard mathematics operators, Visual Basic supports a set of logical operators. These operators only function on integer type numbers. You cannot use these operators on floating style numbers.

NOT	Invert	In case of a Boolean, it inverts the condition. In case of a number, every bit is flipped.
OR	Or	A standard logic operator, the output is true when one input term is true.
AND	And	A standard logic operator, the output is true when all input terms are true.
XOR	XOR	A standard logic operator, the output is true if one and only one of the 2 inputs are true.
EQV	Equivalent	The output is true if both inputs have the same state (this is actually the *XNOR* function)
IMP	Implication	Consult the help system for more explanation. This is a rarely used operator.

5.14 : Shift Operators (NET only)

The NET framework implements two new operands specifically targeted towards bit shifting operations. Even though you could spend your entire life as a regular application programmer without ever using these, as a programmer writing control programs for electronics these can come in quite handy.

The shift operators << and >> allow you to shift a given number of bits in a variable. Ordinarily you could do this also by integer division by a power of2 but the shift operation is executed a lot faster since the CPU has hard coded instructions for that purpose.

```
value = 21282
shifted_Value = Value >> 4
```

The above code shifts the contents of 'value' bitwise to the right by 4 bits. For example chopping up a 16-bit value into 2 bytes becomes easy.

```
Lowbyte = (word_number and &h00FF)
High_byte = (wordnumber and &hff00) >> 8
```

Similarly recombining 2 bytes into a word becomes:

```
Word_number = high_byte
Word_number = word_number <<8
Word_number = word_number and low_byte
```

5.15 : Flow Control

So far, we have seen how to store data and perform basic mathematical operations on data. We also discovered how to group commands and expressions together in functions and procedures and how to pass data to these constructs and obtain results.

Besides these operations, we need some way to control the flow of the program. Some kind of – what if – construct to decide which way the program should continue. That is exactly what is coming next.

5.15.1 : If - Then - Else

The most basic decision routine used in Visual Basic is probably the if-then-else construction

```
if (condition) then
   ' if true
else
   ' if false
end if
```

Where condition is the result of an expression made up of two variables and a comparing function

Operator	Name	Operation
=	Equal	If the two variables contain *exactly the same data*, this operator will set the result to 'true'.
>	Bigger than	If the value contained in the *first variable is bigger than the value of variable 2* then this expression will evaluate as 'true'.
<	smaller than	Like the previous but now it evaluates to 'true' *only if var1 is less then var2*
>=	More then or equal	If the value contained in the first variable is *bigger than or equal to* the value of variable 2 then this expression will evaluate as 'true'.
<=	Less than or equal	Like the previous but now it evaluates to 'true' *only if var1 is less than or equal to var2*
<>	Different	This evaluates to 'true' as soon as the variables contain different data.

If the expression evaluates to true then the ***Then*** clause will be executed. If it does not evaluate then the ***Else*** clause is executed. This construct can be used to compare data and expressions and decide on which step to take next.

You can nest ***if-then-else*** clauses up to 255 levels deep. However, for many of these cases you could use the ***if-then-else if-else*** clause that is explained next.

```
If (x = 5) then
    If y= 2 then
        Debug.print "X=5 and Y=2"
    Else
        Debug.print " X=5 and y <>2"
    End if
Else
    Debug.print " x <>5. "
End if
```

5.15.2 : If-then-else / else if

In some cases, you will have a need for a more complex decision task. You can then use the else if construct

```
if <condition1> then
<statement1>
elseif <condition2> then
        <statement2>
elseif <condition3> then
        <statement3>
else
        <default statement>
end if
```

In most cases, it is easier to use the ***Select Case*** construct. This construct is explained next. However the If-Then-Else / Else If construct is required if you want to process objects. Select case cannot handle conditions resulting from object manipulation. This is a very rare condition however, and can be circumvented by copying the information to a temporary holding variable before evaluating it with a select-case.

I deliberately do not spend much time on this construct, as it leads to confusion and its use should be avoided. Use the more powerful select case instead.

5.15.3 : Select case

If you need to do many tests, or if a given expression can evaluate to many different results, then your best option is probably the Select case clause. The following example gives you an idea of the decision power the select case structure has aboard.

```
Select case (expression or variable resulting in a string)
case "A"
      debug.print "You typed A"
case "B","Z"
      debug.print "You typed either B or Z"
case "D" to "Y",
      debug.print "You typed a letter between D and Y"
case "HELLO","HI","GOOD MORNING"
      debug.print "Hello to you too"
case "BYE","SEEYA"
      debug.print "Goodbye, Have a nice day"
case else
      debug.print "huh?"
end select

Select case (expression or variable resulting in a number)
case 1
      debug.print "You typed 1"
case 2,3,4
      debug.print "You typed 2, 3 or 4"
case 5 to 9, 28 to 30
      debug.print "You typed something between 5 and 9 or 28 and 30"
case else
      debug.print " you typed something else"
end select
```

As you can see, you can specify values or strings, and ranges of values. When the expression or variable is checked against the Case clauses, the compiler will scan from top to bottom. The first clause to match the comparison will be executed. If no match is found the **CASE ELSE** clause will be executed.

An additional construct lets you add equality operands to the 'select case'. The IS keyword lets you add an equality test clause.

```
Select case x
    Case is <5
            ' anything less then 5 will end up here
    Case 6,7
            ' 6 and seven evaluate here
    Case 8 to 10
            ' 8 to 10 brings us here
    Case 11
            ' code for handling 11 goes here
    Case is >=12
            ' anything larger or equal to 12 is handled here
    Case else
            ' anything not covered ends up here
End select
```

5.16 : Loop Constructions

Quite often you will require a process to be repeated a number of times or until a certain condition is met. This calls for LOOP constructions. There are three basic forms of loops. The basic form will run a given number of times whereas the other two will run until depending on a specific condition being met.

5.16.1 : For - Next

This is the Basic looping construction. You use this to execute a certain action a given number of times. The For-Next clause can handle all variable types except objects.

```
For x = 1 to 10
    Debug.print x
    ' more instructions
next x
```

The first example simply counts from 0 to 10 and executes the instructions between the 'For' clause and the Next clause each time. For instance the value of X is printed. In case the counting order needs to be reversed, you can specify this using the Step keyword and a value.

```
for y = 10 to 0 step -1
next y
```

A positive step value will count up, while a negative step value will count down. The above example counts down from 10 to 0.

The step value does not need to be an integer. Any number is acceptable.

```
for z = -1.5 to 125 step +0.01
next z
```

This example will count –1.5 to 125 in steps of 0.01: -1.5, -1.49, -1.48 ... 124.98, 124.99 125.

Note   It is not allowed to change the counter value from within the loop. This common mistake is often made. The construct allows you to do this. However, this can lead to system lock-ups. Programmers often use this technique to prematurely abort the execution of the FOR loop. DO NOT do this. ! There is an **Exit For** statement specifically intended for this kind of functionality.

If you need to exit the For-Next loop prematurely, then you should use the Exit-for statement.

```
For x = 0 to 100000
    If x = 125 then exit for
Next x
```

The counter would normally run from 0 to 10000, however, if the value of x reaches 125 the `Exit for` command will abort the loop end resume program execution after 'Next x'.

5.16.2 : While - Wend

This looping procedure runs as long as a certain condition is true.

The checking of the condition occurs before execution of the sequence. This means that if the condition is already met from the beginning, the sequence will not be executed but skipped.

```
While x <5
    X=X+1
    Debug.print x
Wend
```

The above construction will run until **x = 5**, and then exit.

If the variable **x** were to contain 6, the **While-Wend** will not be executed. The test happens first. As long as the test condition fails, the code between **while** and **wend** is executed. As soon as a match occurs the while-wend terminates.

NET 2005	The 'wend' statement is replaced by the 'end while' construct. The project importer will fix this for you. However, when writing new code this is important. Fortunately, the auto complete functionality in NET automatically inserts the correct construct.

If you need to abort this sequence, you should use the exit-do statement.

5.16.3 : Do Until / While

This is the other looping construct in Visual Basic. It is similar to the While-Wend construct except that the testing of the condition happens at the end of the sequence. This means that, no matter what, the sequence will always be executed at least once.

```
Do
    X =x+1
Loop until x > 5
```

If I start here with x initialized to 6, then it will be incremented to 7, before it is tested against the condition clause.

The same rule as for the While-wend applies. Never jump out of this construction. Use the exit-do command. The problem with jumping out is that some residual stuff is left on the stack of the program execution. The compiler checks for this and inserts cleanup code to work around this. However, this is not fail safe and might eventually lead to a system level crash.

The difference between the do-while and do-until is in the expression evaluation. A do-while runs a certain operation until the given expression evaluates to 'false'. A 'do-until' runs until the test expression evaluates to 'true'. In any case, the loop will at least be run once, as the test happens at the end.

5.16.4 : The For-Each construct

The 'for-each' construct is used in conjunction with objects. It allows you to manipulate collections of objects. As objects are dynamic, you cannot determine how many are actually present. Therefore, an ordinary for-next would not work since you can determine neither the low nor upper bound, and referencing an inexistent object generates an error.

Suppose you have a number of radio-buttons on a form that belong to the same collection i.e. they have the same name but a different index. During startup you want to modify a number of properties. If you know, on beforehand the amount of individual objects, you could use a hard coded 'for-next' construct. The problem arises when objects are added or removed during the design time, or dynamically at runtime. The hard coded loop will not cover all elements or too many elements.

That is where the 'for each' comes in handy

```
For each x in radio_button1
    x.caption= "Hello world"
next
```

The above example will automatically sweep al members belonging to the object radio_button1 and set their captions to 'hello world'.

The 'for each' construct can also be used to retrieve information from regular variables.

```
Dim library(100) as string
Library(7) = "Pinocchio"
Library(12) = "The Wizard of Oz"
Library(13) = "The Tell Tale Heart"
For each book in library
    Debug.print book
next
```

With variables, you can only retrieve information and not assign information back to the array. Then what good is it, you might ask. Well, you can use this to quickly copy an array to a listbox or Combo box for instance.

5.17 : String manipulation Left$ - Right$ - Ltrim$ - Rtrim$.

When working with strings you will often manipulate their contents. In Visual Basic, there is a rich instruction set to manipulate strings.

Suppose a$ contains "How are you?"

5.17.1 : Left$

This command takes the left n characters from a given string.

```
T$ = Left$ (a$,3)  ' t$ now contains "How"
```

5.17.2 : Right$

This command takes the right n characters from a given string.

```
t$ = Right$ (a$, 4)   ' t$ now contains "you?"
```

5.17.3 : Mid$

Just like its smaller brother Left$ and Right$ this allows to you to extract a given amount of characters starting at an offset in a string.

```
a$ = "How are you?"
t$ = Mid$ (a$, 4, 3)  ' t$ will contain "are"
```

The first argument gives the string that needs to be truncated, the second parameter specifies the offset in the string and the last argument gives the number of characters that will be returned starting from the given offset.

5.17.4 : Ltrim$ / Rtrim$ / Trim$

These functions remove 'white space' at the beginning and / or end of the string. 'White space' is any non-printable character. Therefore, everything that is not a letter, number or punctuation mark will be removed. These functions are very useful to manipulate user input or file input from an unknown origin.

```
A$ = LTrim$(b$)
```

5.17.5 : Ucase$ and Lcase$

This function converts a given string to an all-uppercase string or all lower-case string. A very useful combination of these functions is often the following:

```
a$ = Ucase$ (Ltrim$ (Rtrim$ (a$)))
```

This strips off any leading and trailing 'white space' and converts it to an uppercase only string. If you want to write a small command interpreter or macro tool, you will use this construct very often.

Similarly the *Lcase$* would generate an all-lowercase string.

5.17.6 : VAL and STR$

These functions are used to convert numbers to and from strings. The VAL function extracts a number form a string. The routine stops scanning at the first encounter of a non-number character. VAL is also capable of recognizing scientific format numbers (-1.2 e-15) and different based numbers.

```
print val ("10 hello")        ' prints 10
print val ("&h10 bye")        ' prints 16
print val ("-1.55 test")      ' prints -1.55
print val ("-1.5e-55 ok")     ' prints -1.5e-55
```

The *STR$* function has the opposite effect. It converts any number to its string style representation.

```
a$ = Str$(123)          ' will return as string containing "123"
```

5.17.7 : LEN

While not really a string manipulation function, it is used in conjunction with these functions. LEN tells you exactly how long a string is. If it is empty, a Zero is returned.

```
B$ = "HELLO"
For x = 1 to len(b$)
    Debug.print mid$(b$,x,1);" ";
next x
```

This will output *H E L L O* to the debug windows. It checks how long the string is and then will extract the character one by one and print each character followed by a space.

5.17.8 : INSTR

This search routine allows you to find strings in other strings. You can use this to search for words or special characters.

```
X = instr("HELLO","E") ' will return 2
```

Upon execution, X will contain 2. This means that an 'E' was found at position 2.You can also specify an offset:

```
X = instr("HELLO THERE","E",3)  ' will return 9
```

Now the result is 9 because you started searching at position 3 (the first L) and found an E at position 9.

5.17.9 : String concatenation

Historically strings were added using the + operand. Any non-string type variable had to be explicitly converted to a string. In Visual Basic 5.0 and later the ampersand '&' acts as a concatenation symbol that can intelligently convert formats.

```
Dim a as long
Dim b as long
Dim t as string
A= 5
B = 6
Debug.print a & " + " & b & " = " & (a+b)
```

The above yields the following output as result '5 + 6 = 11'.

In a similar fashion, the following code produces the text 'This is a string merged from two strings'.

```
F = "This is a string "
G = "merged from two strings
Debug.print f & g
X = f & g 'the result now also sits in a variable.
```

| NET 2005 | The usage of the ampersand (&) is the only way to concatenate strings in the NET platform. Although a compatibility layer exists, using operator overloading, that still allows you to use the + operator, later versions of NET will no longer support this. |

5.17.10 : String handling in NET.

The NET framework adds a class specifically targeting string manipulations. While the old Basic style operators still work, the new class adds functionality that was previously not available. As explained before, variables are all considered objects under the NET framework. Hence, a variable can have a method attached to it, derived form the class it belongs to.

Any variable belonging to the string class has a number of methods that allow you to manipulate the data. It is preferred to use the NET style when writing new code in the NET framework as this will result in portable code in the NET platform.

5.17.11 : Equivalent String Methods in NET

Len has its equivalent in the length method. *Ucase* and *Lcase* have their equivalent in
ToUpper and *ToLower* respectively.

Old style	New Style
T$ = Ucase$(t$)	T= T.ToUpper()
T$ = Lcase$(t$)	T = T.ToLower()
X = Len(t$)	X = T.length

These methods can be invoked in both the old style and new style but the upgrade wizard will
change them to the new style as later versions of Visual Basic might do away with the old style
operators.

5.17.12 : Padleft and PadRight methods (NET only).

Padleft and *PadRight* allow you to add white space to either the left side or right side of the
string. You specify how much white space is needed. In the event that the string is already
equal to or longer than the desired size no operation is performed.

```
F = "Hello"
F = F.Padleft(10)    ' F now contains "     Hello"
F = F.Padright(15)   ' F now contains "     Hello      "
```

5.17.13 : Insert and Remove (NET only).

These commands allow you to insert and remove sections of a string. The old style constructs
Mid$*, *Left$ and *Right$* can perform a similar operation if you write some surrounding code.

```
A = "This is a string"
B = "manipulated "
C = a.insert (8, B)
' C now contains the string "This is a manipulated string"
```

In a similar fashion, the remove operation can remove a chain of characters from a string.

```
A = "This is a string"
B = "manipulated "
C = a.insert (8, B)
' C now contains the string "This is a manipulated string"
C = c.remove (8, 12)
```

The remove method takes two arguments: the starting position in the string and the number of characters that need to be removed. In the above example, 12 characters are removed starting at the eighth position in the string.

5.17.14 : Join and split (NET only).

These methods allow you to store elements of an array in a string and specify a character to be use as separator.

```
Dim Muffins() as string = {"Blueberry", "Chocolate Chip", "Cinnamon"}
Muffinlist = string.join(",", muffins)

' muffinlist contains a string the looks like this
' Blueberry,Chocolate Chip,Cinnamon
```

This string can now be passed as an argument to a subroutine, or even used as return value from a function. Passing arrays as a return value is hard and these methods give you an escape path.

To break the string into separate units you can use the split method.

```
Dim desserts() as string
desserts = string.split (muffinlist, ",")
dim dessert as string
for each dessert in desserts
    debug.print dessert
next
```

5.18 : File Manipulation under Visual Basic Classic

During your programming work, you will often find yourself in a situation where you need to store something to disk or retrieve it; the information can be all sorts of data, whether it is numerical, text, binary or even an entire database with linked lists, records, custom styles etcetera. Well, you could have not picked a simpler language. Basic in general is probably the only language in which file manipulation is so simple, yet at the same time so extended. This chapter might look overwhelming at first but that is just because there are so many things you can do with files. Since file input and output is one of the most used operations when writing software, I tried to be as complete as possible. This is material that you can read as-you-go. You can easily skip this chapter if you are not going to deal with files yet and come back later.

Files are referenced to using 'handles'. A handle is a storage space that the computer uses to remember where the file resides physically on disk, at what position you are reading, and what the current file status is. This handle points to the information that defines the file to the operating system.

A handle is specified by using the # sign followed by a number. You can use your own numbering scheme or you can ask the system to give you a handle. The function *'freefile'* checks for a free 'handle', allocates it and returns it to you.

5.18.1 : Obtaining a file handle.

In order to be able to perform file operations you will need to obtain a so-called handle. This is a logical link between the actual file as it resides in storage and your program. Since you can have any given number of files open at any time in lots of different modes, this handle also contains information about the access modes.

There are two basic ways to obtain handle information: hard coded and dynamic.

In the hard coded way, you specify a number preceded by the pound (#) sign. This is the style that has been used for years and works fine but it has its drawbacks. You have to keep track of which handles are in use, and, take care not to allocate an open handle to a different file, as this will produce a runtime error. Another disadvantage is that you cannot pass such handles as variables; they are hard coded in place.

Example:
```
Open "myfile.txt" for output as #1
```

Fortunately, there is a better way using dynamic handles. The **freefile** function will find an unused handle, allocate it and return it for you to store in a variable.

```
Myfile = freefile
```

In the above piece of code, the handle will be stored in the variable **MyFile**. You can subsequently use this to access files and perform operations.

```
Open "myfile.txt" for output as myfile
```

The advantage is that you can pass the file handle as an argument to a routine whereas this is impossible using hardcode handles. You can have a maximum of 512 files open at any given time. Per default, the **freefile** function returns a number in the range 1 to 255. You can override this and request additional file numbers in the range 256 to 511 by specifying an argument to the **freefile** functions.

Example:
```
Firstfile = freefile ' default in 1.. 255
' Open file..
Secondfile=freefile(0) ' force 1..255
' Open file…
Thirdfile=freefile(1)' force 256 to 511
' Open file…
```

As explained, you can pass the handle as an argument to code. This saves you a lot of work since you can have all file IO stored in custom routines that become reusable throughout your program.

Example:

```
        Firstfile = freefile
        Open "file1.txt" for output as firstfile
        Secondfile = freefile
        Open "file2.txt" for output as secondfile

        Writecomment firstfile,"this is a line of text in the first file"
        Writecomment secondfile," this is a line of text in the second file"
        Close

        Sub writecomment(handle,info)
                Print #handle,info
        End sub
```

It is very important to note that requesting a file handle does NOT increment the handle. As long as the file has not been opened, the **freefile** function will always return the lowest unused file handle.

Example:

```
        'the following produces a runtime error:
        FirstFile = freefile
        SecondFile = freefile
        Open "file1.txt" for output as FirstFile
        Open "file2.txt" for output as SecondFile ` error as the handle is
        already used in 'firstfile'

        ` this is the corrected code.
        FirstFile = freefile
        Open "file1.txt" for output as FirstFile
        SecondFile = freefile
        Open "file2.txt" for output as SecondFile
```

The first example aborts as soon we open **SecondFile**. Since no file was opened after requesting a handle for **FirstFile**, the **freefile** function returned the same handle for **SecondFile**. This pitfall is often overlooked. **Freefile** returns always the lowest, currently not used, file handle. It is not until you open the file that the handle becomes 'used'. Closing the file releases the handle back to the pool for re-use. Let us look at opening and closing files.

5.18.2 : Basic structure to open and close files

Once you have obtained a unique handle for the file you can proceed and open the file using that handle. There are a number of different possibilities, but let us look at the most basic examples first.

```
        outfile = freefile      ` retrieves a free handle
        open "myfile.txt" for input as #100
        appfile = freefile      ` retrieves another free handle
        open "myfile.out" for output as outfile
        myappfile = "appfile.txt"
        open myappfile for append as appfile
```

The above examples show you the basic modes of operation and the different ways you can specify a filename and handle.

Since Windows is a multi-tasking environment, the risk exists that a separate process attempts to access the same file as we are. When the file is in use, a runtime error will be generated in our program. Therefore, the Open statement provides additional modifiers that control how access is handles. You can even specify which operation is allowed to be performed on a particular file.

The complete syntax of the open command looks like this:

```
Open filepath+name for mode <access method><protection> as handle
```

The file path and name are any legal windows filename and path location.

The mode is one of the following possibilities: *input, output, random, binary* or *append.* The differences are explained in greater detail in the next topics.

The access specifies what you want to do with the file. It is one of the following: *Read, Write* or *Read Write*. As this is an optional parameter and it is assumed to be *Read-Write* by default. The use of the optional modifier allows you to keep tight control over the code that performs file operations, and possible assist in tapping bugs or coding errors.

Protection allows you to define if multiple processes can access the file, and how they should behave. The possibilities are *Shared, Lock Read, Lock Write* and *Lock Read Write.* *Shared* mode allows multiple processes to access a file simultaneously. *Lock Read* prohibits other applications to read the file. *Lock write* prohibits the other applications to write to a file but they can read from it, and lastly *Lock Read* write prohibits any other application to access the file while you have control over it. As this is an optional parameter, it also defaults to *Lock Read Write*.

Example:
```
Open "a.txt" For Output Access Write Lock Write as #1
```

This file can only be written from our program and only be accessed as read by any other program.

Whenever a file has been opened, it should be closed when you have finished with it, and that is exactly what the close command does. If you use *Close* without parameters you will close ALL handles to any file currently open. If you use *close* with a file handle, it will close this file. If the handle does not exist, the close statement will do nothing.

```
Close #1 ' close file with handle 1
Close ' close all files
```

| Note | When a program is terminated by the END command, all open files are closed automatically, so there is no need to worry about that. |

5.18.3 : Output mode

When you open a filename for output then two situations can occur: either the file exists or it does not. If it does not exist, it will be created. If it exists, the file will be overwritten without warning.

Data can be written to a file using the print command in conjunction with the handle.

```
outfile = freefile    ' retrieves a free handle
open "myfile.txt" for output as outfile
print #outfile,"HELLO"
close outfile
```

Of course, the access modifiers described in the previous topic can be applied here as well. It might be interesting to lock a file for reading wile it is being written, even if it is just to prevent a different process from reading outdated information.

5.18.4 : Append mode.

The append mode is an extension of the normal output mode. It allows you to append data to an existing file in case you do not want to overwrite it. The data you send will automatically be written at the end of the current file. To store data you can again use the print method.

```
open "myfile.txt" for append as #1
```

Again, the access modifiers do apply and can be used at will. If the file does not exist, it will be created automatically.

5.18.5 : Input mode.

If you want to read something from a file this is one of the possible ways to retrieve the data. This opens a file for read. In case the file does not exist, a runtime error will occur. You should take care to check for the existence of a file before you attempt to open it for Input.

```
open "myfile.txt" for input as #1
```

It is possible to open a file multiple times if its mode is Input, Binary or Random.

5.18.6 : Binary mode

The Binary access mode is used to be able to treat the file as a collection of bytes. It allows you to retrieve all contents without interpretation. Care has to be taken not to read beyond the end of the file. There are special commands to detect how long the file is.

Example:

```
open "myfile.txt" for binary as #1
```

The Binary mode operation uses special commands such as Get, Put and Seek Non-existing files are automatically created just like in the Output, append or Random modes.

5.18.7 : Random mode

The Random mode is a legacy method to store a record set such as databases. This mode operates only in conjunction with the *Get* and *Put* operators. It is not advised to use this mode anymore, as there are far more powerful data storage mechanisms available.

Example:

```
open "myfile.txt" for random as #1
```

5.18.8 : Storing something in a file

This is easy: just use Print to send it to the file

```
myfile = freefile
open "test.txt" for output as #1
print #1, "Hello world"
close #1
```

Any accepted print expression can be sent to a file.

Note | This is the only place in Visual Basic where you can still use the Print statement, as it used to be implemented in regular Basic. All other cases treat Print as a method of an object even the DEBUG object

Since I have not explained print yet, this is a good point to do so.

5.18.9 : PRINT constructions for object and file output.

Print is a tremendously versatile command. You can send nearly anything to it for printing. In Visual Basic, you can only use the native print command in combination with files. All other print statements are actually methods of objects (textboxes, printers, even the Debug object).

There are two basic ways of invoking print: send it a data list, or first build a string and then send it. The end result is the same but the execution is not. A data list requires the compiler to move all data bit by bit to the printing code. This takes time but does not use memory. The string-building way requires scratch memory to build the string but is a lot faster since only the entry point to the string is passed. Anyhow, in today's optimizing compilers the end result is the same.

5.18.9.1 : Data list Style.

```
Name$="USER"
Number=1
Print #1,"Hello ",name$,"You are my No",number
```

This will output "Hello   USER   You are my No   1". You might think this looks strange but actually, it does not! The comma really means 'move to the next tab'. If you do the following:

```
Print #1,"Hello ";name$;" You are my No";number
```

You will get a string as you would expect it. The string printed automatically gets a CR/LF pair appended (Carriage return Line Feed). If you want to suppress this, you simply append a semicolon at the end of the expression.

```
For a = 0 to 10
    Print a
Next a
```

Results in a list of numbers

```
For a = 0 to 10
    Print a;
Next a
```

Results in "12345678910"

5.18.9.2 : String style

```
Name$="USER"
Number=1
Print #1,"Hello " + name$ + "You are my No" + str$(number)
```

This first builds a complete string and passes it to the print command.

> **Note** You can only pass strings to this style. So you must manually convert any numbers to strings before adding them with the + sign.

The same trick as with the 'Data list' style applies here. By ending with a semicolon, you can omit the CR/LF insertion. Instead of using the + operator you can now also insert the '&' operator. The end result is the same but the way it is done is not. The '&' operator is explained in detail in the chapter in string concatenation.

5.18.10 : Line Input.

Line Input is the counterpart to the Print operation on files. This function retrieves an entire line from a file. It scans the file from the current location to the first occurrence of a CR/LF (carriage return / line feed). There are other ways to retrieve data but they are used to extract records, a known amount of bytes or binary data. These functions will be discussed later on in this book.

```
Open "myfile.txt" for input as #1
while not eof (1)
      line input #1,a$
      textbox1.text = textbox1.text +a$ +Chr$(13) +Chr$(10)
wend
close #1
```

The above piece of code will read an entire text file and dump it into a textbox. Since the **Line Input** statement reads a line, but removes the trailing CR/LF pair, we have to add it to the textbox.

Subsequent calls to the function will retrieve the next lines in the file. You should check not to read past the end of the file by using the **EOF** () function.

5.18.11 : Write.

This is a similar operation to the print command except that it comma separates each argument when writing to the file.

For example:

```
Sub test()
      Open"test.txt" for output as #1
      For x = 1 to 5
            Print #1,x ;
      Next x
End sub
' the file will contain a single line containing the string 12345

Sub test()
      Open"test.txt" for output as #1
      For x = 1 to 5
            write #1,x;
      Next x
      Write "hello world"
End sub
' the file will contain the text  1,2,3,4,5,"hello world"
' note that the text is contained in quotes
```

The advantage of using this scheme is that a formatted file is generated that can be directly read using other programs (Excel for instance), or directly from Visual Basic using the write functions counterpart: the Input command.

The Write command also interprets the data type and inserts padding characters that allow the Input # command to correctly retrieve the information. Strings are contained in quotes, Dates are converted so that it will work regardless of locale and Booleans are written as #TRUE# or #FALSE#.

At the end of the line, a Carriage return/line feed is inserted automatically. Just as with the print command, ending the line in a semicolon suppresses the CR/LF generation.

5.18.12 : Input

The input function is the counterpart of the write subroutine. It can be used to retrieve automatically comma-delimited data.

Example:

```
Input #1,a,b,c,d
```

This will read four parameters from the file defined by handle #1 and store them in variables a, b, c and d respectively.

The combination of the Write and input command can be used to very quickly store and retrieve data arrays to and from disk.

Example:

```
Dim datafield(10,5)
Sub savefield
    Open "datafile.txt" for output as #1
    For x = 0 to 10
        For y=0 to 5
            Write #1,datafield(x,y);
        Next y
    Next x
    Close #1
End sub
Sub loadfield
    Open "datafile.txt" for input as #1
    For x = 0 to 10
        For y=0 to 5
            Input #1, datafield(x,y)
        Next y
    Next x
    Close #1
End sub
```

5.18.13 : Get and Put.

Get and put are operators used in conjunction with files opened in Binary or Random mode. There is a difference in operation depending on the file mode. I will focus on the Binary mode. For the specifics of Get and Put in Random mode please consult the Visual Basic help.

Syntax:
```
Get #filehandle,<offset>,variable
```

The file handle is as usual any valid file handle that points to a file opened in Binary mode. The offset parameter is an optional argument that can be omitted. If specified it sets the location in the file where the command will be executed.

Example:

```
Dim something as integer
Get %1,100,something
```

The above example will read an integer (2 bytes for Visual Basic Classic) from the file at an offset of 100 bytes.

Subsequent calls to Get but without the offset will read the next bytes. Depending on the data type specified one or more bytes would be read. If you specify a fixed size string, then an amount equal to the size will be read.

Example:

```
Dim something as string *100
Get %1,222,something
```

This will read a string of 100 bytes starting at location 222 in the file.

Of course, there is a counterpart to the Get function, which is the Put command. In a similar fashion, the Put command writes variable contents as streams of bytes to a file opened in Binary mode. The same command parameter style is maintained
```
Put #filehandle,<offset>,variable
```

It is again important to note that the actual amount of bytes written depends on the variable type.

```
Dim something as string * 100
Something = "hello"
put %1,,something
```

This will write 100 bytes, of which the first five represent the string 'hello' to the file starting at position 0. Since a total of 100 bytes will be written, there is no telling what will be written there. The content depends on the actual information stored in the file buffers at that time.

5.18.14 : The seek operation.

The **seek** command allows you to set or retrieve the current location a file operation will take place. It is commonly used in conjunction with get/put operations.

Example:

```
X = seek(#1)
```

This will return the current position where file operation will take place in the file defined by handle #1.

You can also use this command to change the position where the next operation will take place.

```
Seek #1,222
```

This sets the file location pointer at address 222.

Since the **Get** and **Put** operations also allow you to specify there is little us for the Seek command except in cases where you have multiple processes running in parallel. For instance, a file holds information about the state of a system. At regular intervals, for example code attached to a timer event, the status is written. Since this runs as an independent process, you have no clue where the main program is performing operations.

The following code would be a case where you can make use of the seek operation.

```
Private Sub Timer1_Timer()
a = Seek(1)
Put #1, 100, StatusCode
Seek 1, a
End Sub
```

5.18.15 : Determining the length and end of a file

When you are reading from a file, you should take care not to read beyond the end of the file since this will result in an error. The **EOF** function can return you whether you have reached the end of an open file.

```
Open "test.txt" for input as #1
While not eof(1)
    Line input #1,a$
    Debug.print a$
Wend
Close #1
```

The above example shows you how to use it. Note that you can use this only in conjunction with the input mode.

If you are manipulating binary files, you should use the **LOF** operator before performing any read. Since a file opened in binary mode is handled as a string of bytes there is no real detection of he **EOF** character. The **LOF** function retrieves the length of the file as stored in the file system.

```
Open "test.txt" for binary as #1
length = lof(1)
```

The above example will return the length of the file in bytes in the variable 'length'. The **LOF** function only works if a file is open. It is possible to read the file length without opening a file by using the **FileLen** function.

```
Open "test.txt" for binary as #1
length = filelen("test.txt")
```

The main difference between the **LOF** and **FileLen** command is that **LOF** represents the actual length of an open file, while **FileLen** returns the size of an unopened file. If **FileLen** is used on an open file, it will return the size of the file as it was prior to opening.

5.18.16 : File names.

Any valid windows file can be opened. Attempting to open a non-existing file can have two outcomes. In case the mode is output, the file will be created. In case the mode is input, you will be stuck with a runtime error. You should especially take care with routines that allow the user to specify a file. Validating a filename can be a very complex matter. Especially resolving a pathname across a network connection can be cumbersome. However, there is a much simpler way. Simply use the CommonDialog File Open and File Save to handle all of this for you. This object is dealt with in Part II.

5.18.17 : The DIR command and File existence

The **Dir** command allows you to retrieve file and directory information. To start the process you invoke the Dir command with arguments. The syntax takes the following format:

```
Dir <Filestring>, <Attributes>
```

The File string contains the file you are looking for. You can use the classic wildcards such as '*' and '?'. The attributes specify what kind of entry in the directory you are looking for. The parameter is optional but its possible arguments are **vbNormal** for regular files, **vbReadOnly** for files that are marked as read-only, **vbHidden** for files that are hidden from normal view, **vbSystem** for system files, **vbVolume** to retrieve the volume header and **vbDirectory** for directories. You can add multiple attributes to your search by adding them together. **VbNormal** is assumed as the default if nothing is specified.

Examples:
```
x = Dir("*.*", vbDirectory + vbHidden) ' find all hidden directories
x = Dir("*.txt") ' find all txt files
x = Dir("*.txt",vbReadOnly) ' find all txt files that are read only
```

The **Dir** function returns a string with the exact filename and path for the first file it finds that matches the given description. When nothing is found, the function returns a blank string. Subsequent calls to the **DIR** function without arguments retrieve the next file that matches the description.

Example: find all regular subdirectories and files

```
entry = Dir("c:\*.*", vbDirectory)
dirlist = dirlist + entry + vbCrLf
While entry <> ""
        entry = Dir ' retrieve next entry
        dirlist = dirlist + entry + vbCrLf
Wend
MsgBox dirlist
```

NOTE Regular files will always be listed. So if you look for directories like in the above examples regular filenames will be returned as well. There is no real way to check if the returned information is a file or a directory until you try to perform **CHdir** and get an error.

Visual Basic Classic does not really provide a means to check if a given file is valid or actually exists. When performing write operations this is not really a problem since the file will be created automatically. The problem arises when you try to read form a nonexistent file.

Fortunately, it is very easy to code such a routine ourselves.

```
Function FileExists(filename As String) As Boolean
    On Error Resume Next
        FileExists = False
    If Dir(filename) <> "" Then
        FileExists = True
    End If
End Function
```

The above piece of code will check if a given file exists. It returns a Boolean (true or false).

NET 2005 This problem has been solved in the NET framework where a collection of methods is available to validate files.

5.18.18 : Removing files using the Kill function

You can remove files using the **Kill** method. **Kill** takes as argument any valid file name. You can also use wildcards '*' and '?' to delete multiple files at the same time, and you can include a search path.

Example:
```
Kill "c:\temp\*.tmp" ' would delete all "tmp" files from the
                     ' path "c:\temp"
Kill "file*.txt" ' will delete all files matching "file*.txt"
                 ' where * is a wildcard, in the current directory
```

No return value is given and, if an inexistent file is specified, nothing will happen.

5.18.19 : Changing directories and drives

Even though you can specify complete paths in all file operation commands it is sometimes easier to perform this once instead of passing the argument all the time. The **CHdir** and **ChDrive** command allow you exactly to do that.

CHdir allows you to change the current working directory for file operations to the argument specified. The argument has to be a valid, existing path.

Example:
```
Chdir "c:\windows"
```

Note that the **CHdir** command changes the directory but does not change the default drive you are working with. For people that remember the DOS command line: this is exactly how the DOS CD command works. If the current selected drive is C and you execute a CHdir "d:\tmp" then the directory has changed on drive D. If you would perform a file operation, it would still be performed on the current selected directory on drive C.

To change drive the **ChDrive** command is used. **ChDrive** takes a string as argument, but only uses the first character.

Example:
```
Chdrive "d"
```

Suppose that on a machine with two disks (c and d) you want to create a file in c:\tmp and d:\tmp you would need to do the following:

```
' using full filepath specifications
x = freefile
Open "c:\tmp\hello.txt" for output as #x
Print #1,aaaa
Close
Open "d:\tmp\hello.txt" for output as #x
Print #1,aaaa
Close

' using Chdir and Chdrive
Chdrive "c"
Chdir "c:\tmp"
x = freefile
Open "hello.txt" for output as #x
Print #1,aaaa
Close
```

```
Chdrive "d"
Chdir "d:\tmp"
Open "hello.txt" for output as #x
Print #1,aaaa
Close
```

5.18.20 : Creating and removing directories

The **MKdir** and **RMdir** commands work in exactly the same way as the old Dos commands did.

In order to create a directory, execute the **MKdir** command. Note that you cannot create nested directories directly. This means that, if you want to create a directory in a nonexistent directory, you have to create the top-level directory first.

Example:

```
Mkdir "c:\test"
Mkdir "c:\test\garbage"
```

To remove a directory, execute the **RMdir** command with the name of the directory to remove. You can specify a complete drive + path but only the last directory will be removed and only if it is empty.

Example:

```
Rmdir "c:\test\garbage"
Rmdir "c:\test"
```

5.18.21 : Retrieving the current location

It is sometime necessary to retrieve the current location the active file path points to. This can be dune using the **CurDir** function in Visual Basic Classic.

Example:

```
Debug.print curdir ' this will tell you the active drive
                   '+ the active path
Debug.print curdir("C") ' this will tell you the current active path
                   ' on the C disk
Debug.print curdir("D") ' this will tell you the active current path
                   ' on the D disk
```

5.19 : Using the FileSystemObject

Windows has a class library you can use to perform other file operations such as getting the number of available drives, finding where windows lives, finding the temp folder and many more. To use this object you need to create a link to it inside the Visual Basic IDE.

Click Project and go to 'References'.

Scroll through the list until you find the Microsoft Script control and check it.

Visual Basic now gets the capability to use all methods, events and properties from the *FileSystemObject* class. Next, we will take a look how to work with this. For the moment, do not worry about classes. That will be explained in detail later on.

There are two entries that both point to the same DLL. It is important you link both, as one entry point is the actual library while the entry point other holds the wrapper layer to be able to use it from Visual Basic. While it might be possible that your code runs with only one, your distributed application might not as the packager can not determine what files to copy.

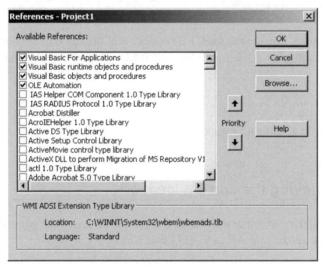

5.19.1 : Instantiating the Filesystemobject

In order to be able to use the methods form the *FileSystemObject* we need to instantiate an object. First, we declare a variable, with name of our choice. The next thing we do assign a reference to the *FileSystemObject* object using the *Set* keyword. Since a class is not an object, we need to use the *CreateObject* method to instantiate the class as an object to the programming environment. Again, this will be explained din detail when we deal with classes.

Example:

```
Dim filehandler
Set filehandler = createobject("scripting.FileSystemObject")
```

5.19.2 : The Drives collection

The **FileSystemObject** has a whole range of methods you can invoke, as well as properties you can retrieve. One such property is the **Drives** collection. This allows you to retrieve all information about a specific drive.

Example:

```
Sub ShowDriveinfo()
    Dim myFSO, DriveCollection, Disk
    Set myFSO = CreateObject("Scripting.FileSystemObject")
    Set DriveCollection = myFSO.drives
    For Each Disk In DriveCollection
        Debug.Print "Disk " & Disk.DriveLetter & ":";
        Select Case Disk.DriveType
        Case 0:
                Debug.Print "Unknown type "
        Case 1:
                Debug.Print "Removable disk "
        Case 2:
                Debug.Print "Fixed disk, ";
                Debug.Print "Volume:";
                If Disk.VolumeName = "" Then
                   Debug.Print "--None--, ";
                Else
                   Debug.Print Disk.VolumeName; ", ";
                End If
                Debug.Print "Free:"; Disk.FreeSpace / 1024; "KB ";
                Debug.Print "Total:"; Disk.TotalSize / 1024; "KB, ";
                Debug.Print "Serial: "; Hex$(Disk.SerialNumber); " ";
                Debug.Print "Filesystem: "; Disk.FileSystem
        Case 3:
                Debug.Print "Network share, ";
                Debug.Print Disk.ShareName; ", ";
                Debug.Print "Free:"; Disk.FreeSpace / 1024; "KB ";
                Debug.Print "Total:"; Disk.TotalSize / 1024; "KB "
        Case 4:
                Debug.Print "CD-ROM drive"
        Case 5:
                Debug.Print "RAM Disk, ";
                Debug.Print "Volume:"; Disk.VolumeName;
                Debug.Print "Free:"; Disk.FreeSpace / 1024; "KB ";
                Debug.Print "Total:"; Disk.TotalSize / 1024; "KB "
        Case Else
                Debug.Print " i was not expecting this"
        End Select
    Next
End Sub
```

The above piece of code will scan through the available drives using a 'for-each' construct. Depending on the **DriveType** returned it will retrieve information such as the volume label, free space, total space, the disks serial number and even what file system it is formatted in.

5.19.3 : FileSystemObject methods

Below is a summary list of what the commands do. A lot of the functionality of the standard basic commands is duplicated since this class can be used by any generic programming language. The list is too long to go on each of these in detail, but the help system of Visual Basic 6.0 has detailed information and examples available.

CopyFile	This command allows you to copy files from one location to another. You can use wildcards like '?' and *.
CopyFolder	This allows you to copy a directory containing files to different locations. You can use wildcards like '?' and '*'.
CreateFolder	The **CreateFolder** method allows you to create folders
CreateTextFile	This allows you to create text files. This returns an object you can manipulate. See next topic
DeleteFile	This keyword deletes a file. You can use wildcards like '?' and *.
DeleteFolder	This method deletes a folder. You can use wildcards like '?' and *.
DriveExists	The **DriveExists** method checks if a certain drive exists. Returns a Boolean
FileExists	The **Fileexists** method checks for the existence of the specified file and returns a **Boolean** which is set to **true** if the file is found.
FolderExists	This method checks for the existence of a specified folder
GetAbsolutePathname	This is a very powerful command that allows you to search for the location of folders.
GetBaseName	This returns you the filename out of a drive-path-file string without the extension. For example a = drivepathname"d:\temp\hello.txt" would return 'hello'.
GetDrive	This returns you the disk number form a drive-path-file string.

GetDriveName	The *GetDriveName* method retrieves the name of the drive form the specified path.
GetExtentionName	This is the counterpart for Get Base Name. It gets you the file extension for the drive-path-file-string. For example a = getextentionname"d:\temp\hello.txt" would return 'txt'.
GetFile	This returns a file object you can manipulate using its own methods form a drive-path-file string.
GetFileName	*GetFileName* returns you the complete path less the drive name.
GetFolder	*GetFolder* returns the folder location where a file is stored.
GetParentFolder	*GetParentFolder* returns the parent folder of the folder where the file is stored.
GetTempName	*GetTempName* finds and returns the location of the temporary folder on the computer.
MoveFile	*MoveFile* is used to move a file from location 1 to location 2. You can use wildcards.
MoveFolder	*MoveFolder* works like *MoveFile* but moves a folder and its contents from location 1 to location 2.
OpenTextFile	*OpenTextFile* opens an existing text file as an object you can manipulate. This is explained in detail in the next topic.

5.19.4 : Text stream I/O using Filesystemobject

The *FileSystemObject* has a number of interesting methods to manipulate plain text files. In order to be able to use this, you need to create the reference for the project to msscr.dll using the previously described method.

First thing we need to do is instantiate the object and define it as a 'text stream'.

Example:

```
Set myFSO = CreateObject("Scripting.FileSystemObject")
Set mytext = myFSO.CreateTextFile("test.txt", True)
mytext.WriteLine("Hello World.")
mytext.Close
```

The above example instantiates the class **FileSystemObject** and pulls an object of the type **TextFile** called **mytext**. The argument **true** allows the file to be overwritten should it exist. The next line writes some text to the file and then the last finally closes the file.

The **FileSystemObject** has a whole range of commands that allow you to perform operation on the **textstream** object. Keep in mind that the object uses the concept of a stream. The direction of time is forward. There is no way to go back and insert something at an earlier position.

Close	This closes a **textstream** file and flushes the buffers to disk. Contrary to the standard Visual Basic method where files are automatically closed upon exit, or when encountering an **END** statement, it is advisable to make sure the file is closed before exiting the program. Otherwise file access errors such as 'sharing violations' may occur
Read	This allows you to read a given number of characters from a file.
ReadAll	This retrieves the entire file and returns it as a string. The drawback is that this function is a memory hog especially for large files. There are other methods to retrieve the file line by line that use far fewer resources.
ReadLine	This retrieves an entire line up to but not including the line feed character.
Skip	The Skip command is used to jump a given amount of characters forward in the file. In essence, it just updates the read location.
SkipLine	This allows you to skip to the next line in the file. This command seeks the next line feed character and places the file index jus beyond that point use in conjunction with **ReadLine** to retrieve the next line
Write	This command writes the given string at the next position in the file. No additional processing is done.
WriteBlankLines	This command allows you to write a given number of blank lines into the file. In essence, it sends a CR/LF pair (ASCII codes 13 + 10) into the stream.
WriteLine	This command writes the given string to the file at the current position. At the end, a CR/LF (ASCII 10+13) is inserted automatically. In Visual Basic Classic, this is equivalent as sending a **vbCRLF**.

5.20 : File I/O under the NET framework

The NET framework has done away with most of the old style file operations. The principal reason was compatibility issues on the common runtime library. They have been replaced by a more powerful way of accessing files. The **Filestream** class builds further on the **FileSystem** object and the **TextStream** object. All file operation objects reside in the IO namespace. **A** second advantage is that all file IO can now be redirected to any object accepting such operations, for instance networked drives. This means that even if the target platform is different the proposed methods will still work. As you might or might not know, the NET platform also allows you to create software for Windows CE, PocketPC and Smart phone devices.

5.20.1 : Using the Filestream Class

The First thing we need to do is to instantiate an object form the class.

```
Dim my_filestream as new io.filestream (<arguments>)
```

Just as with the old style command, you need to specify the filename, the access mode and optional locks

Example:

```
Dim my_file as new io.filestream("test.txt", _
                   IO.FileMode.OpenOrCreate, _
                   IO.FileAccess.read, _
                   IO.FileShare.readwrite)
```

As you can see, there are no more file 'handles' required as the instantiated object represents the file directly. To specify the mode you use the **FileMode** enumeration. Available modes are **Append**, **Create**, **CreateNew**, **Open**, **OpenOrCreate** and **Truncate**.

Append mode opens the file if it exists and puts the file pointer at the end of the current file. Any write operation performed will 'append' to the end of the file without touching its original contents. Should the file not exist then it will be created, just like in Visual Basic Classics append mode.

Create mode will create a new file, or overwrite an existing file with the same name. This is comparable to the Visual Basic Classic **Output** mode.

CreateNew must be able to crate a new file. If the file exists, an error is generated. This construct has no equivalent in Visual Basic Classic.

OpenOrCreate will open an existing file. If the file does not exist, it will be created. This also has no equivalent in Visual Basic Classic.

Truncate allows you to open an existing file and flush it. The contents of the file are cleared.

The **FileAccess** parameter specifies what you want to do with the file. If you open it as **Read** you can only retrieve data from the file. If you specify Write, you can only send information to the file. A third option called **ReadWrite** allows you to perform both operations. This is somewhat similar to the Visual Basic Classic **Random** style.

The sharing property allows you to specify how other processes will be able to access the file. Possible options are **None** for no access at all, **Read** for reading only, **ReadWrite** for full access or **Write** for write access only.

5.20.2 : Reading and writing from and to a stream

To perform operations on a file you can use different methods.

The **BinaryReader** and **BinaryWriter** allow you to perform byte-to-byte operation on the file.
The **StreamReader** and **StreamWriter** can read or write characters from a stream in UTF8 encoding.
The **StringReader** and **StringWriter** also read or write characters but do not perform any decoding like the **StreamReader and StreamWriter** do.

Now that we have created the file stream object, we can instantiate the appropriate object to perform our operations

```
Dim my_file as new io.filestream("test.txt", _
                    IO.FileMode.OpenOrCreate, _
                    IO.FileAccess.write, _
                    IO.FileShare.readwrite)
Dim my_writer as new IO.streamwriter(my_file)
' now we can write using the my_writer object
My_writer.writeline(" hello world")
My_writer.close()
```

The above block of code creates an object called **my_writer** belonging to the **StreamWriter** class and uses the **WriteLine** method to send a string to the file. Finally, the **Close** method is used to end the operations and close the file. At this point the actual data is written to disk.

Contrary to old style operations, the **Filestream** is an object that exists in memory only. The operations do not occur on the disk directly. A shadow image of the file is created. At the moment the close method is executed, the file is actually written to disk. This speeds up the overall performance of the operations as writing a large chunk is faster then hundreds of times writing a small chunk.

To retrieve data form the file, we can use the **ReadLine** method belonging to the **StreamReader** class.

```
Dim my_file as new io.filestream("test.txt", _
                    IO.FileMode.OpenOrCreate, _
```

```
                        IO.FileAccess.read, _
                        IO.FileShare.readwrite)
        Dim my_reader as new IO.streamreader(my_file)
        ' now we can write using the my_writer object
        Dim line as string
        Line =  = My_reader.readline()
        My_reader.close()
```

The above example retrieves a line from the file and returns it in the 'line' variable.

These examples are the generic constructs. Next, we will look at the possibilities in detail.

5.20.3 : StreamWriter and StreamReader in detail

The *StreamWriter* class has a number of methods and properties that allow you to control and perform writing operations. Once an object has been instantiated, you use these interfaces to interact with the stream.

The following properties are of interest. Although this is not a complete list, it covers the core properties of the *StreamWriter*.

5.20.3.1 : AutoFlush Property:

In general, Windows will not access the disk continuously. This is done because disk operations take time and it is far more efficient to perform these in memory and write the data to disk only when the operations are completed. In critical applications, it might be desirable to override this functionality. If the *AutoFlush* property is set to *True,* the data will be written immediately. The default setting is *False*. Closing a file does flush the data to disk. You can force a write to disk by invoking the *Flush* method.

Example

```
        Dim my_file as new io.filestream("test.txt", _
                        IO.FileMode.OpenOrCreate, _
                        IO.FileAccess. write, _
                        IO.FileShare.readwrite)
        Dim x_writer as new IO.streamwriter(my_file)
        ' now we can write using the my_writer object
        X_writer.autoflush = true
        X_writer.writeline ("Hello")
        X_writer.writeline ("World")
        My_writer.close()
```

In the above example, the buffer will be flushed and written to disk on every invocation of the *WriteLine* method.

5.20.3.2 : Encoding Property:

The **StreamReader** and **StreamWriter** can retrieve UTF8 or Unicode streams automatically. The encoding property allows you to find out exactly what kind of file you are accessing. You cannot use it to force the encoding mechanism.

5.20.3.3 : NewLine Property:

The **NewLine** property allows you to specify the end of line character. Normally this is specified as a CR/LF pair (ASCII code 13 followed by ASCII code 10). The **StreamReader** will handle automatically either a LF or a CR/LF pair so reading for instance UNIX files is not a problem. In order to create a UNIX compatible file you can only use a Line-fed (ASCII code 10). Using the **NewLine** property, this becomes very easy

Example:

```
Dim my_file as new io.filestream("test.txt", _
                    IO.FileMode.OpenOrCreate, _
                    IO.FileAccess. write, _
                    IO.FileShare.readwrite)
Dim x_writer as new IO.streamwriter(my_file)
' now we can write using the x_writer object
X_writer.newline=chr(10)
X_writer.writeline ("Visual Basic says Hello")
X_writer.writeline ("to our Unix friends")
My_writer.close()
```

5.20.3.4 : The Close method:

Invocation of this method closes the stream and flushes the buffer to disk. Once a **Close** has been performed, subsequent calls to methods of the **StreamWriter** class may raise errors.

5.20.3.5 : The Flush method:

The **Flush** method forces the current contents of the **Filestream** to be written to disk.

Example:

```
Dim my_file as new io.filestream("test.txt", _
                    IO.FileMode.OpenOrCreate, _
                    IO.FileAccess. write, _
                    IO.FileShare.readwrite)
Dim my_writer as new IO.streamwriter(my_file)
' now we can write using the my_writer object
my_writer.writeline ("Visual Basic says Hello")
my_writer.flush() ' force flush
my_writer.writeline ("to our Unix friends")
my_writer.close()
```

5.20.3.6 : The Write method:

This is the basic operation to be used when sending data to the **StreamWriter**. It allows you to write the contents of any kind of variable to disk. No line feed is inserted, so the next operations write directly behind the current one.

```
Dim my_file as new io.filestream("test.txt", _
                    IO.FileMode.OpenOrCreate, _
                    IO.FileAccess. write, _
                    IO.FileShare.readwrite)
Dim my_writer as new IO.streamwriter(my_file)
' now we can write using the my_writer object
my_writer.write ("Hello")
my_writer.write (" World ")
Dim my_int as int
My_int = 123
My_writer.write (my_int)
My_writer.close()
```

The above example will write the string 'Hello World 123' to the file. The write method can adapt itself depending on what kind of variable type you pass. It can even handle arrays automatically.

```
Dim my_file as new io.filestream("test.txt", _
                    IO.FileMode.OpenOrCreate, _
                    IO.FileAccess. write, _
                    IO.FileShare.readwrite)
Dim my_writer as new IO.streamwriter(my_file)
Dim strary as char() = {"A"c,"B"c,"C"c,"D"c}
Dim numary as int() = {500,600,700,800,900}
' now we can write using the my_writer object
my_writer.write (strary,2,2)
my_writer.write (numary,3,2)
My_writer.close()
```

This example dumps the contents of the array **strary** and **numary** to the stream. The **strary** is dumped from the second position for a total of two entries in the array. The **numary** array is dumped from the third location for a length of two entries. The final string will thus look like this: 'BC700800'

The **Write** and **WriteLine** methods actually interpret the supplied arguments. There is a whole range of commands available most of which are easiest to explain by example:

```
My_writer.write (" This is an ""embedded"" quote")
' output = this is an "embedded" quote

My_writer.write (spc(5), "hello")
' insert 5 spaces then write hello

Dim a as integer =1,b as integer =2
```

```
My_writer.write (" {0} + {1} = {2}",a,b,a+b)
' 1 + 2 = 3

My_writer.writeline (tab(2),"col2",tab(5),"col5")
My_writer.writeline (tab(1),"col1",tab(4),"col4")
'              col2                         col5
'col1                            col4

Dim x as boolean
X=true
My_writer.writeline ("x is",x)
' x is #TRUE#

Dim someday as datetime
someday = datetime.parse("November 10,1970")
my_writer.writeline (someday,"is a date")
' November 10,1970 is a date
```

Any combination of the above variants is possible.

5.20.3.7 : The WriteLine method:

While the **write** command allows you to dump any kind of variable content to the file, it can be annoying if you want to add a new line. The **WriteLine** solves this problem. It works just as the write command does except that it DOES insert the sequence defined by the **NewLine** property.

Example: we modify the previous example to use the **WriteLine** method

```
Dim my_file as new io.filestream("test.txt", _
                  IO.FileMode.OpenOrCreate, _
                  IO.FileAccess.write, _
                  IO.FileShare.readwrite)
Dim my_writer as new IO.streamwriter(my_file)
my_writer.writeline ("Hello")
my_writer.write ("World")
My_writer.close ()
```

This would generate as output

```
Hello
World
```

5.20.3.8 : The StreamReader object

The **StreamReader** is the counterpart of the **StreamWriter** class. It allows you to retrieve information that was written using the **StreamWriter** class. Of course, the **StreamReader** also has a **Close** command just like the **StreamWriter**.

In order to open a file, using the **StreamReader**, you need to instantiate the object and give it permission to access the files. Example:

```
Dim my_file as new io.filestream("test.txt", _
                    IO.FileMode.OpenOrCreate, _
                    IO.FileAccess.read, _
                    IO.FileShare.readwrite)
Dim my_reader as new IO.streamreader(my_file)
Dim x a string
X = my_reader.readtoend
My_reader.close()
```

Once the file has been opened, we can execute methods belonging to the **StreamReader** class on it. Just like the **StreamWriter** object the **StreamReader** has a **Close** method. Once executed, the file is no longer accessible and subsequent operations will raise an error.

5.20.3.9 : The Peek method

By using the **peek** method you can read ahead in the file without incrementing the file pointer. The Peek method returns the next character in the file or it returns -1 if you have reached the end of the file. Thus, you can use the **peek** method instead of the **EOF** function in Visual Basic Classic.

Example:

```
Dim my_file as string ="test.txt"
Dim my_reader as new IO.streamreader(my_file)
Do while my_reader.peek() >=0
   X = my_reader.readline
While end
My_reader.close()
```

The above example keeps reading lines from the file until there is nothing else to read (the peek method returns -1).

5.20.3.10 : The ReadLine method

In the previous example, we have been using the **ReadLine** method already. This function retrieves one line at a time from the open **Filestream**. Each time the method is invoked, the next line is read. You are responsible for checking not to read past the end of the file. That is where the **Peek** command explained in previous topic comes in handy.

5.20.3.11 : The ReadBlock method

The **ReadBlock** method allows you to retrieve any arbitrary block out of the **Filestream**. All you need to provide upon invocation of the method is a variable to hold the result, a start position and a count value representing the number of characters you want to retrieve.

Example:

```
Dim my_reader as new IO.streamreader(my_file)
Dim x a string
my_reader.Readblock(x,5,100)
My_reader.close()
```

The above block of code will retrieve 100 characters starting at the fifth character in the file and return them as a string stored in variable 'x'. Reading past the end of he file is no a problem. If you specify a count value that is larger than the amount of characters available in the file, the **ReadBlock** method will only return up until the end of the file.

Actually, **ReadBlock** is a function that can be used in a different way in order to retrieve immediately the number of characters retrieved.

```
Dim my_reader as new IO.streamreader(my_file)
Dim x a string
Dim block_length as int16
Block_length = my_reader.Readblock(x,5,100)
My_reader.close()
```

If, after executing the **ReadBlock** function, the **Block_length** is less than 500. This means, there were less than 500 characters remaining in the file.

5.20.3.12 : The Read method

The **Read** method comes close to the **ReadBlock** method but is slightly different. You can call this method without arguments to simply retrieve the next character in the stream. At the same time, you can call this with the same arguments as the **ReadBlock** command with one exception, the return value is not a string but an array.

Example:

```
' strem contains the string 'hello world'
Dim my_reader as new IO.streamreader(my_file)
Dim x() as char
my_reader.Read(x,5,5)
My_reader.close()
```

In this example, five characters are read starting at position 5 in the steam. The array x () will thus contain 'world'. If you retrieved element 1 of the array x the contents would be the letter 'o'. The individual characters are returned as elements of an array.

5.20.3.13 : The ReadToEnd method

The **ReadToEnd** method allows you to retrieve the entire file in one shot. An example was given in the topic on the **StreamReader** object.

5.20.4 : StringReader and StringWriter in detail

As explained before the *StringReader* and *StringWriter* do not encode or decode information. Characters are written 'as is'.

The main properties are the same as for the *StreamReader* and *StreamWriter* with the addition of a few new ones

5.20.4.1 : ToString method:

This method allows you to retrieve the data that has been written so far to the stream created with a *StringWriter* object. As data is not really written to disk in real-time, you can use this to retrieve all the data waiting in the queue.

Another possible check is to see if a file has been 'flushed' yet. If the *ToString* method returns something, you might want to flush the buffer to disk.

5.20.5 : BinaryReader and BinaryWriter in detail

This is a completely different animal. The *BinaryReader* and *BinaryWriter* classes allow you byte per byte control of a *Filestream* object. While this gives you full and detailed control, it also requires a lot of work form your part to interact with such files.

As always, the basic construct remains the same. Create a file object and assign it to the *BinaryReader* or *BinaryWriter*.

Example:

```
Dim my_file as new io.filestream("test.txt", _
                IO.FileMode.OpenOrCreate, _
                IO.FileAccess.read)
Dim my_reader as new IO.BinaryReader(my_file)
```

The file is now accessible for the *BinaryReader*. Naturally, for writing the file should be opened in write mode.

5.20.5.1 : BinaryReader in detail

The *BinaryReader* allows you to retrieve information from the *Filestream*. It has lots of methods to allow you to read certain kinds of information or chunks of data directly.

ReadBoolean, ReadByte, Readchar, ReadDecimal, ReadDouble, ReadInt16, ReadInt32, ReadInt64, ReadSbyte, ReadSingle, ReadUInt16, ReadUInt32, and *ReadUInt64* all read a variable of the specified type from the stream. Each of these handlers knows exactly how many bytes need to be read from the file and how they have to be translated to the correct type.

ReadBytes and **ReadChars** allow you to retrieve multiple bytes and chars at a time. You have to specify the count as parameter.

ReadString allows you to retrieve strings stored in a stream. The length of the string must be encoded in the first two bytes retrieved from the stream. This works in conjunction with the **Write** method of the **BinaryWriter**.

All the above methods read from the current position in the file and they advance the file pointer upon return.

The **Read** method allows you to retrieve arbitrary chunks of data from any given position and length. It returns an array of either **Chars** or **Bytes**.

Example

```
Dim my_file as new io.filestream("test.txt", _
                    IO.FileMode.OpenOrCreate, _
                    IO.FileAccess.read)
Dim my_reader as new IO.BinaryReader(my_file)
Dim t() as char
My_reader.read(t,20,400)
```

The above chunk of code will read 400 bytes starting at the 20th byte in the stream.

5.20.5.2 : BinaryWriter in detail

The **BinaryWriter** just features two methods: **Seek** and **Write**. The **Seek** method allows you to set the file pointer to a certain location in the file by specifying simply the offset.

The **Write** method allows you to write any data type that can be handled by its counterpart in the **BinaryReader** class. The data translation is immediate and, for certain data types, the locale is taken into account as well.

Example:

```
Dim my_file as new io.filestream("test.txt", _
                    IO.FileMode.OpenOrCreate)
Dim my_writer as new IO.Binarywriter(my_file)
Dim a_boolean as boolean = true
Dim a_int16 as int16 = 10
Dim a_long as long = 5.2
My_writer.write (a_boolean)
My_writer.write (a_int16)
My_writer.write (a_long)
```

Again, the **BinaryWriter** is very flexible but it leaves all the management up to you.

Normally you should be able to get along without these but the occasion may arise where you need to access binary streams coming from unknown sources. As long as you know exactly how they are formatted you can uses the *BinaryReader* and *BinaryWriter* to read and create such streams. One example may be the creation of WAV files. The file format submits to a specific format and the since *BinaryWriter* class can be used to precisely control how the output is created, this will be far easier than using a different file creation method.

5.20.6 : Detecting file system changes (NET)

Under NET, it is possible to monitor directories for changes to their contents. Just like the explorer window updates automatically whenever a directory gets updated, you can use this object to notify you of changes in the file system. There exists a *FileSystemWatcher* class inside the Net environment, that allows you to monitor the operations going on in the entire file system.

To add this object, you need to load it into your project by grabbing it from the Components toolbox and dragging it onto your form designer. In the image below, I renamed it to *fsw*. As it has no user interface, it comes up underneath the Form designer.

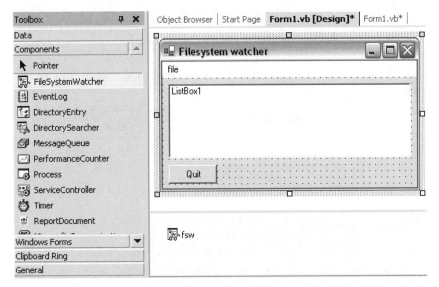

Once added, you can set a number of properties tat define exactly what will be monitored and when the appropriate events will be raised.

5.20.6.1 : Filter

The *Filter* property allows you to specify what files need to be monitored. You can use wildcards such as '*' and '?'. If you set this property to nothing (an empty string), all files will be monitored.

5.20.6.2 : Include Subdirectories

This Boolean property allows you to specify If only the current directory needs watching or all contained subdirectories as well. This works in conjunction with the Path property.

5.20.6.3 : Path

The path property allows you to specify the directory that needs to be monitored. The path accepts *UNC* formatted paths that can point to remote storage such as fileservers.

5.20.6.4 : NotifyFilter

The *NotifyFilter* property allows you to specify exactly what events need monitoring and reporting. You can specify multiple monitors by logically *or*-ing the modifiers. Possible choices are *Filename*, *DirectoryName*, *Attributes*, *Size*, *LastWrite*, *LastAccess*, *CreationTime* and *Security*. These options are available in the *NotifyFilters* collection.

5.20.7 : Example: A file system monitor in NET

The example below will monitor a given directory for changes to a number of events and will report the activity to the console.

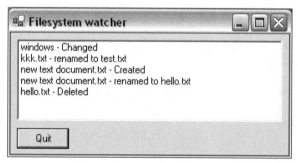

The form has a simple listbox control and a command button. The *FileSystemWatcher* object has been added tot the project and renamed to FSW.

```
    Private Sub Watcher_1 (ByVal sender As System.Object, _
            ByVal e As System.IO.FileSystemEventArgs) _
            Handles fsw.Deleted, fsw.Changed, fsw.Created
            ListBox1.Items.Add(e.Name & " - " & e.ChangeType.ToString())
    End Sub
    Private Sub Button1_Click(ByVal sender As System.Object, _
            ByVal e As System.EventArgs) Handles Button1.Click
            End
    End Sub
```

```
Private Sub Watcher_2 (ByVal sender As System.Object, _
        ByVal e As System.IO.RenamedEventArgs) Handles fsw.Renamed
        ListBox1.Items.Add(e.OldName & " - renamed to " & e.Name)
End Sub
```

The program uses some construction we have not dealt with but that is of no importance yet.

Clicking the 'Quit' button will end the program by executing the END statement.

Whenever the **FileSystemWatcher** detects a **Deleted, Changed** or **Created** event from the object called **FSW**, it will fire the **watcher_1**' subroutine. This will retrieve some properties out of the returned information. Returned information lives in the 'e' collection. By retrieving the **Name** property we know the file name. By converting the **e** object to a string, we know what event exactly was raised. So there is one line of code that creates a string and adds it to the contents of the listbox.

Unfortunately, the collection returned by the **Renamed** event is different from the others, so we are required to write a separate handler: **watcher_2**. This one fires only when a **Renamed** event occurs and retrieves the old name and the new name and sends it to the listbox. So this routine shows exactly what has been renamed to what else.

5.20.8 : File Manipulations (NET only).

The Net framework adds many other classes that allow you to retrieve information about files. One such class is the **FileInfo** class in the **IO** namespace. This class exposes a number of methods and properties that allow you to retrieve or set a number of file parameters.

5.20.8.1 : CreationTime, LastAccessTime and LastWriteTime + UTC variants

These properties allow you to retrieve or set the time properties pertaining to the file. **CreationTime** allows you to retrieve, or set, the date and time the file was created. Its counterpart **CreationTimeUTC** allows you to manipulate the same information but in Universal Time Code (**UTC**). In a similar fashion **LastAccessTime** and **LastAccessTimeUTC** allows you to retrieve, or set, the last time the file was accessed and finally **LastWriteTime** and **LastWriteTimeUTC** allow you to retrieve or set the last time the file was written to.

Example:

```
Dim my_file as new IO.FileInfo("test.txt")
Dim filetime as datetime
Filetime = my_file.creationtime()
Label1.text= cstr(filetime)
```

This example retrieves the file **CreationTime** and stores the result in a variable of the type **DateTime**.

5.20.8.2 : Length

The **Length** property allows you to retrieve the length of a file as it exists on disk.

```
Dim my_file as new IO.FileInfo("test.txt")
Dim filesize as long
Filesize = my_file.filesize()
Label1.text= cstr(filesize)
```

This method can be used instead of the **LOF** function from Visual Basic Classic.

5.20.8.3 : Exists

Before performing operations, such as reading or writing, it may be a good idea to see if there is no file with the specified name yet. The NET platform and Visual Basic provide a lot of error handling for you but you still might want to check for 'user error'. If a given file exists, you may want to provide a message to the user of the program that he is, for instance, about to overwrite an existing file.

Example:

```
Dim my_file as new IO.FileInfo("test.txt")
Dim alive as boolean
alive = my_file.exists()
```

5.20.8.4 : Attributes

It is very easy to retrieve and set file properties in the NET platform.

Example:

```
Dim my_file as new IO.FileInfo("test.txt")
Dim attribs as integer
attribs = my_file.attributes
if attribs and io.fileattributes.hidden then write("hidden")
```

The IO namespace has an enumerated list of flags available that help you manipulate the attributes. The file attributes enumeration consists of the following flags:

Archive	The **archive** flag indicates a file has been archived. Backup programs use this flag to tag files for backup.
Compressed	If this flag is set, the file is stored in a compressed format.

Device	This flag is for future usage and should not be used for now.
Directory	This marks a directory entry.
Encrypted	If the object is a file, the contents are encrypted. If the object is a directory, it means the default mode for newly created files is encrypted.
Hidden	A file or directory with this flag set is hidden from normal view.
Normal	If none of the other flags are in effect, this flag will be set.
Not ContentIndexed	The content of this file is not being monitored by the windows indexing service.
Offline	This is a remote file and is not presently available. The share might no longer be mounted.
Read-only:	This denotes a file that can only be read.
Reparse point	This is a reparse point for the NTFS file system and contains user data attached to a specific file.
Sparse file:	This file mostly contains the same binary information. Only very little in the file is actual data, the rest is just empty space.
System	This flags marks a file that belongs to the operating system.
Temporary	A file marked as temporary is being kept in RAM memory as much as possible. If you create such files the access will b very fast but you need to take care to destroy them upon exit of your program.

5.20.8.5 : CopyTo

The *CopyTo* method allows you to copy the currently selected file to a new location. An argument allows you to specify if the file is allowed to be overwritten in case is should already exist.

Example:

```
Dim my_file as new IO.FileInfo("test.txt")
Dim overwrite as boolean
Dim target as string
Target="c:\copy.txt"
Overwrite = true
My_file.CopyTo (target,overwrite)
```

5.20.8.6 : Delete

The **delete** method allows you to remove a file from the file system. Te method requires no modifiers. Keep in mind that you need to take care not to access the file anymore.

Example:

```
Dim my_file as new IO.FileInfo("test.txt")
My_file.delete()
My_file = nothing    ' destroy object out of safety
```

Out of safety reasons, I implicitly destroy the **my_file** object. Subsequent accesses will generate an error. If your code is well written the error handlers in the other modules will trap this and can display relevant messages to the user like 'File no longer exists' or 'file not found'. Or detailed explanation on error handling see later on in this book.

5.20.8.7 : MoveTo

The companion method to the **CopyTo** is **MoveTo**, which allows you to move a file. However, this does not happen physically. Only the index tables, in either the FAT (The File Allocation Table of the FAT file system) or MFT (the Master File Table of the NTFS file system), are updated.

Example:

```
Dim my_file as new IO.FileInfo("c:\test.txt")
Dim target as string
Target= "c:\temp\test.txt"
My_file.moveto (target)  ' file moved to tempdirectory
Target = "c:\hello.txt"
My_file.moveto (target)  ' file moved and renamed
```

The reference to the file remains valid after the operation so you do not need to redefine an object with the new location. The method updates the file location in the **my_file** object.

5.20.9 : Directory Manipulations (NET only)

Besides the **FileInfo** class there is also a **DirectoryInfo** class we can instantiate to retrieve directory information.

```
        Dim My_Directory as new IO.Directoryinfo("C:\")
```

The ***DirectoryInfo*** class library supports a whole range of operations that are similar the ***FileInfo*** class. This is actually a result of both objects belonging to the same parent class.

5.20.9.1 : Create Method

This method creates the directory as it was defined. If the directory already exists, nothing will happen and no error will be thrown.

Example:

```
        Dim My_Directory as new IO.Directoryinfo("test")
        My_Directory.Create()
```

5.20.9.2 : CreateSubDirectory Method

This method creates a subdirectory, inside the current directory, referenced to by the ***DirectoryInfo*** object. If the subdirectory already exists, nothing will happen and no error will be thrown.

Example:

```
        Dim My_Directory as new IO.Directoryinfo("test")
        My_Directory.Create()
        My_Directory.CreateSubDirectory("sub_test")
```

The sub_test directory will be created as a subdirectory of 'test'. Then you can instantiate again an object referencing to it. However, there is a better way. It is possible to retrieve the handle to the subdirectory directly, and instantiate it as a new object.

Example:

```
        Dim My_Directory as new IO.Directoryinfo("test")
        My_Directory.Create()
        Dim my_sub as Directoryinfo = _
            My_Directory.CreateSubDirectory("sub_test")
```

In this case the newly create subdirectory is directly available as a new object called my sub.

5.20.9.3 : Delete Method

This allows you to delete a directory and optionally its contents.

Example:

```
Dim My_Directory as new IO.Directoryinfo("test")
My_Directory.Delete()
My_Directory = Nothing
```

This creates a directory and immediately destroys it. Setting the object to nothing destroys it, so that the garbage collector can free up space in memory.

Should the directory have contained information an error would have been thrown. In order to automatically delete a directory, and all its content, you need to provide a flag to do so.

Example:

```
Dim My_Directory as new IO.Directoryinfo("test")
My_Directory.Delete(True) ' delete contents
My_Directory = Nothing
```

5.20.9.4 : GetDirectories Method

The **GetDirectories** method returns an array of **DirectoryInfo** and can be used in conjunction with a **for-each** construct to walk through an entire directory and retrieve information about the subdirectories.

Example:

```
Dim subDirectory as IO.Directoryinfo
For each subdirectory in IO.GetDirectories()
    Listbox1.additem subdirectory.name
Next
```

5.20.9.5 : GetFiles Method

In a similar fashion as the **GetDirectories** the **GetFiles** method retrieves all files in a given directory. The returned data type belongs to the **FileInfo** class.

Example:

```
Dim file as IO.Fileinfo
For each file in IO.Getfiles()
    Listbox1.additem file.name
Next
```

5.20.9.6 : GetFileSystemInfos Method

The **GetFileSystemInfos** method allows you to retrieve information about the contents of a directory. This is a very complex and extensive method. It is advisable to read the online help to see what you can do with this.

However, a small example to show what is possible.

```
Dim My_Dir as new IO.Directoryinfo("c:\")
Dim Dirs as FileSystemInfo () = My_dir.getdirectories("*")
Dim single_dir as DirectoryInfo
For each single_dir in dirs
    Single_dir.GetfileSystemInfos("*").length
next
```

The above example first creates an object of the type **DirectoryInfo**. Secondly, an object of the type **FileSystemInfos** is created that contains the result of the **GetDirectories** method applied to our first object. The resulting collection is a list of all directories since a single wildcard (*) was specified.

Thirdly, an object of the **DirectoryInfo** kind is defined. Each entry in the **Dirs** object is of that type. Finally a **for-each** clause scans through all entries and retrieves the length of each object that matches.

5.20.9.7 : MoveTo Method

Similar to the **MoveTo** method of a **FileInfo** object this allows you to move a directory and all its contents to a new location.

Example:

```
Dim My_Directory as new IO.Directoryinfo("test")
My_Directory.Create()
Dim My_Directory_2 as new IO.Directoryinfo("test_2")
My_Directory_2.Create()
My_directory_2.MoveTo("test_2")
```

In the above example, we create two directories and then move the last one created inside the first one created.

5.20.9.8 : FullPath Property

This method returns you the complete path. A complete path is defined as a '\\server\drive\directory (s)' structure.

5.20.9.9 : Attributes Property

This has been explained in the previous topic on NET file operations.

5.20.9.10 : Exists Property

This has been explained in the previous topic on NET file operations except that now it is applied to an object belonging to the *DirectoryInfo* class. Its operation is similar.

5.20.9.11 : CreationTime, LastAccessTime and LastWriteTime + UTC Properties

These properties have been explained in detail in the previous topic on the File Manipulation under the NET framework.

Chapter 6 : The NET platform in more detail

As we have seen in the past topics, the NET platform introduces an impressive set of new features not found before in Visual Basic Classic. Throughout this book, I will point out the key differences between the Classic style and NET style where appropriate. Concepts that are similar in nature between the two generations are interspersed with each other. However, There are a number of concepts that have no relations whatsoever to Visual Basic Classic.

6.1 : Namespaces

This is a pure NET concept that has no equivalent in Visual Basic Classic. Since NET is a true object oriented environment, it makes extensive usage of classes. As we have seen before we are instantiating objects from various classes such a file handlers, collections, graphics elements. Even user interface objects we put on a form belong to one class or another. Because of the sheer volume of available classes the management becomes quite complex. And that is where namespaces fit in.

A namespace is a collection of classes. For example, the largest collection of classes in the NET platform is the System namespace. When instantiating an object directly from a class, we provide the full path to the object including the namespace.

Example:

```
Dim x as new System.IO.Directoryinfo()
```

Of course, this is an elaborate way of referencing but it does guarantee you an exact object. It is possible for namespace to contain classes with the same name in which case there is a possible conflict.

If you are not into creating your own classes and namespaces, you may use a shortcut and import the entire class namespace into your project directly. This allows you to use a shorter notation.

Example:

```
Imports system.io
…
Sub …
Dim x as nes directoryinfo()
End sub
```

The 'imports' clause needs to be placed on the topmost line of the code belonging to a form or module. You can import as many namespaces as you want. The compiler will throw out unused information anyway.

6.1.1 : Creating your own namespace

It is perfectly possible for you to create your own namespace and add classes to it. This allows you to build a code library of often-used routines and it makes managing large projects a lot easier.

Example

```
Namespace My_Library
     Public class My_firstclass
          Public sub My_method_1
          End sub
     End class
     Public class My_secondclass
          Public sub My_method_1
          End sub
          Public sub My_method_2
          End sub
     End class
End namespace


Dim some_object as new My_library.My_Firstclass
Some_object.my_method_1
```

6.2 : Threads

While writing threaded code in Visual Basic is not a truly new concept, the NET environment makes it a lot easier and safer. Most of us will probably never write threaded code as it involves a great deal of careful planning and testing to make sure the thread remains safe and does not 'run away'.

A thread is essentially a program within a program. While belonging to the main program it runs its own course. It interacts with the main program, or other threads, by sending messages and exchanging flags and variables. it is even possible to write a program that can thread itself. Most web-browsers are written that way. Every time you open a new window, a duplicate of the main program is instantiated and run as a thread.

Other applications are background handlers such as printing, saving files or other tasks that can take a while and would block the user from doing something else in the meantime.

6.2.1 : Creating a thread

Creating a thread is not harder than writing any other fragment of code.

Example:

```
Sub Mythread_1
     Dim x as integer
```

```
    For x = 1 to 10000

          Console.writeline ("Thread 1 count =" & x)
        Next x
        Console.writeline ("Thread 1 terminated")
    End sub

Sub Mythread_2
    Dim x as integer
    For x = 1 to 10000
          Console.writeline ("Thread 2 count =" & x)
        Next x
        Console.writeline ("Thread 2 terminated")
    End sub
```

The above are two routines that do a similar same operation. In order to start these routines as threads, you need to launch them as objects belonging to the thread class.

Example:

```
Sub main()
    Dim th1 as new system.threading.thread(addressof mythread_1)
    Dim th2 as new system.threading.thread(addressof mythread_2)
    Th1.start()
    Th2.start()
End sub
```

By instantiating a new object from the thread class, and pointing it to the subroutine, the code becomes threaded. Invoking the tart method, launches the code.

The above example showed you how to thread two independent routines. It is equally possible to instantiate the same code as multiple threads.

Example:

```
Dim thrd as integer

Sub Mythread()
    Dim x as integer
    My_number = thrd
    For x = 1 to 10000
          Console.writeline ("Thread " & my_number & "count =" & x)
        Next x
        Console.writeline ("Thread " & my_number &" terminated")
    End sub

Sub main()
    Dim th1 as new system.threading.thread(addressof mythread)
    Dim th2 as new system.threading.thread(addressof mythread)
    Thrd = 1
    Th1.start()
    Thrd = 2
    Th2.start()
    Console.writeline ("main program halted")
    End sub
```

Later on, I will show how you can control thread behavior and how to pause, continue and abort threaded processes.

6.2.2 : Ending a Thread and joining the main program

A thread will terminate itself when it reaches the end of the code; however, sometimes it is necessary to cancel a thread. Suppose the user launches a process to save all open files. This process runs in the background and sits in a thread. The code detects that a given file already exists and prompts the user to Overwrite, Save As or Cancel. The Cancel event needs to close the thread. Whereas it is perfectly possible to terminate the thread, by jumping out of the code and to the end of the process, this is not the case if the thread needs to be stopped from outside the thread process itself.

Visual Basic provides the Abort method to stop the thread. In essence, all that this method does is, raise an error event. The error handling inside your thread will catch the exception, cleanup and exit, hence closing the thread.

Example:

```
Dim thrd as integer

Sub Mythread()
    Dim x as integer
    My_number = thrd
    For x = 1 to 10000
        Console.writeline ("Thread " & my_number & "count =" & x)
    Next x
    Console.writeline ("Thread " & my_number &" terminated")
End sub

Sub main()
    Dim th1 as new system.threading.thread(addressof mythread)
    Dim th2 as new system.threading.thread(addressof mythread)
    Thrd = 1
    Th1.start()
    Thrd = 2
    Th2.start()
    Th1.abort()
    Console.writeline ("Thread 1 abort requested")
    Th1.join()
    Console.writeline ("Thread 1 aborted")
    Console.writeline ("main program halted")
End sub
```

The above code executes the Abort method on thread 1. The Join method waits for the Thread to completely stop. It is important to wait for this to happen, as a thread may not stop immediately. Since the abort command interacts with the error handling inside the thread (through a try-catch clause we will see later on), there will still be code that is running. The main process has to wait for this to complete before continuing, hence the Join method. Join waits for the thread to terminate and halts the main program until this happens.

6.2.3 : Monitoring and Modifying thread execution

It is possible to monitor and control the execution of a thread. We have already seen that a thread can be aborted and the main program can be re-synchronized by waiting for the thread to join the main program

6.2.3.1 : Suspending and Resuming

There are other things we can do to a threaded process. It is possible to suspend a process in order to resume it at a later point in time.

Example:

```
Dim thrd as integer

Sub Mythread() …

Sub main()
    Dim th1 as new system.threading.thread(addressof mythread)
    Dim th2 as new system.threading.thread(addressof mythread)
    Thrd = 1
    Th1.start()
    Thrd = 2
    Th2.start()
    Th1.abort()
    Th2.susspend()
    Console.writeline ("Thread 1 abort requested")
    Th1.join()
    Th2.resume()
    Console.writeline ("Thread 1 aborted")
    Console.writeline ("main program halted")
End sub
```

The code above will suspend the TH2 thread until TH1 has stopped and joined the main program. At that time the thread TH2 will continue where it was suspended.

6.2.3.2 : Putting a thread to sleep

If a thread is waiting for the arrival of certain data, you might want to switch it into a lower priority mode. Normally a thread is dividing its time automatically with other threads and programs. Even if the thread is doing nothing and just sits there waiting, the process scheduler will allocate time to it. The *Sleep* method allows a thread to switch itself into a low priority mode and wake up when the time expires.

Example:

```
Sub Mythread()
    Dim x as integer
    My_number = thrd
    For x = 1 to 10000
        Console.writeline ("Thread " & my_number & "count =" & x)
        If x = 5000 then
            Threading.Thread.CurrentThread.Sleep(1000)
        End if
    Next x
    Console.writeline ("Thread " & my_number &" terminated")
End sub
```

The Thread will go to sleep for 1 second when X reaches a value of 5000.

6.2.3.3 : Waking a sleeping thread

Suppose something happens in the program and the sleep process needs to be aborted. This is possible using the Interrupt Method.

Example:

```
Th1.interrupt()
```

This will cause the Sleep operation to be aborted prematurely and the thread will continue running.

6.2.3.4 : Monitoring a thread

A number of properties can be retrieve do check the operational state of a thread using the *IsAlive* and *Threadstate* properties. If a thread still exists, the *IsAlive* property will return true. When the thread has terminated, it falls back to False.

The *Threadstate* property returns a value for the *ThreadState* enumeration. Possible values are:

- Aborted: The thread has been stopped.

- *AbortRequested*: An Abort has been executed but the thread has not received the *System.Threading.ThreadAbortException* that will terminate it.

- *Background*: The thread is running as a background process. A Thread can run as foreground or background processes, more on that later.

- *Running*: The thread is in full operation and no state changes are pending, e.g.: an Abort request.

- *Stopped*: The thread has stopped.

- **_StopRequested_**: The thread has received a STOP request. This is for internal use only.

- **_Suspended_**: The thread is in a 'low power' state as the result of a suspend request. Only minimal overhead code is running and the actual processes inside the thread are frozen in time.

- **_SuspendRequested_**: The thread has been requested to go into Suspend mode and is in the process of doing so.

- **_Unstarted_**: The thread object does exist but has not been started yet, by using the **_Start_** method.

- **_WaitSleepJoin_**: The thread is frozen due to a Wait, Sleep or Join command. This state can be broken by issuing an Interrupt to the thread.

All these states belong to the **_Threadstate_** enumeration and can thus easily be tested for, but you have to keep in mind that certain combinations are possible. The states are represented by individual bits in a so-called control word. Therefore, you need to perform logical operations on the result of the **_Threadstate_** method, as it is possible to have, for example, both a **_SuspendRequested_** and **_AbortRequested_** pending.

Example:

```
If Th1.ThreadState and (Threadstate.Stopped) then …

If Th1.ThreadState and (Threadstate.Abortrequested or Stoprequested)
then …
```

The first line checks for a single state while the second line monitors two different states. If you used a simple comparison method, instead of logical operations, the second line would not evaluate since it contains multiple states and an equality operator would not find an exact match.

6.2.4 : Background / foreground and priority

All threads essentially run as a background process as far as the user is concerned, however for the operating system there is a difference. A Thread running in the Background is considered as 'expendable' while a thread running in foreground is not. What does this mean?

Well, suppose you have a program that contains two Threads, one that updates a Statusbar and a thread that saves data to a file. The status indicating thread can be considered as unimportant. If the user decides to shut down the program, we do not really care about this thread. It can shut down pretty much immediately, we could not care less. On the other hand, suppose the program is still writing data to disk, we would like to see the execution of the other thread completed before the program really exits.

6.2.4.1 : Background and foreground

That is where **Foreground** and **Background** comes into play. A foreground process will only terminate once it has reached the natural end of its run. A background process is shut down automatically when the main program terminates. In the case above, you absolutely want to run your file saving routine as a foreground process, so that it will be allowed to complete its work before shutting down. Actually the foreground process will 'hold up' the main program until it has finished.

You can change the state of a thread by changing the **IsBackground** property.

Example:

```
Th1.IsBackground = False ' switch to foreground
Th1.IsBackground = True ' switch to background
```

6.2.4.2 : Thread priority

All threads of a program are controlled by a threading scheduler. This scheduler allocates the amount of time each thread is allowed to run before the CPU switches to a different thread. Normally each thread is assigned an equal 'importance'. It is possible to change this priority and allocate more or less time for a particular thread.

By invoking the **Priority** method, and passing parameters from the **Threadpriority** enumeration, you can control program behavior.

Example:

```
Th1.Priority = Threadpriority.lowest
```

There are 5 levels: **Highest**, **AboveNormal**, **Normal**, **BelowNormal** and **Lowest**. A new thread has a default assignment of **Normal**. If setting a priority higher then normal the system may be impaired in terms of responsiveness to the user's actions since more processing power is devoted to handling the process than performing other tasks.

6.2.5 : Thread safety

Threading is a powerful mechanism that allows you to write multitasking programs in a snap, but at the same time, it can be very dangerous. All threads run in the same memory space (the program) and can access any object at any given point in time. Most objects do not contain code to deal with this correctly.

There is a synchronization mechanism provided that lets you Queue threads. This is especially handy if you have threads that deal with the user interface.

The **SyncLock** method allows you to specify to what object the thread needs to synchronize itself when performing operations. The **SyncLock** method will check when it is safe to access a particular object.

Example:

```
Sub mythread()
    Dim y
    Y=x
    Synclock (my_list)
    My_list.add("something from thread " & y)
    End synclock
End sub

public x as integer
For x = 1 to 10
    Dim a_thread as new system.threading.thread(addressof mythread)
    A_thread.start()
Next x
```

This program launches 10 independent threads. Since each thread **synclocks** itself to the listbox, they will neatly queue up and execute one at a time. Actually, they will wait for access to the listbox. Whenever the listbox is available, the thread currently in process will lock the listbox for access so that other threads have to wait for the operation to complete.

Chapter 7 : Creating a user interface

Now that we have a basic understanding of the syntax, commands and data types at our disposure, it is time to look on how we give our program a user interface. After all, Windows is a graphical user interface and the user will need to interact with the program. In the old DOS era, the user interface had to be built from scratch through coding every single element. Fortunately, Windows has a vast array of user interface elements that are available for us to rapidly build the interface without writing code or with only some minimal code.

7.1 : Creating the Form

We start the Visual Basic environment and select standard EXE format. An empty form is being displayed. To add control you select a control out of the Control Toolbox and then drag the outline of it on your form.

All controls on a form take up control handle space available to the form. A form has a handle space limited to 255 (one-byte) handles. This means a form can have a maximum of 255 controls. There are ways to extend this number. Actually, a 'parent' can contain 255 'children'. In Windows, normally any User interface (UI) object can act as a parent for other UI objects. Due to certain limitations and practical constraints inside Visual Basic only a form, a picture box and a frame can act as a parent to other UI objects. It is possible to 'nest' objects on one another. This limitation only exists on one level. Therefore, a form could have 100 frames each having 100 sub frames with three buttons each. Such a form would be unmanageable but technically possible to construct.

The only limitation is that a project cannot contain more then 32000 identifiers. An identifier being a non-keyword such as: an object name, variable, constant, procedure or function. A form containing two buttons with code attached to the click events calling 1 subroutine that calculates with 2 arrays, 1 variable and 1 constant; would thus consume 1 form + 2 buttons + 2 click events + 1 user subroutine + 2 array names + 1 variable name + 1 constant = 10 identifiers.

> **Note**
>
> In a project containing multiple forms, this still means that every form can have 255 controls.
>
> An array of controls counts as 1 control. Therefore, an array of 1.000.000 buttons still counts as only one object.

Let's add a button to our form and edit the properties **Caption** and **Name** of it The Name has been set to **MyButton** and the caption to 'Go'. As you can see, an ampersand (&) also denotes a hotkey, just like in the menu editor.

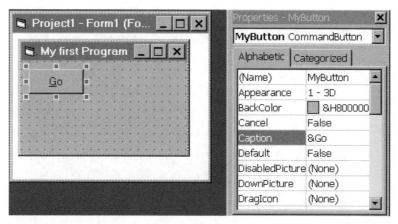

Now let us add another object. Let's say a label. We will call the label *Mylabel* and set its caption to an empty string.

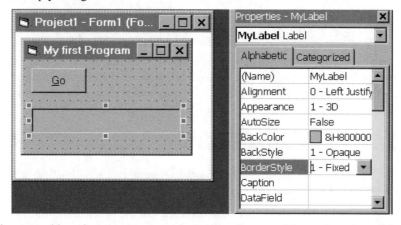

Now we have an object that can generate events (the Command button), and an object that can be used to display something. We now still need a way to give the user the option to terminate our program. A Windows program is not like a classic program with a beginning and an end. The flow of a windows program is not linear. When the program is started, a lot of things are happening at the same time. It is the user's option to terminate it. Therefore, you need to have an explicit means of terminating a program. We could give the user this means using another command button, but a menu looks nicer.

So let's open the menu editor and create a simple menu.

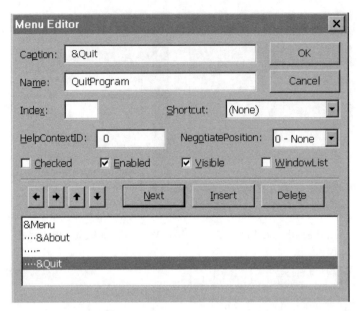

This menu has three entries. The first will show the user a message about the program. The second entry is a divider line and the last one will allow the user to quit the program. We have now come to the stage where the user interface is ready and we can start attaching code to our program.

7.2 : Arrays of Objects and Controls

ctrlarray.vbp

There is a tutorial program available that explains the constructs, explained in this topic, by example.

In some cases, you will have more than 255 controls. On the other hand, you might want to have an easy indexing system using controls. A typical example is a keypad. Instead of placing 10 command-buttons on the form, you can place an array of 10 command-buttons. This uses only one handle. Furthermore, the attached code is common for all controls; you have to write only one procedure to handle all these events.

Creating arrays of objects is easily done by drawing the first object, giving it a name and then copying it. (<CTRL> - C / <CTRL>- V)

After you have placed the first copy, the environment will ask you if you want to create a control array. By answering yes, the array will be created. You will notice that the **index** property will contain a value. This value indicates the position of the control in its control array.

For a keypad you would create a button called Keypad and give it as caption '0'. This will be the item 0 in the array.

Make a copy by selecting this control and perform a copy-paste operation on the edit menu or by hitting Ctrl-V Ctrl-Von the keyboard. The IDE will prompt you if you want to create a control array. Simply confirm this by clicking YES. The newly placed object will get 1 as index. Subsequent paste operations will no longer prompt you if you wan to create the array, as it already exists. The index will automatically increment. All you have to do now is change the caption accordingly, or you could do that from code using a 'for-each' construct.

When you double-click any of the controls in the control array to view the attached code, you will see the same piece of code. However, remark that now an additional parameter called 'index' is being passed. The value of 'index' indicates you which one of the elements in the array really generated the event. In case of our keypad, the index relates directly to the number, provided we have kept the labeling according to the index and not mixed up the order.

7.2.1 : Using control arrays to preserve storage space.

Another application of control arrays is to store labels. A typical form might contain many labels that are wasting valuable resource space. As explained before only a limited number of objects per parent can be used and the entire project is limited to 32.000 elements. Since labels have no use in generating events, (nobody will ever do something with them apart from reading them) it is a good idea to store them in an array. That way you only use one handle.

NET 2005	In NET a special form of label is available that contains a clickable hyperlink. You can store information in the Link property and process this information using the `LinkClicked` method. In essence, this object behaves as a button but has the appearance of a hyperlink and a couple of additional properties that allow you to make smarter applications than when using buttons.

7.2.2 : NET does away with control arrays

The NET framework does not support arrays of controls. A much more powerful method of handling 'collections' has been added to this version of Visual Basic.

One of the main problems with control arrays was that the associated code could only handle events coming from controls of the same type. Suppose you wanted to write a universal chunk of code that could handle all the *mouseover* events for any control on the form. This was not possible up till now.

Thanks to the changes in the way a subroutine is attached to an event, this has now become possible.

Additionally, this has opened up the possibility to fix a problem that has plagued the IDE of Visual Basic for a long time: changing the name of an object would break the link with the attached code and manual editing was required to re-attach all code in the correct place.

There is no longer a direct relation. The syntax of a subroutine definition has been changed.

Old style:
```
Sub button1_click()
End sub
```

New style:
```
Sub My_Handler(byval sender s System.object, _
Byval e as System.Eventargs) handles button1.click
```

In the new definition, the subroutine **My_Handler** will inherit two arguments (sender and e) from the event button1.click. The **handles** clause defines to which events the routine is attached. In the above case, this is **button1.click**. In order to add more controls it is sufficient to specify a comma delimited list

New style:
```
Sub My_Handler(byval sender s System.object, _
Byval e as System.Eventargs) handles button1.click, button2.click
```

The code above links **My_Handler** to both button1 and button2 **click** events.

There is a detailed explanation in the next chapter on how to attach code to events. I have also added a detailed example on how this functionality works in the calculator example. There is an example for Classic Visual Basic and a completely reworked Calculator for the NET framework.

7.2.3 : Creating controls at runtime in VB Classic

I will deliberately only talk about Visual Basic Classic in this topic. A detailed explanation on how it is done in NET, is given in the next topic.

7.2.3.1 : Creating individual controls and arrays of controls

It is possible to create a control or object in runtime, actually creating objects in runtime is something we did earlier on but you may not have noticed this. When we were dealing with the file system, we actually instantiated objects at runtime. Besides this, all the user interface builder does when you design a form, is writing this code for you. This is even more obvious in NET since there you can actually see this code.

Things change a bit when creating controls at runtime. Just like any object, a control can be created at runtime as well. First of all, we define a variable of the type **control** and assign it a newly created control.

The Add method of the controls collection creates new instance of a control.

Example:

```
Dim x As Control
Set x = Controls.Add ("VB.label", "newcontrol", Form1)
x.caption="my new label"
x.Visible = True
```

The arguments provided are the type of control that needs to be created, the name under which it will be known and the parent it will be assigned to. In the above case this translates to a **Label** known under the name **newcontrol** and belonging to **form1**

You can equally create arrays of controls. The only problem is that you cannot handle events generated by these controls. While it is perfectly possible to add 5 buttons to the screen from code, you cannot attach to the click event with the presented method. The next paragraph will show a way to circumvent this restriction.

The method just presented is perfect for controls that provide feedback to the user such as labels on read-only textboxes. If you need a control that interacts with the user and that needs to be able to raise events, you have to use a different method.

7.2.3.2 : Creating arrays with events (classic)

When you need to be able to respond to events from the newly created objects or controls things get a bit more complicated. There is no provision to attach a newly created object to an event handler in Visual Basic Classic. Actually, it can be done using API calls to the windows kernel but it is tricky.

There is a cleaner way that handles all the hard parts for us. It is possible to add elements to an existing control array by invoking the Load method to it.

Example:

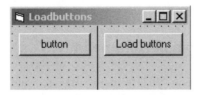

We define a form with two buttons. The first commandbutton is labeled 'Button' and also called 'button'. It is made part of a control array by setting its index property to 0 instead of a blank. It is also set hidden.

A second button is labeled 'Load buttons'. The following code is attached:

```
Option Explicit
Dim x As Integer
Private Sub button_Click(Index As Integer)
      MsgBox ("button " & Index)
End Sub

Private Sub loadbuttons_Click()
    For x = 1 To 5
        Load button(x)
        button(x).Top = button(x - 1).Top + button(x - 1).Height
        button(x).Caption = "Click me " & x
        button(x).Visible = True
    Next x
```

```
            loadbuttons.Visible = False
      end sub
```

When you click the **Loadbutton** a loop is iterated 5 times. The loop code invokes the Load method on the existing Button () and thus ads an element to the list of available Buttons.

The remaining three lines of code are merely used to position the newly created button on the form. Finally, the newly created button is set visible.

7.2.3.3 : Removing objects

Objects created with the above method can be unloaded simply by specifying the name of the object.

Example:

```
      For x = 1 To 5
            UnLoad button(x)
      Next x
```

Be careful not to reference an object once it has been unloaded or you will be presented with a runtime error.

Note	You cannot remove the first item in a control array. Typically, the first item is set invisible and then items are added as needed with the visible flag turned on.

7.2.4 : Creating controls at runtime in NET

Adding controls from runtime in NET is more structured and simpler than in Visual Basic Classic. All that needs to be done is instantiate a new element form the **Windows.forms** class and assign it to a parent.

Example:

```
      My_label= new system.windows.forms.label
      My_label.text = "runtime label"
      Me.controls.add (my_label)
```

The first line instantiates a new object and derives it from the **windows.forms** namespace a label. The second line just sets some property and finally the third line adds it to the current form (accessed through the **Me** collection). Once added to the form, you can use **My_label** just as any regular control.

Note	Keep in mind that simply setting the visible property to true does not make the newly created control active or visible. As long as it is not assigned a parent using the **controls.add** method, it is not being handled by the user interface.

7.3 : Console applications (NET)

The NET framework allows you to create command line based programs. Sometimes you just need a quick tool that performs a certain job and does not really need a user interface. Let us take for example a piece of code that performs a certain task, and will be called from a script or batch file. That's were a console application comes in handy.

Console applications will be described in further detail later on in this book. However, here is a quick preview:

Begin a new project in NET and select Console application as project type. You will not get a user interface builder this time as all screen interaction is done using the console object.

7.3.1 : Writing something to the command line:

To send text output to the screen you can use the *Write* or *WriteLine* methods of the console object.

Example:

```
        Console.writeline("Type your name")
```

This will write the message to the console and move to the next line. If you do not want to move to the next line, you can either use the *Write* method or specify modifiers. Check for a detailed explanation of the *Write* and *WriteLine* methods in the section on File I/O.

7.3.2 : Getting input from the command line

Besides sending output to the console, it is equally possible to retrieve information from the console such as user input.

Example:

```
        User_input = Console.readline()
```

Anything the user types will be returned into the variable *user_input* the moment the user hits the enter key. Program execution is halted until this actually happens. It is possible to create this as a separate process so that other parts of your program can continue running. After all we are still writing in the NET platform, and can use all functionality including multitasking and threading.

More details will be given in the chapter devoted to console applications.

Chapter 8 : Attaching code to handle events

The events generated by user activity, program activity or operating system activity will invoke different parts of your program. To specify what you want to be done, you have to start writing code. Since you are working in an event-driven world, the actual code writing will be limited to whatever cannot be handled automatically by the system.

8.1 : Attaching code to events in VB Classic

To add code to an object you simple double-click it. A code editor window will open and show you the code attached to it. By default, the most used event for the particular object you double-clicked on is displayed. In case of the button, this is the *Click* event. This can be different for other controls or objects. In case of the textbox, the default event will be the *change* event. You can select events belonging to an object using the right pull-down menus on the code window. With the left pull-down menu you can also select an object belonging to the current form. The code editor shows you all code belonging to one form, class or module.

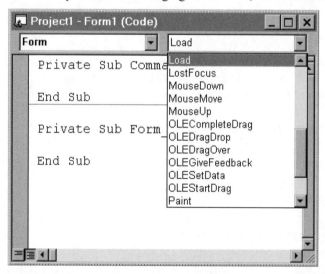

The code editor has a number of very interesting features which make programming very easy. As you are typing code, the editor evaluates what you are typing and shows online help. If you type the name of one of the objects and put a dot behind it, the system will automatically show you a list of all the properties and methods you can control from within code.

If you are calling functions or procedures, it will automatically show you what arguments they expect, in what order and their type. This even works for your own defined procedures and functions. Similarly, this will work for custom enumerated data types, structures, types and classes.

The moment you reach the end of the line and press return, the editor evaluates what you just wrote and will comment if it finds any syntactical errors in your line. This will help you already eliminate typing errors and syntax errors before you even compile it the first time.

8.1.1 : Let's attach some code.

So let's attach some code. First, we want to display the text 'Hello World' when we click on the Go button. To do this you simply double-click the Go button and the code viewer will present you with the correct routine. Since in the example below the button was called **MyButton** the code editor will automatically create the correct definition of the subroutine if it was not already present and put the cursor where you can begin writing code. Of course, if the particular piece of code already existed no new definition will be generated. In that case, only the cursor will jump to the correct location.

Note	In Visual Basic Classic, the code editor will not 'update' the definition should you modify the object in any way. For example if you change the control to a control array then 'index' argument will not be added. You will need to update your code manually.
	Should you change the name of the control, a blank definition will be created for the new control name. The code definition for the old control name still exists. It is up to you to move these blocks of code and re-align them with the new control name.
	Since Visual Basic NET uses a different approach, it can update the definitions automatically so this is no longer an issue.

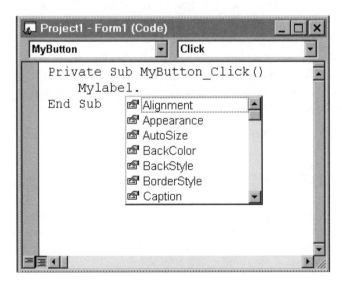

While you are typing, the editor evaluates what you are typing and attempts to assist you. Since we want to change a property (the Caption) of **MyLabel**, we start typing **Mylabel.** (Note the dot!), and then the editor kicks in and shows a list of what properties can be changed. It is sufficient to type now a few letters of the property name until the selector bar is highlighting the desired property method or event. You can now select this by pressing the TAB button and the Visual Basic IDE will write the code for you, or you can type the name completely.

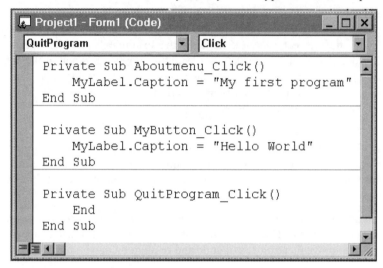

```
Project1 - Form1 (Code)

QuitProgram          ▼   Click                    ▼

Private Sub Aboutmenu_Click()
    MyLabel.Caption = "My first program"
End Sub

Private Sub MyButton_Click()
    MyLabel.Caption = "Hello World"
End Sub

Private Sub QuitProgram_Click()
    End
End Sub
```

The above figure shows you the complete program. When you click the 'Aboutmenu' item (on the Menu bar), then the caption of the **Mylabel** object is going to be changed into 'My first program'. The same goes for a click on **MyButton**. Finally, a click on the Quit button will terminate the execution of the program.

Note	In general, the code attached to a form should only contain directly linked subroutines or functions. If you need to define a dedicated function, store it in a Module. This keeps your code transparent, easier to read and maintain. For more information refer to chapter 9.

Now that we have written the code for the desired functionality, we are ready to run and compile our first program.

8.2 : Attaching event handlers in NET

Since NET considers anything to be an object, the syntax has been amended when dealing with event handlers. As explained before any subroutine can now handle any event. There is no longer the requirement to have the routine named for the control it is attached to.

8.2.1 : The Handles construct

Visual Basic NET introduces the 'handles' keyword that lets you assign the subroutine to an event. A big change is that any routine now can handle multiple objects, and in some cases multiple events.

8.2.1.1 : Dealing with Multiple objects

It is perfectly possible to service multiple objects and events. There some consideration to be made when handling different kinds of events, but that is explained in the next topic. Let's focus on handling similar events from different objects. Suppose you have two buttons and you want to have one routine service the click events

In Visual Basic Classic, you would create the button as a control array and use the index property to fid out exactly which one triggered the click event.

Example:

```
Sub button1_click(index as integer)
    Msgbox ("sender =" & index)
End sub
```

In Visual Basic NET this is rewritten using the Handles keyword

```
Sub Test(ByVal sender As System.Object, _

        ByVal e As System.Eventargs)
        Handles button1.click, button2.click
        Dim keyhit as button.
        Keyhit = sender
    Msgbox("sender =" & keyhit.text)
End sub
```

In order to find out who sent the event, you can examine the 'sender' property passed to you upon invocation of the event handler.

8.2.1.2 : Dealing with multiple events

Under NET, you can deal with multiple different events in the same handler. The only reservation is that the renamed set of arguments needs to be the same. Therefore, in practice, there will only be a few cases where you can exploit this construction. One such an example is the File System Watcher explained previously.

You can trap multiple different events and have them handled by the same routine.

```
Private Sub Watcher_1 (ByVal sender As System.Object, _
        ByVal e As System.IO.FileSystemEventArgs) _
        Handles fsw.Deleted, fsw.Changed, fsw.Created
        ListBox1.Items.Add(e.Name & " - " & e.ChangeType.ToString())
End Sub
```

8.2.2 : The AddHandler method

When writing code there will be situations where you need to be able to handle events dynamically. For instance when you have just instantiated a new button or a menu entry, you might want to add the click event to an already existing handler.

```
Private Sub my_Handler (ByVal sender As System.Object, _
        ByVal e As System.eventargs)
        Handles something.click
Msgbox ("You clicked me")
End Sub

Sub create_and_attach
        Dim somethingelse as new button()
        Me.controls.add somethingelse
        Addhandler somethingelse.click, addressof my_handler
End sub
```

In the above chunk of code, a control named *somethingelse* of the type *button* will be created and added to the current controls collection using the Add method. Finally, the handler *handler* is attached to the 'click' event of the newly defined control.

8.2.3 : The RemoveHandler method

In a similar fashion, it is possible to detach event handlers from a subroutine.

```
Sub detach_and_destroy (something as object)
        removehandler something.click, addressof my_handler
        Me.controls.remove something
End sub
```

In the above chunk of code will detach the control form *My_Handler* and then remove it from the control collection.

Chapter 9 : Running and debugging a program.

Now that you have created a user interface and attached code to it, it is about time we check if it actually does something. The Visual Basic environment allows you to run and debug your code in an easy to use, interactive way. More, you can modify code in place without having to recompile or restart the program being debugged. The 'immediate' window even lets you execute code on the fly. This chapter will concentrate on how to trace and fix errors rapidly.

9.1 : Running a program

Once you have written a block of code you will want to start it and see how it behaves. In order to run a program you can either select the Run-Start (F5), Run-Start with full compile (shift-F5) or the Run button on the toolbar. When you press the Run button on the Toolbar, you are actually just executing the Start command. (F5)

9.1.1 : Start, Break, Stop

When you lick the Start button, the program will be compiled to a machine-readable form and executed. The same happens if you start with a full compile. Then what is the difference, you might ask?

Well, the difference with them is the following: When you come from the situation where your code is not running, it doesn't really matter. Both options will compile your code into an **exe** file and launch them. The difference is when the program aborts due to an error. If you are in the process of debugging your code and you are modifying it, you can continue the run by executing the Start command. The line that caused the program to 'halt' will be re-executed. When the program is halted, you get the change to analyze the problem and correct it on the fly. Hitting the start button will attempt to execute that line again. If this time it does work, the program will continue its course. This is a major advantage of Visual Basic over any other programming language. With other languages, you have to restart the program completely. This can lead to tedious and frustrating work, especially if you are chasing a bug that only pops up occasionally, and after lengthy manipulation. Each and every time you want to try a fix you will have to recreate the problem. In Visual Basic, everything is preserved.

If you select the *Start with full compile,* your program will restart its run completely. All internal variables and objects are destroyed and the program restarts from scratch.

When your program is running, you can halt execution by using CTRL-Break. Alternatively, by clicking the Break button on the toolbar.

Upon executing a break, you will be shown your code at the location where the program is currently processing. The actual line that was going to be executed next will be highlighted. At this point you can examine various elements, such as variables, possibly edit the code and then continue running the program. This allows you to make on-the-fly modifications and see their impact as you go.

| Note | During a break, you cannot edit the user interface. Only the code can be modified. The reason is that the control structures need to be recompiled if you change the interface. Your code is interpreted on the fly. When you really make an EXE then your code also is compiled into machine language |

The stop button finally ends the execution. If, during the execution of your program, a real unrecoverable error occurs, Visual Basic will halt execution and ask you what to do.

9.2 : Debugging a program

If for some reason, something goes wrong (now how did that possibly happen?), you will be presented a warning screen with a brief description of the problem and a number of options on how to proceed.

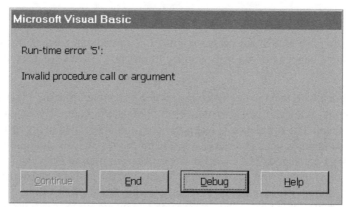

The runtime error-code is displayed together with a brief explanation on what the particular code means. You will have to select what to do next.

If you select 'End' then the execution simply halts. Pressing 'Help' will display information about the nature of the error. However, the Debug button is the most interesting one as it allows examining in great detail what went wrong, and possibly correcting it on the fly.

When you press debug, the code viewer will take you immediately to the line in your code where the error occurred. Now you can examine variables and parameters that may learn you a great deal on what causes the problem and how to remedy it.

9.3 : Examining Variables

You can examine the contents of the variables and properties you access inside the current procedure. This is useful to detect if some parameters are being passed correctly, or if you do not abuse the type of certain variables.

To do this just move your mouse over a variable or property and a small box will appear below the mouse-pointer to show you what is stored in the variable. Most problems are related to variable abuse.

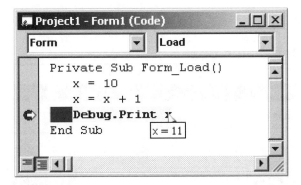

9.4 : Advanced Debugging: The Watch Window

This window appears when watch expressions have been defined in the project.

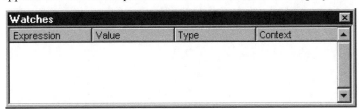

To monitor a variable, simply drag it to either the Immediate window or the Watch window.

9.4.1 : Watch Window Elements

Expression	This column lists the watch expressions.
Value	The Value column lists the value of the expression the moment you enter Break mode. It is possible to modify the variables contents by simply clicking on one and typing in a new value.
Type	This lists the type of expression.
Context	This lists the context of the expression.

Of course, in order for the value to be displayed it needs to be in the scope of the current routine.

9.4.2 : Add Watch command

The Add watch command on the toolbar allows you to add watch expressions. You can do this either at design time or in break mode. The expression can be any valid Basic expression. The watch expressions are displayed in the Watch window as soon as you enter break mode.

Toolbar shortcut:

9.4.3 : Add watch dialog box

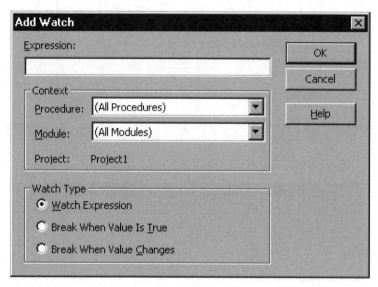

This dialog is used to define the watch expression. It can be a variable, a property, a function call, or any other valid Basic expression. The information is displayed in the Watch window as soon as you enter break mode, or if you are running from the immediate window, as soon as the command is executed.

You can also drag a selected expression from the Code window to the Watch window.

 The more watches you define the slower your program will execute. Try to narrow the selected element down as much as possible.

The watch type defines what will be monitored.

Watch Expression	This displays the watch expression and its value in the Watch window.
Break When Value Is True	If this option is chosen the program execution will automatically enter break mode when the watch expression evaluates.
Break When Value Changes:	This is similar to previous option but any change will trigger an Execution halt.

9.4.4 : Quick Watch command (Shift F9)

The Quick watch command opens the Quick Watch dialog box. You can use this command to check the current value of a variable, property or expression, even it is not defined in the watch window.

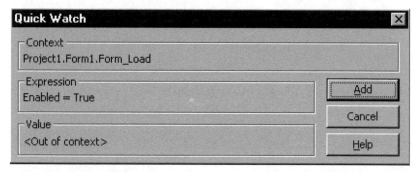

The Quick Watch dialog box displays the current value of a selected expression. This functionality is useful when debugging your code, if you want to see the current value of a variable, property, or other expression.

9.4.5 : Edit Watch command

The Edit Watch command displays the Edit Watch dialog box in which you can edit or delete a watch expression.

Toolbar shortcut: .Keyboard shortcut: CTRL+W.

9.4.6 : Edit Watch Window

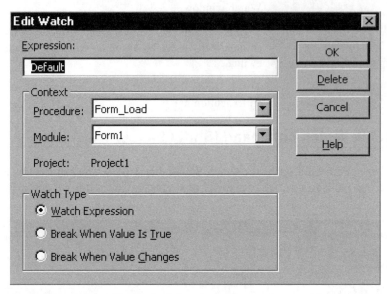

This window is similar to the Add watch dialog. It can be used to modify a watch expression or delete it.

9.5 : Using Breakpoints

Breakpoints may well be the most important trick in the debugger's hat. You can set a breakpoint on any executable line of code. When, during execution, the compiler reaches a line of code with a breakpoint set, it will halt the execution. You can then examine variables or change the flow of the program.

Note	Breakpoints are saved into you project. When you compile code containing breakpoints, they are suppressed. Compiled code cannot be halted by breakpoints. They only work inside the IDE of Visual Basic

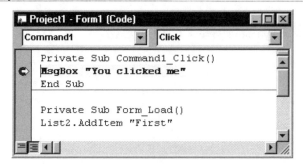

You can set a breakpoint by clicking in the column before the line you want to set it. A red dot will appear showing you a set breakpoint. Clearing it is equally simple. Simply repeat the action. When the code is running and reaches the breakpoint, a yellow arrow will appear in front of the line where the run was halted. You can examine variables now. You can also move the arrow down or up. This way you can alter the program flow. Be careful however, this is tricky stuff and might not always lead to what you intended it to.

Note	Breakpoints halt before the tagged line. If there are multiple commands separated by semicolons on a single line, then the first of them is halted. The others cannot be halted. In order to use breakpoints fully, you should make sure only one statement per line of code is present in your program.

9.6 : The Debug Object

Another way of examining data and program flow is to insert calls to the DEBUG object. This is an embedded object of the IDE. When compiling code this objects is made empty. This means that the calls are omitted. Therefore, the end user will not see these messages. You can call the immediate window (debug window) by pressing CTRL-G. You can simply print messages to debug by referring it as **debug.print** "something".

```
Sub Form1_load()
    Debug.print " program started"
End sub

Sub Quit_click()
    Debug.print " Bye !"
    End
End sub
```

The contents of this immediate window are preserved even after the run of the program is terminated. This means it can be used to track nasty bugs in bailout code, or things that happen even before a user interface is visible.

You cannot delete text from this window while the program is running. Once it is stopped, you can select lines, use cut copy and paste commands, just like you can with any regular window.

9.7 : Debugging NET style

The NET framework defines its own debug concept. The output can be redirected anywhere depending on the parameters provided. The expected behaviors like setting breakpoints, watch points and examining variable contents while in break mode are all available.

There are, however, a few things that have changed in NET, that are important enough to highlight here.

9.7.1 : Debug.Print and the Debugger in NET

Debug.Print is no longer available and had been replaced by *debug.write* and *debug.writeline*. So far so good, you might say, but ... you also need to specify what you are going to use as output device. In Visual Basic Classic, the immediate window was the default output window for debugging information. In NET, the output can go anywhere, to file to a remote debugger over Ethernet or even to the console if you want to. It is equally possible to use multiple output channels in parallel and replicate information.

In its most simple implementation, all you need to do is provide an output channel. This is done by adding the channel to the *Debug.listeners* collection.

Example:

```
Debug.listeners.add (new TextWriterTraceListener(console.out))
```

The above code creates a new text trace listener and points it to the *Console.Out* class that handles all console output. There are other types of trace listeners available that allow interfacing to other debugging interfaces but this is beyond the scope of this chapter.

The newly created debug channel is added to the *Debug.Listeners* collection.

Since this collection runs independently it is necessary to force it to update continuously. Just like when we were dealing with the file system, the debug object also features an *AutoFlush* property.

Example:

```
Debug.autoflush = true
```

And finally, we can send information to the debug channel by using the *Write* or *WriteLine* methods exposed by the debug object.

Example:

```
Debug.writeline ("hello world")
```

Chapter 10 : Distributing a program

Now you have come to the point where you have program that is to your best knowledge bug free. The last step is to make a distributable version of the program.

10.1 : The First steps ...

The first step is to compile it to an executable format. Clicking on the 'File' menu and selecting 'Make Executable' in the design environment can easily do this.

If you click this menu item, the compiler will build an executable version of your program.

You can now run this project on your computer without needing Visual Basic. However if you would like to distribute it you might run into some trouble. For starters, your project might use certain controls that reside in separate VBX, OCX or DLL files. Sometimes it is not always easy to figure out what exactly is needed. Furthermore, your target user might not have the correct version of the files you use in your program.

However, do not despair! Visual Basic has a wizard aboard which does all this work for you and creates a nice set of floppy disks you can use to install your program onto another computer. More, it even creates a nice Setup and uninstall program that gives an extra Pro-touch to your application.

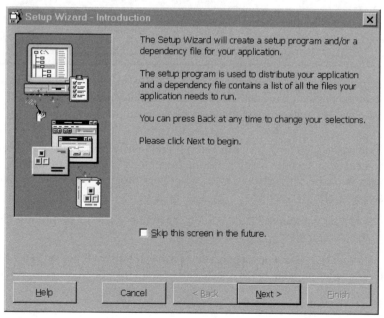

This wizard can be found in the program group of Visual Basic. It will guide you step-by-step through the creation of the distribution kit. For the most part of the process, all you have to do is, keep clicking the Next button. However, some pages are interesting, and will be dealt with next.

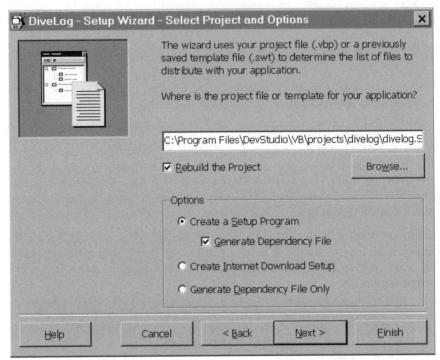

The first step you have to do is select the program's VBP file. It is a good idea to select the option 'Rebuild the project'. This will force a clean compile of all of your code. Furthermore, you will be sure the latest changes and bindings are installed.

Note Bindings are the links between your program and external modules. These bindings contain also module version information. It is important to distribute the right version of the external files. Otherwise, your program might not be able to run on someone else's computer.

In the Options section you can select the kind of operation you want to perform. For now, the standard 'Create a setup program' will do just fine.

However, make sure the 'Generate Dependency File' option is switched on. This again is used for the bindings in your program.

10.2 : Specifying the Media

The next screen allows you to specify the kind of setup you want.

If you specify 'floppy disk', you will have to make sure to have enough empty and formatted floppy disks at hand. A better option in that case is to specify 'disk directories'. This will store the contents of the floppy disks in files on your hard disk. You can then later make the distribution floppies.

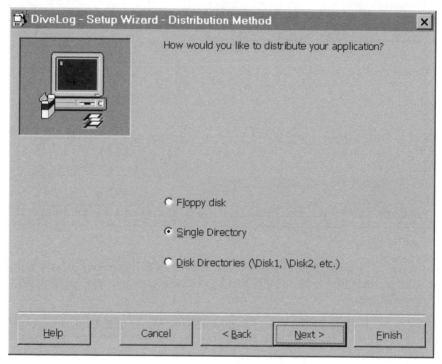

Single directory is used if you want to store everything in one huge file or want to write a CD with the software on.

The setup wizard will now ask you where you want the distribution files to be located. You can select any valid directory. It is a good idea to start in an empty directory. The wizard will not touch existing files in the directory (if any should exist). Therefore, if the directory is not empty you might end up with more files then you bargained for.

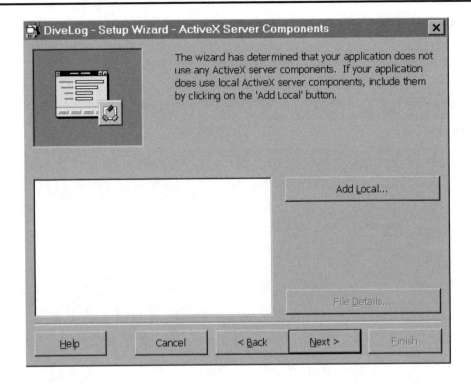

The next screen will allow you to add custom files. This is interesting if you want to add 'readme' files or setup files to the distribution kit. These files will be packed also and installed on the target computer.

After this, you will see a list of files that the wizard thinks are necessary for your program. You can edit this list at will. However, this is not such a good idea since you might accidentally delete necessary files.

For the remainder of the work you can simply click 'Next' all the time. At a certain point, you will see that the wizard starts gathering the required files and will compact them. In the final stage, it will compile the actual Setup.exe program.

When all is done, the only thing you have to do, depending on the output format you selected, is send the floppies to your user, or copy the files onto floppies or other media, zip them or send them over the internet.

Chapter 11 : Multi-module projects

During your programming work, situations will arise where you will need more than one form. You might want to give the user an options form, setup form or an about form. Sometimes your program will include also custom routines that are not directly related to events, but are called from other routines.

In any of these cases, your project will be a multi-module project. To be honest, nearly every project, no matter how small, will most likely turn out to be a multi-module project. Anyway, this dividing of a project keeps things manageable. Furthermore, you can re-use chunks of code you once wrote easily by adding the file they reside in to the project you are working on right now.

You can add items using the Project menu. To create a form, simply select 'Add Form'. Similarly, a module can be created using the Add Module item.

11.1 : Multiple Forms

Remember when we discussed the basic project form, we talked about the startup form. Typically, the first form you ever draw in a project is the startup form. Other forms remain hidden until you call them. There is a substantial difference between Visual Basic Classic (5.0 and 6.0) and later versions such as NET, NET2003 and Visual Basic 2005.

11.1.1 : Visual Basic Classic Forms

You can call a form on to the screen with the Show method. In a similar way, you can hide the form using the Hide method.

```
MySecondform.Show
```

When the form is loaded then the **focus** is automatically set to the new form. This means that keyboard and mouse operations will refer to this form. You can select a different form by clicking it. In some cases, you might want to 'lock' the form. This means the user can do nothing until ha closes the new form. This can be done using the **vbModal** option. If you specify this option then the user can only work with this form until it is closed.

```
MySecondform.show vbModal
```

To ease the programming work, Visual Basic has also something called a message box. This is a kind of predefined simple form, which you can use to interrogate the user. A number of parameters allow you to change the look and feel of this form:

```
MsgBox "Hello World", vbOKOnly + vbInformation, _
       "My first Message"
```

This gives the following result:

11.1.2 : Visual Basic NET Forms

Loading and unloading forms in Visual Basic NET is still done with the Show method but the way it is invoked is different. As explained before Visual Basic NET is completely object oriented. Any form, module or any other component that makes up your project is treated as a class. So if you create a second form with its own controls that is actually a class.

Therefore, it is now necessary to first instantiate and object of that class.

Example:

```
'Consider thehe project has 2 forms called form1 and form2

Dim my_form2 as new form2 ' create a new object form the class
                          ' form2 and call it my_form2
My_form2.show ' now apply the Show Method to the freshly created
              ' object
```

11.2 : Modules

Apart from forms there are also things called modules. A module is a piece of code that has no user interface. It generally contains variable definitions, and user subroutines and or functions. It provides a means to neatly organize your own functions.

A calculator program might have a custom function called calculate which takes in two numbers and an operator and returns the result.

```
Function Calculate (a, b, operator)
select case operator
case   plus
                result = a + b
case minus
          result = a - b
end select
        calculate = result
end function
```

A module is also the place where you define your variables and constants. You have to consider a module as a separate process. When your application is compiled, all modules are evaluated and their definitions are created. Then the remainder of the module is compiled to a library and linked to the other parts of the program.

11.3 : Accessing items from other parts of the program

Since every form acts like a standalone unit this also means that two different forms can have a control with the same name. The controls are completely different since they have different handles.

Suppose you have a project with three forms, and every form has a command button to close the form. Logically you would call every close button simply *CloseForm*. Now suppose you have a routine that closes all three forms. You could simply invoke the commands from this routine. The only problem is figuring out what command.

Well the answer is simple. You just specify the parent object and then the desired object belonging to this parent. In our case the code would look like this:

```
Sub Closeall()
    call form1.close_click ()
    call form2.close_click ()
    call form3.close_click ()
End Sub
```

This same rule applies to procedures inside a module. Actually, your own built procedures are no different than the ones attached to objects. You have to specify the target object using its complete denominator. You can make an analogy between a project and a hard disk.

The hard disk is the project itself. The user interface is the root account. In the root of the project are forms (subdirectories). Each form contains objects (files). Every object on this form can contain further objects (another layer of directories. To reach an object from any given location you have to specify the complete search path. Objects belonging to the same level (directory) can find each other since they reside at the same level.

The only quirk in this analogy is that in the root there can only be a special kind of object (forms) and they can only reside there. Once you go down then you can have directories made of other objects.

11.4 : Root structure analogy of a project

```
project1.vbp

├─Form1
│     ├──Menu(menubar)
│     │         ├─────File
│     │         │         ├─Save
│     │         │         ├─Save As
│     │         │         ├──
│     │         │         └─Quit
│     │         ├─────Edit
│     │         │         ├─Cut
│     │         │         ├─Copy
│     │         │         └─Paste
│     │         └─────Help
│     │                   └──About
│     ├──Close(button)
│     ├──MyMessage(label)
│     └──MyStatusbar(statusbar)
│                   ├─────Panel1 type:text(first panel)
│                   ├─────Panel2 type:Date(second panel)
│                   └─────Panel3 type:capsLock(third panel)
├─Form2
│     ├──Close(button)
│     └──mytext(textbox)
└─Form3
      ├──Mypanel(frame)
      │         ├─────OK(button)
      │         └─────Turbo(checkbox)
      ├──Cancel(button)
      └──Close(button)
```

As you can see in this graphical representation, even a menu is a collection of objects. Keep in mind, though that some objects could contain others. Some special objects like Forms and menus are 'awkward'. These objects have a special function. They are called parental object. This means that they form the basis from which the operating system detaches messages. A menu bar is also an object, but a special kind that can only be linked to a parent of the class 'Form'.

The particularities of this matter are dealt with later on where the creation of custom objects will be discussed.

Chapter 12 : A couple of case studies

This chapter will guide you step-by-step through the creation of a couple of small programs. This will provide you with a better understanding on how a program is written in Visual Basic.

The first program is a small text viewer / editor. It allows you to view and edit files.

Topics such as add-on objects and system objects, textboxes and menus will be explained. You will see how to open, read and write, and close files. Furthermore, it makes use of some of the components built into windows such as the clipboard

The second program describes a calculator.

This will deal with arrays of controls and creating a multi-module project. It will show you how you can heavily optimize code by creating arrays of objects and writing your own custom functions and procedures.

12.1 : Case Study 1: A small Text Editor

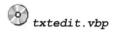 **txtedit.vbp**
There is a tutorial program available that explains the constructs, explained in this topic, by example.

In this case study we will create a small text editor. Basic file manipulation, using the CommonDialog control and accessing the windows Clipboard will be explained.

12.1.1 : Designing the user interface

As usual, we first start Visual Basic and create a new Standard EXE project.

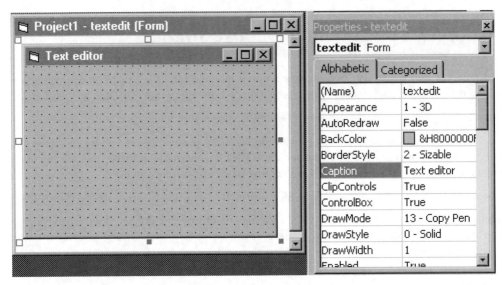

Since we will make a text editor, the next logical step is to put a textbox on the form. If look to the properties of the textbox you will find a property called *Multiline*. When you set this to true, then the textbox can contain multiple lines of text. A *CRLF* will force the textbox to add a new line to its contents.

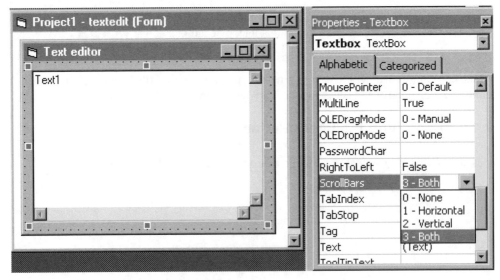

Since our editor can read files up to 32000 characters, it might be a good idea if we would have some means to scroll through the text. Browsing through the properties quickly reveals the Scrollbars property. Setting this to 'Both' displays both scrollbars: a horizontal and a vertical scrollbar.

The next thing we should do is, give the user a means to load and save files. We could go on, design our own **load** and **save** forms but, since this is Visual Basic, these forms already exist under the CommonDialog object.

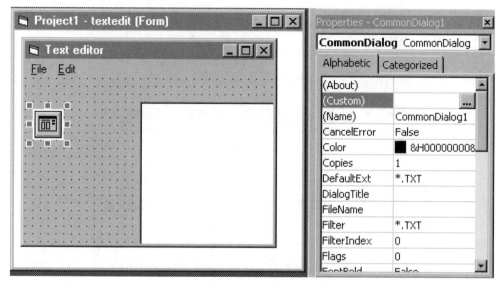

Placing the **CommonDialog** custom control on the form gives you instant access to interface to automate such things as loading and saving files, selecting colors, selecting printers etc.

We give this control also a name. The control position on the form does not really matter. This is a kind of control that has no runtime GUI element attached to it. This means that when your code starts running nothing appears.

Now we should build a menu to allow the user to access the file load/save dialogs and to perform some basic editing operations on the text in the textbox.

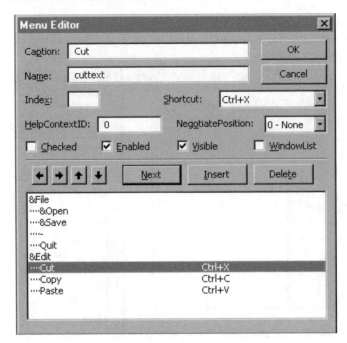

To ease the editing work we attach the standard windows hotkeys to the controls for cut, copy and paste.

If you would run your program now you would see that you already could type some text in the textbox. However, this is of no use since you could not save or retrieve any document.

12.1.2 : Attaching Code

The first thing to do is attach code to the Quit option on the menu. We will simply terminate the execution using the 'end' keyword. Enhancements could be detecting if the user has not saved his work and display a warning that he might lose information.

Now let us take a look into the Editing functions. The textbox control features a property called *SelText*. This property holds any text the user selects (highlighted text). You can read and write this property. This means that, when reading, you extract the text; and when writing, you change the selected text.

So all we need to do is, store the contents of this property in a variable. Now we could do this but then we have to define a global variable. Then what if we want to support copying and pasting across applications? Well, fortunately Windows has something called the 'clipboard'. We can use this clipboard from within Visual Basic. A virtual object called 'clipboard' exists. This object does need to be put somewhere on your design form since it resides inside the operating system itself. Just like the printer or debug object, it is directly accessible.

To learn more about the clipboard object it suffices to type **clipboard** with a dot behind in the code window. The Visual Basic editor will show you your options immediately.

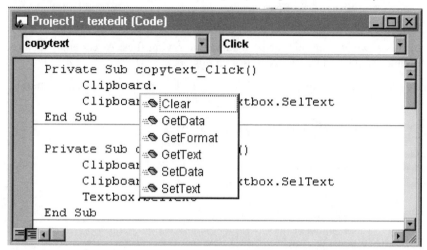

As you can see, the clipboard is a universal storage space for temporary data. You can store and retrieve texts, images and formatting commands with it.

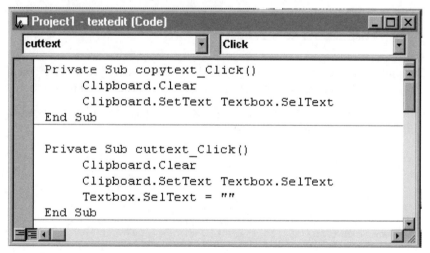

The copy routine clears the clipboard and then retrieves the text the user has selected, and stores it onto the clipboard.

The Cut routine does the same but afterwards it sets the selected text to an empty string. This way the text disappears from the edit window.

For the paste routine, we only have to extract the stored text from the clipboard and dump it into the selected text. Now one nice thing about the *SelText* property is that, when no text is selected, the text is dumped at the current cursor location. This means the user can insert text wherever he want by placing the cursor at a position of his linking and executing the 'paste' operation, or overwriting text by first selecting the chunk to be removed and then performing a 'paste' operation.

Now this is done, we can concentrate on loading and saving files. As explained before, we will use the CommonDialog control to assist us with this operation.

The control has a several methods attached to it. The ones we are concentrating on, are **ShowOpen** and **ShowSave**.

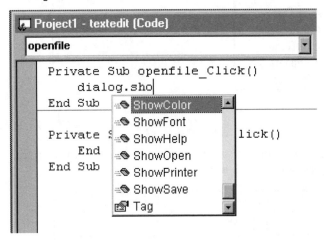

To ask the user for a filename, you just call in the **CommonDialog.ShowOpen** method. The user can then navigate his hard disk and select a file. He can also cancel this operation

When a file has been successfully selected, the complete path and filename is stored in the property Filename of the CommonDialog control.

```
Private Sub openfile_Click()
    dialog.ShowOpen              ' show the commondialog
    On Error GoTo invalidfile   ' if no file should be selected
    filename$ = dialog.filename    ' retrieve the filename
    Open filename$ For Input As #1 ' open the file
    Textbox.Text = ""       ' clear contents of the textbox
    While Not EOF(1)        ' as long as not end of file
       Line Input #1, a$
       Textbox.Text = Textbox.Text + a$ + vbCrLF
    Wend

invalidfile:
    Close #1 ' close the file
End Sub
```

When the user cancels the operation, then no file has been selected and the property filename will be empty. In this case attempting to open a non-existing file will yield an error. Therefore we will test for errors during the execution of the code and takes measures to solve it.

Since a CommonDialog is always *application modal*, the user cannot do anything else with our program in the mean time. The user has to close the file selector first and then be able to continue to work with the text editor.

The final code for the entire text editor looks like this:

```
Private sub QuitProgram_Click()
    End
End Sub

Private sub savefile_Click()
    dialog.ShowSave
    On Error GoTo invalidfile
    filename$ = dialog.filename
    Open filename$ For output As #1
    Print #1, Textbox.Text

invalidfile:
    Close #1
End sub

Private Sub openfile_Click()
    dialog.ShowOpen              ' show the commondialog
    On Error GoTo invalidfile  ' if no file should be selected
    filename$ = dialog.filename    ' retrieve the filename
    Open filename$ For Input As #1 ' open the file
    Textbox.Text = ""       ' clear contents of the textbox
    While Not EOF(1)        ' as long as not end of file
        Line Input #1, a$
        Textbox.Text = Textbox.Text + a$ + vbCrLF
    Wend

invalidfile:
    Close #1                                ' close the file
End Sub

Private Sub Cuttext_Click()
        ClipBoard.Clear
        ClipBoard.Settext Textbox.Seltext
        Textbox.Seltext=""
End Sub

Private Sub CopyText_Click()
        ClipBoard.Clear
        ClipBoard.Settext Textbox.Seltext
End Sub

Private Sub PasteText_Click()
        Textbox.Seltext=ClipBoard.Gettext
End Sub
```

12.2 : Case Study 2: A Calculator

 calc.vbp

There is a tutorial program available, which explains the constructs explained in this topic.

The goal of this exercise is to show you how to create control arrays and how to create a project with multiple forms.

12.2.1 : Designing the user interface

First of all, you start up Visual Basic and create a new standard exe project.

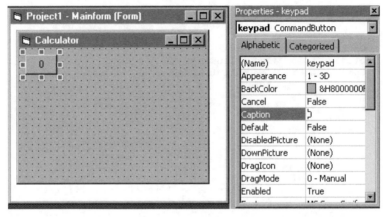

Rename the main form to **calculator**, set its caption to 'Calculator' and create a command button. The command button gets as caption '0' and as name **Keypad**.

The keypad we are about to design will be roughly divided into two sections. You will have the numerical field that will be designed as a control array and the other keys that are regular keys.

To create the array of objects you select the command button and copy it (ctrl-c or *copy* on the *edit* menu). Then you paste the object on the form by pressing ctrl-V or edit-Paste via the menu bar.

Visual Basic will now ask you if you want to create a control array since you already have an object named 'keypad' on your form.

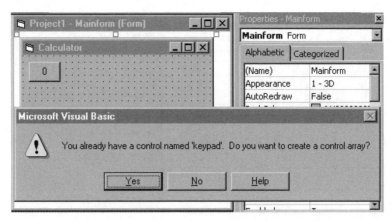

You click 'Yes' and a new control will be placed on your form. This control is an exact copy of the original, except that its *index* property has been set to 1. The original button will automatically have his index set to 0.

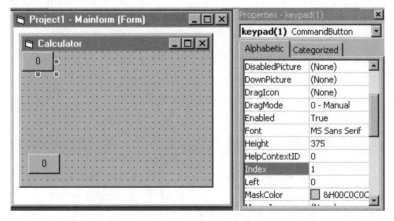

You move the object now into place and select it. Change the caption property using the property navigator to '1'. Continue this until you have all the numbers from 0 to 9. The result should look like the image on the next page. Make sure that the captions correspond to the index given to the controls, and re-arrange where necessary in order to get a nice looking keypad.

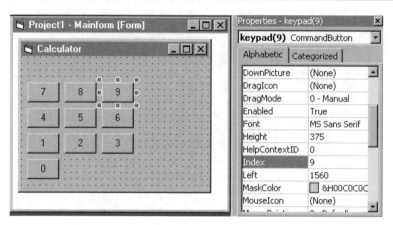

The last placed object will have index 9 and caption 9.

Now we can continue placing the other control buttons. The four buttons for the operators will be called **plus**, **minus**, **divide** and **multiply**. A command button with a dot will also be created. The next and last 3 buttons will be command buttons with **CE**, **C** and **=** as caption. These will allow you to correct errors and to actually execute the calculation.

Set the name of the **CE** button to **clearerror**, name the **C** button **clearall** and rename the **=** button to **calculate**.

Finally, a textbox is placed on the form and named **display**.

The result should look somewhat like this:

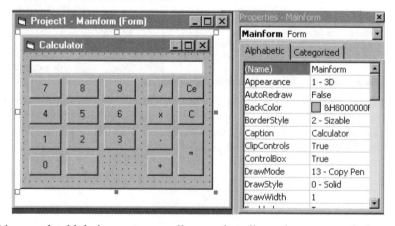

The last thing we should do is, create a small menu that allows the user to exit the program. To do this you start the menu editor and build a small menu.

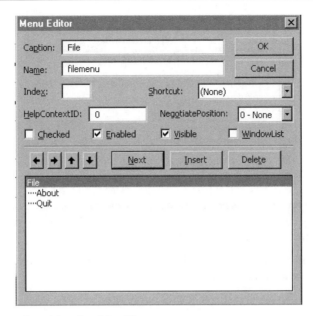

A top level and two sub entries should suffice.

Now that we have the user interface in place, we can start writing code for our application.

12.2.2 : Writing Code

The first thing that needs to be done is deciding if we need any variables and or constants. If yes, they should be stored in a module.

It might be a good idea to store entered values in two variables. In addition, the selected operator should be stored somewhere. To make the code readable, we will define constants for the operators. This will allow us to refer to names instead of numbers. The code will be easier to understand later.

To do this you select the Project menu and click on 'Add-Module". In the project browser, you will see that an empty module has been created and attached to your project.

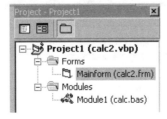

In this module, we will define the variables and constants discussed above.

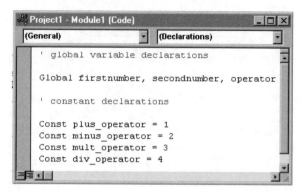

The variables *firstnumber*, *secondnumber* and *operator* have been defined as *global*. This means that they can be accessed and modified from anywhere in the program. The same is true for the operators that are stored as global constants.

As you type, you will see again that the Visual Basic code editor will color the text. This gives you immediate feedback on the correct syntax of your code.

Now this is done, we can start creating code for our project.

12.2.3 : Attaching code to the user interface

We will start with the keypad. Double-click any of the buttons of the keypad. The code editor will open up and show you the appropriate section of the program code.

As you can see, the keypad's click event returns an index to show you which one of the keys in the array of objects actually invoked the event. We will use this index value to update the contents of the display.

Every time the user clicks on one of the buttons belonging to the array, the *keypad_click* routine will be fired and the index will let us know exactly which one was clicked. All we do is simply convert this index number to a string using the *STR$* function and write it to the textbox. Since the *STR$* returns a string beginning with a leading space, we strip off this space using the *LTRIM$* function

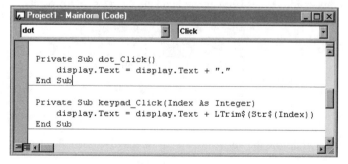

The dot operator will simply add a dot to the display. A point for improvement would be to check if there already is a dot and decide whether to put it or not.

Since we are programming in Basic this is dead easy by simply adding an if-then-else construct to the **dot_click** routine.

```
if instr (display.text, ".") = 0 then
      display.text = display.text + "."
end if
```

The above piece of code is executed every time the '.' Button is clicked. Using the **Instr** function a check is made to see of the property 'text' of our display has a dot. If the **Instr** function returns a zero, then none was found. In that case, we allow the dot to be written to the display.

So far, two functions will allow you to enter a decimal number using the mouse and the keypad, and all with only three lines of code. Pretty neat, huh?

Now let us create the code for the operators and other buttons. To do this, simply double-click any of the remaining controls and you will be able to attach the rest of the code. The Visual Basic IDE will automatically create the subroutines for you.

For each of the operators we will set the variable operator to one of our constants. Later, in the real calculation part, we will use these constants again to decide what needs to be done.

The CE and C buttons do nothing else than clear the display (CE) and the variables holding the two numbers and the operator (C).

The code for the other buttons will look like this:

```
Private Sub clear_Click()
      display.Text = ""
End Sub
Private Sub clearerror_Click()
      display.Text = ""
      firstnumber = 0
      secondnumber = 0
      operator = 0
End Sub
Private Sub divide_Click()
      firstnumber = Val(display.Text)
      display.Text = ""
      operator = div_operator
End Sub
Private Sub minus_Click()
      firstnumber = Val(display.Text)
      display.Text = ""
      operator = minus_operator
End Sub
Private Sub multiply_Click()
      firstnumber = Val(display.Text)
```

```
            display.Text = ""
            operator = mult_operator
      End Sub
      Private Sub plus_Click()
            firstnumber = Val(display.Text)
            display.Text = ""
            operator = plus_operator
      End Sub
      Private Sub quitProgram_Click()
          End
      End Sub
```

Now for the real workhorse: the '=' button. This button will actually calculate and display the result. This takes some programming logic to figure out exactly what to do and, most importantly, how to do it.

Fortunately, there is the *Select Case* construction that will help us out here.

```
      Private Sub calculate_Click()
            secondnumber = Val(display.Text)
            Select Case operator
            Case plus_operator
                result = firstnumber + secondnumber
            Case minus_operator
                result = firstnumber - secondnumber
            Case mult_operator
                result = firstnumber * secondnumber
            Case div_operator
                result = firstnumber / secondnumber
            End Select
            display.Text = result
            firstnumber = result
            secondnumber = 0
            operator = 0
      End Sub
```

The last part of our work is to attach a few blurbs of code to the two menu items. The about item will simply brag a bit about our program and the Quit menu will neatly terminate our program.

When finished the complete code should look like this:

```
      Private Sub aboutprogram_Click()
          display.Text = "Calculator v1.0"
      End Sub
      Private Sub calculate_Click()
            secondnumber = Val(display.Text)
            Select Case operator
            Case plus_operator
                result = firstnumber + secondnumber
            Case minus_operator
                result = firstnumber - secondnumber
            Case mult_operator
                result = firstnumber * secondnumber
```

```
                Case div_operator
                     result = firstnumber / secondnumber
                End Select
                display.Text = result
                firstnumber = result
                secondnumber = 0
                operator = 0
        End Sub
        Private Sub clear_Click()
                display.Text = ""
        End Sub
        Private Sub clearerror_Click()
                display.Text = ""
                firstnumber = 0
                secondnumber = 0
                operator = 0
        End Sub
        Private Sub divide_Click()
                firstnumber = Val(display.Text)
                display.Text = ""
                operator = div_operator
        End Sub
        Private Sub dot_Click()
                display.Text = display.Text + "."
        End Sub
        Private Sub keypad_Click(Index As Integer)
                display.Text = display.Text + LTrim$(Str$(Index))
        End Sub
        Private Sub minus_Click()
                firstnumber = Val(display.Text)
                display.Text = ""
                operator = minus_operator
        End Sub
        Private Sub multiply_Click()
                firstnumber = Val(display.Text)
                display.Text = ""
                operator = mult_operator
        End Sub
        Private Sub plus_Click()
                firstnumber = Val(display.Text)
                display.Text = ""
                operator = plus_operator
        End Sub
        Private Sub quitProgram_Click()
            End
        End Sub
```

Well that's it. We have just made a calculator with only 37 lines of code, which has a complete GUI and is entirely event driven.

12.3 : The Calculator NET style

The previous calculator example looks a bit different in the NET framework. As explained before, NET no longer supports control array. Instead, you can specify the controls a particular subroutine is attached to.

Let us again start with the form and put the numerical keyboard in place. We will place ten buttons in total. You can do it two ways: simply draw ten buttons or draw one button, select it, edit-copy (ctrl-c) end then paste it nine more times. Contrary to Visual Basic Classic you will not be prompted with the question 'do you want to create a control array' since the NET framework no longer has arrays of controls.

Rename the last placed button to Button0 and organize the buttons to form the keypad.

Double-click any of these buttons to open the code editor.

I clicked Button1 so I got the following piece of code:

```
    Private sub button1_click(Byval sender as System.Object, _
            Byval e as System.Eventargs) Handles button1.click
        End sub
```

I will rename this subroutine to a more generic name: **keyboard_click**

```
    Private sub keyboard_click(Byval sender as System.Object, _
            Byval e as System.Eventargs) Handles button1.click
        End sub
```

Even though the function is no longer called **button1_click** it still handles the **button1.click** event, and this is a big difference with Visual Basic Classic. There the function name reflected directly what object and event it was servicing. In NET, this is specified by the **Handles** construct.

The next step is to let this routine handle more than one button. So we need to add the other events to the **handles** list.

```
    Private sub keyboard_click(Byval sender as System.Object, _
            Byval e as System.Eventargs) Handles button0.click, _
                Button1.click, Button2.click, Button3.click,
                Button4.click, Button5.click, Button6.click,
                Button7.click, Button8.click, Button9.click
        End sub
```

The **sender** property contains a handle to the calling object and the **e** property contains the collection of all associated interfaces of the class that 'sender' belongs to.

Since our buttons will have their text property set to their numerical representation, we can retrieve the **text** property.

Now add a textbox and call it **display**. To update the textbox whenever a key on our keyboard is hit, we would have to write the following piece of code:

```
Display.text = display.text & sender.text
```

While this will work, it is impaired in the sense that the development environment will not show you the familiar list of interfaces of the object *sender*, since it has no idea what kind of object *sender* is. For the same reason the actual generated code will be slow, since this has to be figured out at runtime.

By adding a temporary variable and correctly typecasting it, we can circumvent these two problems.

```
Dim keyhit as button.
Keyhit = sender
Display.text = keyhit.text
```

Since the NET framework considers anything an object, we can actually define a variable that points to an object. In this case, I declared it as the type Button that resides in the *System.windows.forms* class.

By assigning the sender object to *keyhit*, the *keyhit* subroutine will take over all interfaces from 'sender'. Since *keyhit* is typecast, the compiler can generate much tighter and thus faster code.

The full code looks like this:

```
Private sub keyboard_click(Byval sender as System.Object, _
        Byval e as System.Eventargs) Handles button0.click, _
            Button1.click, Button2.click, Button3.click,
            Button4.click, Button5.click, Button6.click,
            Button7.click, Button8.click, Button9.click

        Dim keyhit as button.
        Keyhit = sender
        Display.text = keyhit.text
    End sub
```

At the same time, the development environment knows as what type *keyhit* has been cast. As soon as you put the dot behind *keyhit* the IDE will pull up the list of available interfaces.

This might seem a cumbersome way of working, but it has many advantages.

- You can handle multiple objects with one routine.
- The name of the routine that services an object's events is no longer coupled with the object name. The IDE can no update the logical link.

The rest of the code pretty much remains the same, except for the names of the subroutines and their arguments of course.

Introduction to Part II

After reading part 1, you have got an all-round overview of the Visual Basic programming environment and language. We have covered the basic methods and objects. Nevertheless, even though we have covered extensive ground, we have barely scratched to surface of Visual Basic. The presented material is the foundation stone for additional techniques that will be presented in this part.

Part II takes you one step further into the nuts and bolts of Visual Basic programming, building on the material presented in the first part. The main block of this part will explore the richness of the standard controls and objects. Things like Popup menus, MDI forms, Menu lists, and Timers and more will be explained.

I will also show you how to have other applications embedded inside your programs; we will dig deeper in Windows and the things it is composed of.

I will expose some of the inner workings of windows and of what use they can be to a programmer. Topics such as API accessing through DLL libraries will be extensively covered since they allow us to extend our programming environment and programming language practically limitless.

Finally, we will dig deeper into the different channels the computer uses for communication to the outside world. Topics such as serial communication, printing and communication such as TCP/IP operations will be explained.

Chapter 13 : One step beyond

So far you have learned about objects, methods, properties and events. You have seen what they are and touched some of the things you can do with them. You also studied the command set of the Basic language. By this time you will probably have written a small program yourself. Now it is time to dig a little bit deeper in this new world.

13.1 : Advanced Form manipulations

Let us take a closer look at the forms and what you can do with them. Typically, a program will consist of multiple forms. You should already know that you can 'show' and 'hide' a form. You can also Load and Unload a form. Now what is the real difference? A form is typically the startup place of your program. Almost 100% of normal window applications have at least one form. Exceptions might be ActiveX controls without a user interface or custom classes.

NET 2005	Visual Basic NET also allows you create so called console applications. These do not use the windows graphical user interface but perform their screen I/O through the command line interface, pretty much like in the old DOS days.

Unless you change the project settings, the program begins with the *form_load* code of the main form. The compiler defaults to this procedure upon executing the code. It is possible to change this behavior by changing this in the projects property dialog of Visual Basic. You can switch this to any custom subroutine. This allows you to perform certain operations before anything visible is shown, like checking for a program running two instances.

13.1.1 : The Load event

Loading a form means that windows allocated memory for the graphical part, the event processors, and the message queue. The moment a form is loaded, it starts consuming resources. The more controls there are on a form the more resources will be allocated, and the more time windows has to divert to it, even if the form is not being used.

When you execute the *Form.Show* command, Windows checks if the referred form is already loaded. If not it loads it into memory, builds all required links and finally renders it as an image on the monitor. If you hide a form, the window manager removes the form from the screen but not from memory. All controls and objects are still in place. Furthermore, you can still call *public* procedures and manipulate exposed variables and objects just like when the form is visible. All the resources allocated to it, still remain locked.

From the above the following should be observed: if you extensively use forms, then you should take care to unload the unnecessary forms whenever you can. Do not simply hide them.

You do not need to explicitly *Load* a form in order to use it. Any reference to a form or object belonging to a form will trigger the load process automatically.

Any standard dialog boxes that can be displayed using the Visual Basic internal functions, such as *MsgBox* and *InputBox*, can simply be called directly.

13.1.2 : Unload

The *Unload* method unloads a form or control from memory.
        `Unload (object)`

It may be necessary in some cases where the memory is needed for something else, or when you need to reset properties to their original values, to unload a form entirely from memory.

When a form is unloaded, all controls belonging to the form are destroyed and thus no longer accessible. In case Unload is used to unload objects that were created in run-time, it can only be used to destroy control array elements.

13.1.3 : Show

The Show method makes a form visible. If the form is not already loaded, it will be loaded automatically.

        `Object.show style,ownerform`

Object	An optional object name. If no object is specified the currently focused form is assumed as default.
Style	An optional Integer that defines if the form is modal or modeless.
Ownerform	A string expression that specifies the component that "owns" the form being shown. For standard Visual Basic forms, use the keyword Me.

Visual Basic will automatically load a form when the *Show* method is invoked so you do not have to deal with that.

Note	A form is bound to a certain mode. Typically a form is 'modeless'. This means that it acts just as any other form. You can however force a certain 'mode'. You can, for instance, stop windows until a particular form is closed. The user is then forced to respond to this form before the program can continue.

A modal form locks down all input (keyboard or mouse click) to itself. You need to close a modal form before other parts of the program can receive further input. It is possible to set a form modal for either the current application or the entire system. Modal forms are explained in detail a bit further on.

13.1.4 : Hide

The **Hide** method hides a Form object, but does not unload it form memory. It is essentially the counterpart for the **Load** method.

`object.` **Hide**

If no object is specified the current form will be hidden. Note that hiding a form does not unload it from memory. All the attached code remains active and can be accessed fro other parts of the program.

Hiding a form merely removes it from the screen and its **Visible** property is set to **False**.

13.1.5 : Modal / Modeless forms

In general, a form is **Modeless**. This means that it is just a window on the GUI. If you want to, you can also create a **Modal** form. When a form is **Modal** this means that it has the focus for input. All other forms belonging to the same project are disabled. You can use this to notify the user of something and waiting for a response. The user cannot deny the information since the program stalls until he does something. Visual Basic supports the two types of Modal forms. **VbAppModal** means that the other windows of the application are disabled. **VbSystemModal** means that all applications are disabled until the form is hidden.

The code below shows both implementations. Simply comment out one line and run the form.

```
Private Sub form1_load ()
     Form2.show vbApplicationModal
     Form2.show vbSystemModal
End Sub

Private sub ok_click()
     Form2.hide
End sub
```

The ok_click event is attached to a simple button that is present on form2.

13.1.6 : MDI forms

Besides the standard look, you can also create interfaces in what is called the Multiple Document Interface or MDI for short.

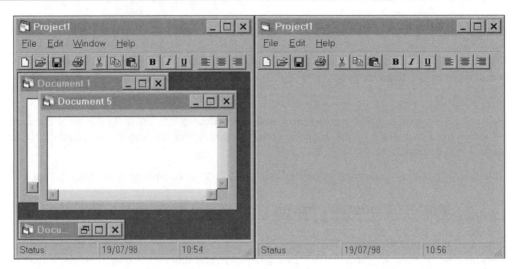

The left part shows an MDI interface. The right part shows a standard interface. Creating a program that does handle MDI is a bit more complex than a normal program; but fortunately, Visual Basic has a wizard that enables you to build an MDI program very fast. To access this wizard, simply start a new Visual Basic program (File - New application) and select Visual Basic application wizard. In the first form, simply specify that a MDI interface should be used and the wizard will generate all necessary stuff for you.

13.2 : Additional Form properties in NET

The NET platform adds a newer graphical look to your program. As such, the base controls have been upgraded, not only visually but in terms of properties and methods as well.

13.2.1 : Opacity

This allows you to change the background opacity of a form. You can program this from 0%, which is in essence invisible, to 100%, which is solid. This allows for interesting visual effects like fading windows, but can also be used to make a program easier to operate. You could 'dim' a foreground window while working on the background window.

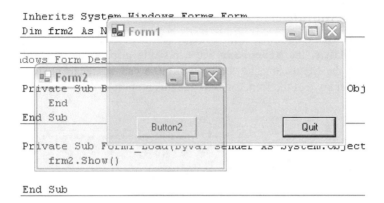

```
Inherits System Windows Forms Form
Dim frm2 As N
idows Form Des
Private Sub B
    End
End Sub
Private Sub Form1_Load(ByVal Sender As System.Object
    frm2.Show()

End Sub
```

Note that all controls remain fully functional.

13.2.2 : AcceptButton and CancelButton

The **AcceptButton** property allows you to specify a default button. Suppose you want to make a messagebox that can display information for the user. This form would just have a button labeled 'Ok'. By specifying that button as the **AcceptButton** the user can confirm the message by clicking the Ok button or by simply hitting enter on the keyboard.

The only exception is that, when a control that knows how to handle the enter key (like a textbox), has the focus, it takes priority.

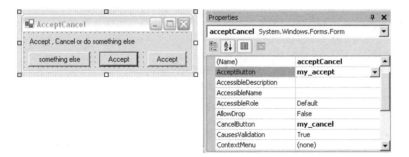

The counterpart for the **AcceptButton** property is the **CancelButton**. The **CancelButton** reacts to the pressing of the <ESC> key on the keyboard. Suppose you have a small form with an Ok and Cancel button.

By specifying them as **AcceptButton** and **CancelButton** you can have them react to Enter and Esc. In classic Visual Basic, there was no real way to do this except as to tap into the keyboard stream using API calls.

13.2.3 : Sizegripstyle

In Visual Basic Classic, the *Statusbar* had a resizing grip. In the NET platform, this no longer belongs to the Statusbar. The *Sizegripstyle* can be set to hidden, show or auto. Changing the border style of the form can override this property.

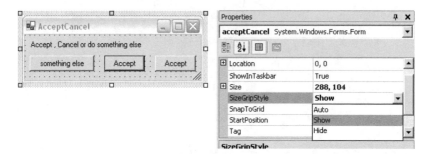

Keep in mind that if you are going to use the *Autoscroll* property, which is explained next, you should set the *Sizegripstyle* to either *None* or *Auto*.

13.2.4 : Autoscroll

The *Autoscroll* is a mayor advantage in NET. In Visual Basic Classic it was a nightmare to make a form with a movable view port. Suppose you have a form with so many controls it actually doesn't fit the screen or you program was written to run in 1280x1024 and the user only has a 1024x786 pixel screen.

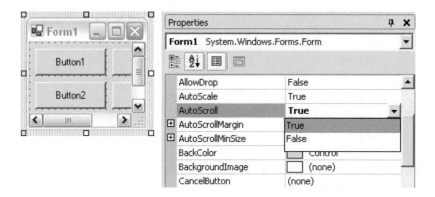

By switching *Autoscroll* to 'True', Visual Basic will automatically make the window scrollable and the scrollbars will appear if the contents of the form do not fit the screen.

13.3 : Menu's

Let's talk a bit more about menus. You have seen how to create them and how to assign hotkeys to them. You can do more things with menus: Create a popup menu for instance, or add items at runtime.

13.3.1 : Popup menus (classic) and Context Menus (NET)

A special kind of menu is the *Contextmenu*, which is similar to the Visual Basic Popup Menu.

The Pop menu is a menu that can be pulled up, for instance, by right clicking an object on the screen. For instance, the textbox has a default pop menu that allows you to cut copy and paste text.

Creating such menus is no harder than any other menu. Define your menu inside the main menu of your form and set the top-level entry's visible property to false so it remains hidden. When the time comes to display the menu, just call the *PopupMenu* function Visual Basic 6.0.

Example:

```
Private Sub Command1_Click()
    PopupMenu popmenu1
End Sub
```

The *PopupMenu* function takes optional arguments that allow you to fine-tune its behavior. You can specify in the given order, a flag to specify alignment, an x and y coordinate on the screen and the name of a particular entry to be displayed bold.

The complete syntax looks like this:
```
object.PopupMenu menuname, flags, x, y, boldcommand
```
The *PopupMenu* method syntax has these parts:

Menuname	This is the name of the pop-up menu to be displayed. There must be at least on submenu attached to it.
Flags	This value specifies the location and behavior of a pop-up menu.
X	If specified the popupmenu will be displayed at this the x-coordinate. If not specified the current mouse X coordinate will be used.
Y	Similar to the X coordinate this geves the vertical location for the popup window.
Boldcommand	This gives the name of a menu control to be displayed in Bold in the pop-up menu.

The settings for flags are:

Constant (location)	Value	Description
vbPopupMenuLeftAlign	0	(Default) The left side of the pop-up menu is located at x.
vbPopupMenuCenterAlign	4	The pop-up menu is centered at x.
vbPopupMenuRightAlign	8	The right side of the pop-up menu is located at x.

Constant (behavior)	Value	Description
vbPopupMenuLeftButton	0	(Default) An item on the pop-up menu reacts to a mouse click only when you use the left mouse button.
vbPopupMenuRightButton	2	An item on the pop-up menu reacts to a mouse click when you use either the right or the left mouse button.

Note	The flags parameter has no effect on applications running under Microsoft Windows version 3.0 or earlier. It is possible to combine flags using the Or operator.

You can find the predefined constants in the Visual Basic (VB) object library in the Object Browser.

The x and y coordinates will respect the *ScaleMode* property. Code following the *PopupMenu* command is not executed until the user has actually selected an item from the menu. When an element on the menu is clicked, the attached event handler for that menu item is executed before the code following the *PopupMenu* command is executed.

Example:

```
Private Sub Command1_Click()
    PopupMenu popmenu1,,,fatentry
End Sub
```

Fatentry is a menu with that name. As shown, it is possible to omit optional parameters just by specifying nothing between the commas. It is also possible to create a *PopupMenu* without having a main menu. If you set all top-level entries as hidden then no menu will be visible but the *PopupMenu* will still work. It is equally possible to have more then one of these popup menus on a form, just as you can popup normally visible menus as well.

Of course, it is better to attach this to a specific button click. To this effect, we will adapt the above code so it responds only to right-clicks. Select the **MouseUp** method of the button and adapt the code as follows:

```
Private Sub Command1_MouseUp(Button As Integer, Shift As Integer, _
                             X As Single, Y As Single)
    If Button = 1 Then
        PopupMenu popmenu1,, , , fatentry
    End If
End Sub
```

When right clicking on the button this is the result of our code:

13.3.1.1 : How NET handles the Contextmenu

The **PopupMenu** construction has been removed from the NET Visual Basic language and replaced by the Contextmenu class. The advantage is that you have much more control but the disadvantage is that it requires more code. However, it is nothing to be scared of.

First of all, add a **Contextmenu** control to your form and give it a name. The object appears below the form in the form editor. Select it by clicking and you will see that the menu editor pops up on the form with the text **Contextmenu** in it. Note that you cannot change the text of the top entry. Build your menu just as you would do with any other menu in NET.

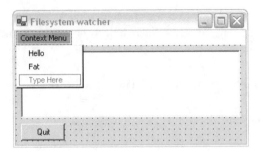

Now let's add a button to our form and set its text property to 'Quit'. In the properties dialog for the button find the Contextmenu property and click the arrow on the list to edit. You will see a list of all available context menus attached to this form, which in this case is just one. Select the contextmenu1.

The link is no made between the command button and contextmenu1. All that remains is to decide when we want the menu to be displayed. Just like with Visual Basic Classic, we attach a piece of code the *MouseUp* event handler.

```
    Private Sub Button1_MouseUp(ByVal sender As Object, _
            ByVal e As System.Windows.Forms.MouseEventArgs) _
            Handles Button1.MouseUp
        If e.Button = MouseButtons.Right Then
            Button1.ContextMenu.Show(Button1, New Point(e.X, e.Y))
        End If
    End Sub
```

At first sight, it looks more complex but that is not true. We are still only checking for the right mouse button to be clicked and then tell the *Contextmenu* associated with button1 to show itself on button1 at location *x,y*, which we retrieve using the *e.X* and *e.Y* methods and convert to a graphics point on the screen using the point function from the graphics operators.

And here is the result on windows XP:

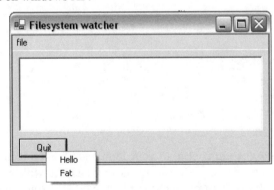

Well, you can do this in Visual Basic in a simple manner too.

13.4 : Modifying menus from code

The menus you create at design time, can also respond dynamically to run-time conditions. For example, if a menu item action becomes inappropriate at some point, you can prevent users from selecting that menu item by disabling it. In the MDI Notepad application, for example, if the clipboard does not contain any text, the Paste menu item is dimmed on the Edit menu, and users cannot select it.

You can also dynamically add menu items, if you have a menu control array. This is described in "Adding Menu Controls at Run Time," later in this topic.

You can also program your application to use a check mark to indicate which of several commands was last selected. For example, the Options, Toolbar menu item from the MDI Notepad application displays a check mark if the toolbar is displayed. Other menu control features described in this section include code that makes a menu item visible or invisible and that adds or deletes menu items.

13.4.1 : Enabling and Disabling Menu Commands

All menu controls have an **Enabled** property, and when this property is set to **False**, the menu is disabled and does not respond to user actions. Shortcut key access is also disabled when **Enabled** is set to **False**. A disabled menu control appears dimmed.

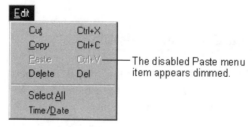

The disabled Paste menu item appears dimmed.

For example, this statement disables the Paste menu item on the Edit menu of the MDI Notepad application:

```
mnuEditPaste.Enabled = False
```

Disabling a menu title in effect disables the entire menu, because the user cannot access any menu item without first clicking the menu title. For example, the following code would disable the Edit menu of the MDI Notepad application:

```
mnuEdit.Enabled = False
```

13.4.2 : Displaying a Check Mark on a Menu Control

Using the *Checked* property, you can place a check mark on a menu to:

- Tell the user the status of an on/off condition. Choosing the menu command alternately adds and removes the check mark.

- Indicate which of several modes is in effect. The Options menu of the MDI Notepad application uses a check mark to indicate the state of the toolbar.

You create check marks in Visual Basic with the *Checked* property. Set the initial value of the *Checked* property in the Menu Editor by selecting the check box labeled Checked. To add or remove a check mark from a menu control at run time, set its *Checked* property from code. For example:

```
Private Sub mnuOptions_Click ()
        ' Set the state of the check mark based on
        ' the Visible property.
        mnuOptionsToolbar.Checked = picToolbar.Visible
End Sub
```

13.4.3 : Making Menu Controls Invisible

In the Menu Editor, you set the initial value of the *Visible* property for a menu control by selecting the check box labeled *Visible*. To make a menu control visible or invisible at run time, set its *Visible* property from code. For example:

```
mnuFileArray(0).Visible = True
        ' Make the control
        ' visible.
mnuFileArray(0).Visible = False
        ' Make the control
        ' invisible.
```

When a menu control is invisible, the rest of the controls in the menu move up to fill the empty space. If the control is on the menu bar, the rest of the controls on the menu bar move left to fill the space.

 Note   Making a menu control invisible effectively disables it, because the control is inaccessible from the menu, access or shortcut keys. If the menu title is invisible, all the controls on that menu are unavailable.

13.4.4 : Adding Menu Controls at Run Time (VB Classic)

A menu can grow at run time. In the image below, for example, as files are opened in the SDI
Notepad application, menu items are dynamically created to display the path names of the most
recently opened files.

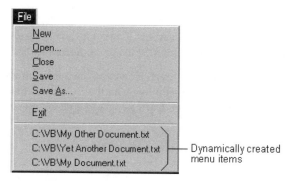

Dynamically created
menu items

You must use a control array to create a control at run time. Because the **mnuRecentFile**
menu control is assigned a value for the **Index** property at design time, it automatically
becomes an element of a control array — even though no other elements have been created yet.

When you create **mnuRecentFile** (0), you actually create a separator bar that is invisible at
run time. The first time a user saves a file at run time, the separator bar becomes visible, and the
first file name is added to the menu. Each time you save a file at run time, additional menu
controls are loaded into the array, making the menu grow.

Controls created at run time can be hidden by using the **Hide** method or by setting the control's
Visible property to **False**. If you want to remove a control in a control array from memory,
use the **Unload** statement.

13.4.5 : Adding Menu Controls at run time (VB NET)

In NET, the menu is a collection of objects. It is possible to add menu entries and attach events
to the newly created menu items in a similar manner as creating a new control.

The **MenuItems.Add** method can create a new item on the menu. Since this is an overloaded
method, there are multiple possibilities in passing information to determine the look and feel of
the menu item

It is even possible to create the menu completely at runtime using the **Dim** method and
instantiating an object from the class MainMenu.

Example:

```
Private Sub build_my_menu ()
        Dim my_menu as new MainMenu()
```

```
                My_menu.MenuItems.Add("&File")
                My_menu.MenuItems.add(("&Help", _
                        New eventhandler(AddressOf helphandler))
        End sub

        Sub helphandler (sender As System.Object, e As System.EventArgs)
                end
        End sub
```

The above code creates a new menu and assigns it two top-level entries: File and Help. The Help menu button gets an event handler appointed using the **AddressOff** method.

It is equally possible to create multilevel menus. However, the approach is a bit different. In the previous example, we were just creating menu items on the fly but we have not really provided a symbolic name to reference them later on. Even assigning a check mark would be pretty hard this way.

A better way is to create a menu structure using **MenuItem** objects and then assigning them to the main menu.

Example:

```
        Private Sub build_my_menu ()
                Dim a,b,c as MenuItem
                A = New MenuItem("1")
                B = New MenuItem("2")
                C = New MenuItem("3")
                B.checked = true
                C.Shortcut = Shortcut.CtrlX
                My_menu.MenuItems.Add (a, new eventhandler(AddressOf(ah)))
                My_menu.MenuItems.Add (b)
                My_menu.MenuItems.Add (c)
        End sub

        Sub ah (sender As System.Object, e As System.EventArgs)
                end
        End sub
```

This code creates three objects of the **menuitem** class and assigns various data to their properties. Subsequently, the three created objects are added to an existing menu in the form called **my_menu**.

Note	It is equally possible to use these methods on a context menu. The syntax and possibilities are exactly the same as in a MainMenu.

There are many more properties and possibilities to explore. Just keep in mind that you are always adding to the end of a menu. There is no real means to 'insert' elements in an already existing menu except for using the **Merge** method. You can clear an entire menu by invoking the **Clear** method on the parent.

13.5 : Special Menu features

The menu system has a number of interesting features that can make life a lot easier for the programmer.

13.5.1 : The WindowList

A *WindowList* is a menu entry that automatically displays a list of available windows in your program. This is only useful if you are programming MDI interface. It allows the user to quickly jump from one window to another.

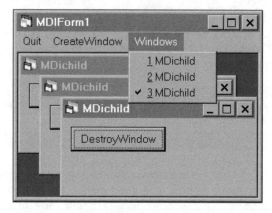

To add this to your application, you simply select an entry in the menu editor and check the *WindowList* checkbox.

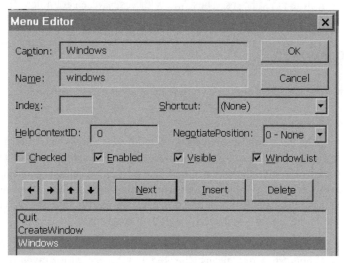

Note, however, that you can have only one *WindowList* in your menu bar.

13.5.2 : Negotiating menu's

When programming MDI style programs, you can use a feature called 'Negotiate Menus'. You will find this property on any normal (non MDI-main) form. When this is set to true, the menu of the child window will be displayed on the parent window.

Option selectors are simple visual components that allow you to specify certain selections or options. The simplest are Radio buttons and checkmarks. More advanced selectors let you select from a list (*Combobox* and *ListBox*). Finally, I will show how to group selectors by using the Frame object.

Another type of selectors is list boxes. These allow the user to select an item from a predefined list. Or in case of the *Combobox* he can also type in an in-existing item.

13.6.1 : Checkboxes

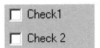

The checkbox is one of the simplest selectors in Windows. It allows you to turn options on and off. A *Checkbox* control displays an X when selected; the X disappears when the Checkbox is cleared. Use this control to give the user a True/False or Yes/No option. You can use Checkbox controls in groups to display multiple choices from which the user can select one or more. To display text next to the Checkbox, set the *Caption* property. Use the *Value* property to determine the state of the control—selected, cleared, or unavailable.

You can also set the value of a Checkbox programmatically with the *Value* property. A value of 0 means it is not checked. A one means Checked and 2 means it is grayed-out. If you set the value to 2, it will not respond to click actions.

13.6.2 : Option Buttons or Radio Buttons

An Option Button control displays an option, which can be turned on or off. Usually, Option Button controls are used in an option group to display options from which the user selects only one.

Note	Checkbox and OptionButton controls function similarly, but with an important difference: Any number of Checkbox controls on a form can be selected at the same time. In contrast, only one OptionButton in a group can be selected at any given time.

13.6.3 : Grouping Radio Buttons (VB Classic)

You group RadioButtons or OptionButton as they sometimes are called, by drawing them inside a container such as a Frame control, a PictureBox control or a form. To group OptionButton controls in a Frame or PictureBox, draw the Frame or PictureBox first, and then draw the OptionButton controls inside. All OptionButton controls within the same container act as a single group.

Controls that are grouped together, especially RadioButtons, work together. For RadioButtons your only option to have multiple groups that work independently is to assign them to a different parent.

13.6.4 : Grouping Radio Buttons (VB NET)

In Visual Basic NET, the functionality to group Option or RadioButtons together is retained from Visual Basic Classic. Visual Basic NET also provides a different kind of parent that can be used to group these buttons: the Panel. The Frame control has been renamed to a GroupBox but retains all functionality of the Visual Basic Classic Frame.

The Panel has a couple of advantages over the Old style Frame, notably: it has a switch-able border style and it can have scrollbars.

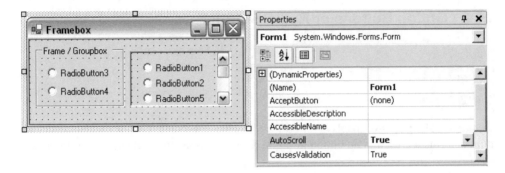

The border size of a Panel can be set to none, recessed or Simple2d.

13.6.5 : List boxes

There are two standard windows list boxes you can use to allow the user to select something from a list. **ListBox, FileListBox, DirListBox, DiskListbox** are simple list boxes. **ComboBox** is a more versatile Listbox variant. This discussion will focus on the **Combobox** used as a plain listbox. For the full capabilities if the **Combobox** read on in the next chapter.

A **Listbox** is a simple control that allows you to display a list of items from which the user can select one or more. A scrollbar is automatically displayed if the list is too long to be contained inside the visible bounding box of the control.

By default, nothing is selected in the list and thus the **ListIndex** property value is set to -1. Items in the list are sequentially numbered starting at 0 for the first item and increasing until the end of the list is reached. The value of the **ListCount** property gives you the number of items available in the list. In order to add or delete items in a Listbox control you can use the **AddItem** or **RemoveItem** method.

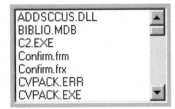

A **FileListBox** is basically a listbox that automatically lists all files in the specified directory given by the **Path** property.

A *DirListBox* does the same as a *Filelistbox* except that it lists the subdirectories available to the given path.

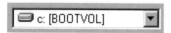

A *DriveListBox* control enables a user to select a valid disk drive at run time. Use this control to display a list of all the valid drives in a user's system. You can create dialog boxes that enable the user to open a file from a list of files on a disk in any available drive.

NET

The *DirListBox* and *Drivelistbox* have been removed form the NET platform. As the requirement for standardization becomes greater, the NET platform provides a universal File selector box. Coding your own file selector using the *Drivelistbox* and *FileListBox* was a tedious and error-prone job that became obsolete at the introduction of the Common controls in Visual Basic 4.0

13.7 : Timer objects

The *Timer* control allows you to generate timed events. The number of timers is virtually unlimited. Keep in mind that every timer uses system resources and simply having too many timers will ground the system to a halt. In general, it is OK to have one or two timers running things in the background, but it is bad programming practice to write half the program attached to hundreds of timers. You should consider using threads if a lot of background processing is required.

The most important property of timer is the interval. It returns or sets the number of milliseconds between calls to a *Timer* control's *Timer* event.

```
object.Interval [= milliseconds]
```

The settings for milliseconds are:

Setting	Description
0	(Default) Disables a Timer control.
1 to 65,535	Sets an interval (in milliseconds) that takes effect when a Timer controls **Enabled** property is set to **True**. For example, a value of 10,000 milliseconds equals 10 seconds. The maximum, 65,535 milliseconds, is equivalent to just over 1 minute.

You can set a Timer control's *Interval* property at design time or run time. The *Timer* control's Enabled property determines whether the control responds to the passage of time. Set *Enabled* to *False* to turn a Timer control off, and to *True* to turn it on. When a *Timer* control is enabled, its countdown always starts from the value of its Interval property setting.

13.7.1 : Precision Timing

Even though the timer provides an easy means to generate a timed event, sometimes you need more precision. Visual Basic does not provide a standard method to do such a thing, but the windows API does.

All that is required, is to declare the routine and we can start using it. For further information on API calls, you can check further on in this book.

Example:

```
Public Declare Sub Sleep Lib "kernel32" (ByVal uDuration As Long)
Sleep 10
```

The above code will put us to sleep for 10 milliseconds. Keep in mind that the granularity is operating system dependent. Older version of Windows might not provide millisecond resolution in which case the actual time will be rounded to the closest tick of the clock.

13.7.2 : Time measurement

In order to measure time you can of course use a timer, and some creativity, but you will be faced with the overhead of coding it and the unavoidable delay that is present in executing all the code.

There is again an API call that can be performed, that gives you the tick count since the last boot as a long and a call that lets you set the precision of the tick. It is again a matter of referencing the correct API library and declaring the prototype for the functions.

Example:

```
Public Declare Function timeGetTime Lib "winmm.dll" () As Long
Public Declare Function timeBeginPeriod Lib "winmm.dll" _
            (ByVal uPeriod As Long) As Long
```

The *TimeBeginPeriod* allows you to set the step. If you call this and pass it a value of 10 then the resolution is 10 milliseconds. If you pass it a value of 1 the resolution becomes 1 millisecond.

The *TimeGetTime* function retrieves the number of milliseconds since boot. Therefore, you can easily write code like this:

```
Public Declare Function timeGetTime Lib "winmm.dll" () As Long
Public Declare Function timeBeginPeriod Lib "winmm.dll" _
        (ByVal uPeriod As Long) As Long
Dim start_time as long
Dim stop_time as long
Dim call_time as long
Dim eal_time as long
Dim x as long
Start_time = timegettime
Call_time = timegettime
Start_time = timegettime
For x= 1 to 10000: next x
Stop_time = gettime
Real_time = Stop_time-start_time-cal_time
```

Note that I perform a calibration in this loop. I retrieve the number of ticks and store it in **start_time**. I immediately retrieve the counter again and store this in **call_time**. The difference gives me exactly how long it took to retrieve the time in the first place, so I can consider this later on.

Now I retrieve the **start_time** once more and launch my for-next loop. Upon exit of the loop the **TimeGetTime** function is called once more to retrieve the final tick count. To finish, I perform the calculation to find out exactly how long the machine took to execute my 10,000 iterations in the for-next loop.

There is one unavoidable problem in this method. Since the **TimeGetTime** function returns a long this means that it can overflow and fold around to zero. In order for the value to overflow, it does take more then 25 days! So if you are going to write code that checks for a condition, be careful to test for overflow of the timer.

Example:

```
Public Declare Function timeGetTime Lib "winmm.dll" () As Long
Public Declare Function timeBeginPeriod Lib "winmm.dll" _
        (ByVal uPeriod As Long) As Long


' Don't':
start_time = timegettime
next_time = start_time +100
while timegettime < next_time
wend

'Do:
start_time = timegettime
next_time = start_time +100
while (timegettime < next_time) and (timegettime >start_time)
wend
```

The above **AND** clause checks that **TimeGetTime** indeed is larger then the time at which we started. If not, the loop will be aborted since an overflow occurred.

13.8 : User entry objects

Any given program interacts with the user in one way or another. The user can click on buttons to execute tasks, or select options using RadioButtons and so on, but sometimes stuff needs to be entered using the keyboard. That is where the user entry objects and controls come in to play. *Textboxes*, *Comboboxes* and more allow the user to verbally specify information to the program.

13.8.1 : Textboxes

Textboxes can de useful to allow the user to – fill in the blanks. In some cases, you want the user to see information but modify it only when a certain condition is met. The textbox has two interesting properties:

13.8.1.1 : Locked and Enabled.

The Locked property controls the capability of the user to modify the contents of a textbox. It does not become grayed out, but the user cannot change the contents. In addition, no *Change* event is generated but it will still generate click events. If you set *Enabled* to false, this means that the textbox is detached from the command stream. It will become grayed out and no longer generate any event. It will also no longer respond to changes of its content from code.

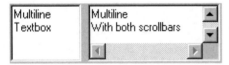

Other interesting features are the *Multiline* and *Scrollbar* properties. By switching on *Multiline* you allow the user to type multiple lines of text. If you also cared to set the scrollbars property to anything else than none, then scrollbars of the selected style will automatically appear when the text no longer fits in the visible portions of the textbox. The user can then use these to walk trough whatever input he made in the textbox.

13.8.1.2 : KeyPress Event

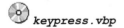
keypress.vbp

There is a tutorial program available that explains the constructs, explained in this topic, by example.

This is an event generated by every key press when the textbox has the focus. It will return the ASCII key code. You can use this to make textboxes that behave in a particular way.

Sample:

```
Private Sub Text7_KeyPress(KeyAscii As Integer)
    Static password$
    If KeyAscii = 13 Then
        MsgBox "Password:" + password$
        Text7.Text = ""
        password$ = ""
    Else
        password$ = password$ + Chr$(KeyAscii)
        x = Len(Text7.Text)
        Text7.Text = String(x, "*")
        KeyAscii = Asc("*")
    End If
End Sub
```

The above routine will react to any key press. If enter (Carriage return = ASCII 13) is detected, a message box is displayed that shows the type password.

If the character is not a CR then the character is added to the password. Finally A number of stars representing the length of the typed password is printed. But why on earth would I assign an asterisk (*) to the **keyASCII** code? Well simple: reading the value returned from this routine does not prevent it from being sent to the textbox. Furthermore, it will overwrite the first character in the textbox. Therefore, if I set it to an asterisk, it will simply overwrite the first asterisk that was already there.

13.8.2 : The Combobox

I already explained the basics of a *ComboBox* when used as a simple listbox. However, it goes far beyond that. The user can also type something. So when using combo-boxes you should retrieve the text property of the *ComboBox*. You can then match it against whatever is in the *ComboBox*. If it is not in there, it means the user made a totally new selection. You can then decide to either reject it or maybe create something new.

You use the **AddItem** or **RemoveItem** methods to add or delete items in a *ComboBox* control.

Note	A *Scroll* event is generated by a *ComboBox* control only when the contents are being scrolled. This means that as long as no information is actually moving on the screen this event will not fire. This is something to keep in mind when writing code that interacts with the Combo box.

The *ComboBox* control supports a number of different styles:

Constant	Value	Description
VbComboDropDown	0	(Default) Dropdown Combo. Includes a drop-down list and a text box. The user can select from the list or type in the text box.

| VbComboSimple | 1 | Simple Combo. Includes a text box and a list, which doesn't drop down. The user can select from the list or type in the text box. The size of a Simple combo box includes both the edit and list portions. By default, a Simple combo box is sized so that none of the list is displayed. Increase the Height property to display more of the list. |
| VbComboDrop-DownList | 2 | Dropdown List. This style allows selection only from the drop-down list. |

You can set the **List, ListCount** and **ListIndex** properties to enable a user to access items in the **ComboBox**. Alternatively, you can add items at design time by modifying the **List** property. By modifying the **Style** property settings for the **ComboBox** you can change its behavior. You will probably most of the time use it as **Dropdown** List. When styled to this mode it is easier to work with then the **Listbox**.

Possible settings are:

Constant	Value	Description
VbComboDropDown	0	Acts as aDropdown Combo. This Includes a drop-down list and a text box. The user can select from the list or type in the text box.
VbComboSimple	1	A Simple Combo includes a text box and a list, which doesn't drop down. You can select from the list or type in the text box.
VbComboDrop-DownList	2	As a Dropdown List, the combo-box allows you to select from the drop-down list only.

13.9 : Printing

The **Printer** object enables you to communicate with a system printer (initially the default system printer).The **Printers** collection enables you to gather information about all the available printers on the system.

13.9.1 : The printer object

You can use graphic methods to draw text and graphics on the **Printer** object. Once the **Printer** object contains the output you want to print, you can use the **EndDoc** method to send the output directly to the default printer for the application.

You should check and possibly revise the layout of your forms if you print them. If you use the **PrintForm** method to print a form, for example, graphical images may be clipped at the bottom of the page and text carried over to the next page.

The **Printers** collection enables you to query the available printers so you can specify a default printer for your application. For example, you may want to find out which of the available printers uses a specific printer driver.

The following code searches all available printers to locate the first printer with its page orientation set to portrait, and then sets it as the default printer:

```
Dim X As Printer
For Each X In Printers
    If X.Orientation = vbPRORPortrait Then
        Set Printer = X ' Set printer as system default.
        Exit For        ' Stop looking for a printer.
    End If
Next
```

You designate one of the printers in the Printers collection as the default printer by using the Set statement. The preceding example designates the printer identified by the object variable X, the default printer for the application.

| **Note** | If you use the Printers collection to specify a particular printer, as in Printers (3), you can only access properties on a read-only basis. |
| | To both read and write the properties of an individual printer, you must first make that printer the default printer for the application. |

13.9.2 : Sending something to the printer

Since we have obtained a handle to the default system printer, we can now simply send information to the printers drawing canvas. You have to think of the Drawing canvas as the sheet of paper. You first send all information to the sheet of paper and finalize the operations using and **EndDoc** method. Once the **EndDoc** is invoked, the printer engine in Windows will process the information and send it off to the printer driver that will rasterize it and actually print it.

Example:

```
Dim X As Printer
x.newpage
x.fontheight=30
x.print "Hello.world"
x.line (100,100)-(200,200),7,bf
x.enddoc
```

The above code simply sends the text "hello world" to the printer and draws a filled rectangle from coordinates 100,100 to 200,200.

Most graphics methods and properties can be used on the printer object, so that you can actually make pretty complex print output. Since graphics methods are explained in great detail elsewhere in this book, I will not re-iterate this information here.

13.9.3 : Making a preview window in VB Classic

In Visual Basic Classic it is sometimes annoying to get an idea of what the print output will look like. Since the printing canvas supports the same methods as a **PictureBox** you can actually redirect the output to a **PictureBox** for preview.

Example:

```
Sub create_output (target as object)
    On error goto next
    Target.print "Hello World"
    ' more output code goes here
    '...
    Target.enddoc
End sub

Sub Print_something()
    Dim my_printer as printer
    Create_output (picturebox1)
    Create_output (my_printer)
End sub
```

The above code is an example of a re-directable output generator. Since the **create_output** routine accepts an object as argument, we can actually pass it either our printer or a PictureBox on some form. The **On Error Goto next** clause will automatically skip methods that would not apply to one or another thus preventing stalling the program. Although this construction is not perfect, it will get you a pretty close preview of what will be rendered on the printer output.

13.9.4 : The Print Preview (NET)

The NET platform has its own **PrintPreview** engine, so there is no need for the trickery under Visual Basic Classic. The **PrintPreview** dialog is the standard dialog as used by many programs. All you need to do is, pass it a **PrintDocument** and it will render the output into the control. The Same **PrintDocument** method is used to send data to a printer.

Note	**PrintDocument** is actually what was known as the drawing canvas under Visual Basic Classic. You can consider it as a collection of instructions and primitives that make up a document.

13.9.5 : Adding text to the printout

Even though the IDE will not display the **Print** method in its list, you can still use it in regard to sending text to the printer. You can set the font, font size and font styles using the normal properties associated with them.

One thing to be careful of is when printing text on a dark background. The printer object does not know the same drawing styles as the screen. You need to set the background correctly or otherwise nothing will show up.

For example on a dark background, printing something in white will result in a white rectangle that encompasses the text completely. You need to set the text background to black and the text foreground to white before printing such information.

An additional problem is that many printers do not exactly know how to handle every possible combination of elements you may come up with. It is wise to thoroughly test your code on an actual printer.

13.9.6 : Adding graphics to the printout

You can use any graphics method that is available in your platform including the scaling and positioning methods. The explanation of these functions and methods will not be re-iterated here since it is covered in great detail elsewhere in this book.

13.9.7 : EndDoc

Once all information has been added to the document you conclude by sending an **EndDoc**. Upon reception of the **EndDoc** call, the print processor in windows will start creating output and send it to the printer.

13.10 : Taking Advantage of the Windows 95 Look

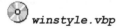 **winstyle.vbp**   There is a tutorial program available that explains the constructs, explained in this topic, by example.

So far, I have shown you how to use the embedded controls that windows provides us. As you know, Windows has a long history and the user interface has changed from time to time. The Windows 95 look brought some new graphical features. The controls available to us can often be switched from style. **OptionButtons**, **RadioButtons**, **Comboboxes** and **ListBoxes** can adopt either the standard look or a newer Win95 look. In order to change the look there is a property called Style.

The look differs rather drastically.

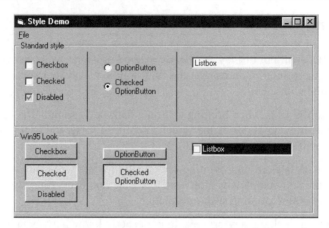

Changing the **Checkbox** and **OptionButton** changes them to buttons that assume depressed or unpressed states. The listbox changes by adding a checkbox in front of an item. Using this you can make multiple selections (normally not possible with a listbox).

Other interesting options are the features that allow you to insert images on controls. This is a new thing that the Win95 GUI brings with it. For Win NT users: You need Release 4 or later.

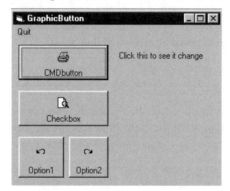

You can assign a picture to the Down position, the Disabled and to the standard look. The standard picture (when nothing is happening or has happened with the control) is set with the Picture property. The properties **DownPicture** and **DisabledPicture** allow you to set the image that should appear when they are selected and disabled.

13.11 : The XP look

Windows XP is yet another step in user interface design. Besides more a modern look than the windows 95/98/2000 interface it also adds a more 'browsing' style look. As computers become more and more network centric, people have grown accustomed to the look and feel of an internet browsers user interface. Hyperlinks, single click interfaces, drag and drop, resizable panes and windows, movable controls to name a few, are all concepts anyone takes for granted.

Fortunately, the NET platform adds lots of this functionality and takes care of all the low-level stuff for us.

It is possible even with Visual Basic 6.0 to write programs that adhere to this windows XP style look. The control library, which holds all user interface controls, has both styles on board starting from windows 2000 on. By default a program runs in the '95' look but this can be changed by providing a so-called manifest file that specifies what look should be used. It is even possible to switch Visual Basic Classic into this interface mode, albeit the form designer will still show the old controls style. Once a program s compiled to an executable, it will adhere to the Win XP control style provided a manifest file is available for it to let the operating system name know it should use the XP style interface.

Example:

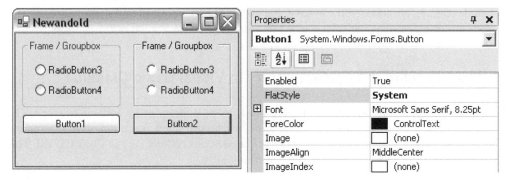

13.11.1 : The manifest

In order for the operating system to know it should use the new controls, you need to provide it with a manifest file. A Manifest is an XML file that contains directives for the operating system on how to behave.

The Manifest file is common for any program that wishes to use the XP Style.

Manifest file:

```
<?xml version="1.0" encoding="UTF-8" standalone="yes"?>
<assembly xmlns="urn:schemas-microsoft-com:asm.v1"
manifestVersion="1.0">
<assemblyIdentity
version="1.0.0.0"
processorArchitecture="X86"
name="WindowsXP"
type="win32"
/>
<description>Your application description here.</description>
<dependency>
<dependentAssembly>
<assemblyIdentity
type="win32"
```

```
name="Microsoft.Windows.Common-Controls"
version="6.0.0.0"
processorArchitecture="X86"
publicKeyToken="6595b64144ccf1df"
language="*"
/>
</dependentAssembly>
</dependency>
</assembly>
```

This file must be saved in the installation directory of your program where the.EXE file resides and should be named **yourappname.exe.manifest**, where **yourappname** is the name of your application. For Example: **Myprogram.exe.manifest** if the executable is called **program.exe**.

While developing programs you can save this also in the Visual Basic installation directory on in your projects directory. For NET users: this manifest file needs to go in the Bin subdirectory of the project in order to work.

13.11.2 : Forcing the correct library in Visual Basic Classic

Visual Basic Classic has on little thing that needs to be done in order for this to work. The correct version of the control library needs to be instantiated upon execution of your program. This is easily done by calling the function **InitCommonControl** residing in Comctl32.dll. This function needs to be called as soon as your forms initialize.

Example:

```
Private Declare Function InitCommonControls Lib "Comctl32.dll" () _
        As Long

Private Sub Form_Initialize()
    Dim x As Long
    x = InitCommonControls
End Sub
```

This piece of code together with the manifest will switch your program to XP style if you are running on Windows XP. If you are running on older version of the operating system, nothing will happen.

13.11.3 : XP style in NET

In order to use this new style in NET, besides providing the manifest, you need to set the **FlatStyle** property of the controls to 'System' instead of 'standard'. While still developing code you can save the manifest file in the 'Bin' directory inside your project directory.

If the **FlatStyle** property is set to standard, then the Windows 2000 look will be used and the system cannot use the new controls that are available.

Chapter 14 : Graphics

You can also create graphics using Visual Basic. Graphics can be drawn on almost any control. Visual Basic supports a set of methods that allow you to create drawings very easily. All drawing commands use an object called the Brush. This brush is an internal windows object that determines what drawing will look like. The brush has a coordinate system and properties that specify color, style, fill style etc.

A number of basic statements are available to change these properties.

Visual Basic NET also has extensive graphics capabilities but they belong to graphics objects and behave a bit differently. Later on in this chapter, I will explain in detail the functions of the graphics objects as they pertain to NET, but let us focus on Visual Basic Classic first.

14.1 : Basic coordinate operations

Drawing requires the use of a coordinate system of some kind. Windows handles the translation between your coordinate system and the physical display all by itself. The *CurrentX* and *CurrentY* parameters know the point where the next drawing will commence. You can also use these to set a new point.

14.1.1 : CurrentX, CurrentY

These functions return or set the horizontal (*CurrentX*) or vertical (*CurrentY*) coordinates where the next printing or drawing method will take place. They are not available at design time since the graphics objects are created in runtime only.

```
object.CurrentX [= x]
object.CurrentY [= y]
```

All coordinates are measured from the top-left corner of an object. Zero is defined as completely left for *CurrentX* and completely top for *CurrentY*. Coordinates are expressed in twips, or in the unit of measurement defined by the *ScaleHeight*, *ScaleWidth*, *ScaleLeft*, *ScaleTop*, and *ScaleMode* properties.

14.2 : Drawing setup

A number of properties allow you to specify exactly how all graphics methods will relate to the coordinate system and how they will perform their operations.

14.2.1 : Drawwidth

The **Drawwidth** property allows you to retrieve or set the line width for output from graphics methods.

```
object.DrawWidth [= size]
```

The setting for Size can be any number from 1 to 32767. Increasing the value of this property results in a thicker line. If the **DrawWidth** property setting is greater than one, **DrawStyle** property settings 1 through 4 produce a solid line (the **DrawStyle** property value is not changed).

14.2.2 : DrawMode

The **DrawMode** property determines the appearance of the output generated by a graphics method, or the appearance of **Shape** and **Line** controls.

```
object.DrawMode = [mode]
```

The possible settings for the **DrawMode** are listed below.

Constant	Setting	Description
VbBlackness	1	Blackness.
VbNotMergePen	2	Not Merge Pen — Inverse of setting 15 (Merge Pen).
VbMaskNotPen	3	Mask Not Pen — Combination of the colors common to the background color and the inverse of the pen.
VbNotCopyPen	4	Not Copy Pen — Inverse of setting 13 (Copy Pen).
VbMaskPenNot	5	Mask Pen Not — Combination of the colors common to both the pen and the inverse of the display.
VbInvert	6	Invert — Inverse of the display color.
VbXorPen	7	Xor Pen — Combination of the colors in the pen and in the display color, but not in both.
VbNotMaskPen	8	Not Mask Pen — Inverse of setting 9 (Mask Pen).
VbMaskPen	9	Mask Pen — Combination of the colors common to both the pen and the display.
VbNotXorPen	10	Not Xor Pen — Inverse of setting 7 (Xor Pen).
VbNop	11	Nop — No operation — output remains unchanged. In effect, this setting turns drawing off.
VbMergeNotPen	12	Merge Not Pen — Combination of the display color and

		the inverse of the pen color.
VbCopyPen	13	Copy Pen (Default) — Color specified by the ForeColor property.
VbMergePenNot	14	Merge Pen Not — Combination of the pen color and the inverse of the display color.
VbMergePen	15	Merge Pen — Combination of the pen color and the display color.
VbWhiteness	16	Whiteness.

You can use this property to produce effects with *Shape* or *Line* controls or when drawing with the graphics methods. Visual Basic performs bitwise operations by comparing each pixel in the pattern to be drawn with the pixel information already present. For example, setting 7 (XOR Pen) will use the XOR operator to combine a new pixel with a background pixel and update the existing information with the result.

14.2.3 : DrawStyle

The *DrawStyle* defines the line style for output from graphics methods.

```
object.DrawStyle = [style]
```

The possible settings for 'style' are:

Constant	Setting	Description
vbSolid	0	(Default) Solid
vbDash	1	Dash
vbDot	2	Dot
vbDashDot	3	Dash-Dot
vbDashDotDot	4	Dash-Dot-Dot
vbInvisible	5	Transparent
vbInsideSolid	6	Inside Solid

The above codes 1 to 4 work only correctly if *DrawWidth* is set to 1. A value greater than 1 will render a normal solid line. Modes 5 and 6 will work correctly with any *Drawwidth* settings.

14.2.4 : FillColor

The **FillColor** retrieves or sets the color that will be used to fill shapes. **FillColor** also applies to circles and boxes created using the **Circle** and **Line** graphics methods.

```
object.FillColor =[color]
```

Any system color is accepted. You can use the Visual Basic color definitions, a hexadecimal number in RGB format.

Note	As with all color settings, you can still use the old DOS style colors by calling the **QBcolor** function.

14.2.5 : FillStyle

This returns or sets the pattern used to fill shapes, circles and boxes created with the **Circle** and **Line** graphics methods.

```
object.FillStyle = [number]
```

Possible settings are:

vbFSSolid	0	Solid
vbFSTransparent	1	(Default) Transparent
vbHorizontalLine	2	Horizontal Line
vbVerticalLine	3	Vertical Line
vbUpwardDiagonal	4	Upward Diagonal
VbDownwardDiagonal	5	Downward Diagonal
VbCross	6	Cross
VbDiagonalCross	7	Diagonal Cross

When **FillStyle** is set to 1 (Transparent), the **FillColor** property is ignored, except for the **Form** object.

14.3 : Drawing primitives

Visual Basic has a number of commands available that you can use to draw primitives such as boxes, lines, circles and points. Using a combination of these commands, allows you to render custom graphics on almost any control visible on the screen.

14.3.1 : PSet

Using the *PSet* method, you can a point on an object to a specified color.

```
object.PSet [Step] (x, y), [color]
```

The *PSet* method syntax has the elements:

Step	A keyword specifying that the coordinates are relative to the current graphics position given by the *CurrentX* and *CurrentY* properties.
(x, y)	Single values indicating the horizontal (x-axis) and vertical (y-axis) coordinates of the point to set.
color	An optional long integer value indicating the color specified for point. If not specified, the current *ForeColor* property setting is used. You can use the RGB function or *QBcolor* function to specify the color.

The *DrawWidth* property has a direct impact on the size of the point drawn. If *DrawWidth* is equal to 1, then the *PSet* method sets a single pixel of the specified color. When *DrawWidth* is larger than 1, the point is centered on the specified coordinates.

The *DrawMode* and *DrawStyle* properties further control the behavior of the *Pset* method. After *PSet* has executed the *CurrentX* and *CurrentY* properties will hold the reference point specified by the arguments of the *Pset* method.

In order to clear a single pixel using the *PSet* method, simply specify the coordinates of the pixel and pass the contents of the *BackColor* property setting as the color argument.

Example:

```
Me.Pset(100,100),qbcolor(14) ' using qbcolor
Me.pset(102,102),#aaff5555 ' using RGB color value
Me.pset(102,102),me.backcolor ' erase pixel
```

14.3.2 : Line

The *Line* method allows you to draw lines, boxes, filled boxes, shaded boxes and more.

```
object.Line [Step] (x1, 1) - [Step] (x2, y2), [color], [B][F]
```

The Line method is built of following parts:

Step	This modifier specifies that the start point is relative to the current graphics position as stored in the *CurrentX* and *CurrentY* properties.
(x1, y1)	Single values that indicate the starting point for the line or rectangle. The

	unit of measure is defined in the **ScaleMode** property. This parameter is optional in which case the **CurrentX** and **CurrentY** are used.
Step	Specifies that the end point is relative to the starting point.
(x2, y2)	**Single** values that indicate the coordinates of the end point for the line or rectangle being drawn.
Color	A **long integer** that specifies the RGB color used to draw the line. This is optional. If omitted, the current **ForeColor** property value is used. You can use the RGB function or **QBcolor** function to specify the color.
B	If included, creates a rectangle from (x1,y1) to (x2,y2) .
F	Can be used only, if B is already specified. This fills the box with the current **FillColor** and **FillStyle**. The default value for **FillStyle** is transparent.

To draw connected lines, begin a new line at the end point of the previous line. Since the (X1, Y1) coordinates are optional you can simply draw a line to a new endpoint.

Example:

```
Me.ScaleWidth = 500
Me.ScaleHeight = 300
Me.Line (100, 100)-(200, 200)
Me.Line -(300, 100)
Me.Line -(400, 200)
Me.Line -(420, 220), 7, B
```

The above code gives the following result:

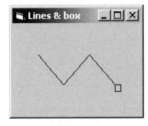

The width of the line drawn depends on the **DrawWidth** property. **DrawMode** and **DrawStyle** properties control the way it is drawn corresponding to the background. Once the Line method completes the **CurrentX** and **CurrentY** properties are referencing the ending coordinates from the command.

14.3.3 : Circle

This command allows you to create circles and ellipses.

```
object.Circle [Step](x, y),radius,[color,start,end, aspect]
```

The Circle method takes the following arguments:

Step	A keyword that forces the center of the circle, ellipse or arc, to be relative to the *CurrentX* and *CurrentY* properties.
(x, y)	Two *Single* values defining the coordinates for the center point of the circle, ellipse or arc. The *ScaleMode* property governs the units of measure used.
radius	A *single* indicating the radius of the circle, ellipse or arc.
color	A *Long integer* specifying the RGB color of the circle's outline. If *color* is not specified the value of the *ForeColor* property is used. You can use the RGB function or *QBcolor* function to specify the color.
start, end	Two single-precision values. In order to draw an arc, the *start* and *end* parameters specify (in radians) the beginning and end positions of the arc. The value ranges from -2 pi radians to 2 pi radians. The default value for start is 0; the default for end is 2 * pi radians resulting in a closed arc.
aspect	A single-precision value indicating the aspect ratio of the circle. The default value is 1.0, which yields a perfect (non-elliptical) circle on any screen.

To fill a circle you can set the *FillColor* and *FillStyle* properties of the parent object. Only a closed figure can be filled. Closed figures include circles, ellipses or pie slices (arcs with radius lines drawn at both ends).

When omitting an argument, simply type a comma and move on to the next argument. As with all graphics methods, the *CurrentX* and *CurrentY* properties are updated according to the commands arguments. Note that for circle this means the center coordinates.

14.4 : Saving and loading graphics

Every time you need a graphic, you could of course build it from scratch. You must be joking, right? There are functions that allow you to store and retrieve graphics from disk.

14.4.1 : Saving Graphics

So you have created a nice graphic and would like to save it. Well, nothing is simpler. Typically, you use a *PictureBox* or an *Image* control to doodle on. However, you can also use other objects to draw on. As long as an object has a *Picture* or *Image* property, you can extract the graphical data from it. The problem is, extracting this data and storing it in the appropriate format. To do this there is a function built into WINDOWS! After all, the GUI system knows how to treat the graphics. Visual Basic gives you direct access to this via the *SavePicture* method.

```
SavePicture picture, stringexpression
```

Picture:	A Picture or Image control from which the graphics file is to be created.
String expression:	The filename of the graphics file to save.

If the image assigned to the *Picture* property of an object is saved, it will default to the type it had at the moment it was assigned, if, and only if, it was a bitmap, icon, metafile, or enhanced metafile when loaded. GIF and JPEG files will be saved as a bitmap file.

For graphics attached to an *Image* property this rule does not apply, they are always saved as bitmap (.bmp) files regardless of their original format. Any image that has been made with the drawing controls can be stored in this format.

Example:

```
Private Sub Form_Click ()
    Dim radius,cx,cy as integer
    AutoRedraw = True ' Turn on AutoRedraw.
    Me.scalewidth = 300
    Me.scaleheight = 300
    CX = 150
    CY = 150
    For Radius = 0 To 300
        Circle (CX, CY), Radius, RGB(Rnd * 255, Rnd * 255, Rnd * 255)
        DoEvents        ' Yield for other processing.
    Next Radius
    Msg = "Click OK to save the graphics to a bitmap file."
        MsgBox Msg
    SavePicture me.Image, "TEST.BMP" ' Save picture to file.
End Sub
```

14.4.2 : Loading Graphics

If you can save graphics, it should be equally possible to load graphics. That is exactly what the *LoadPicture* is intended for. Any object supporting the *Picture* or *Image* property can be used as target for this operation

```
LoadPicture([stringexpression])
```

The string expression argument is the name of a graphics file to be loaded.

Graphics formats recognized by Visual Basic include bitmap (.bmp) files, icon (.ico) files, run-length encoded (.rle) files, metafile (.wmf) files, enhanced metafiles (.emf), GIF files and JPEG (.jpg) files.

Graphics are cleared from forms, picture boxes, and image controls by assigning *LoadPicture* with no argument. To load graphics for display in a *PictureBox* control, Image control, or as the background of a form, the return value of *LoadPicture* must be assigned to the *Picture* property of the object on which the picture is displayed. For example:

```
Set Picture = LoadPicture("PARTY.BMP")
Set Picture1.Picture = LoadPicture("PARTY.BMP")
```

To assign an icon to a form, set the return value of the *LoadPicture* function to the *Icon* property of the *Form* object:

```
Set Form1.Icon = LoadPicture("MYICON.ICO")
```

Icons can also be assigned to the *DragIcon* property of all controls except *Timer* controls and Menu controls. For example:

```
Set Command1.DragIcon = LoadPicture("MYICON.ICO")
```

Load a graphics file into the system *Clipboard* using *LoadPicture* as follows:

```
Clipboard.SetData LoadPicture("PARTY.BMP")
```

That's it: very easy.

```
Private Sub Form_Click ()
        Dim MSG as String       ' Declare variables.
        On Error Resume Next    ' Set up error handling.
        Set Picture = LoadPicture("PAPER.BMP")
        ' Load bitmap.
        If Err Then
                MSG = "Couldn't find the.BMP file."
                MsgBox MSG        ' Display error message.
                Exit Sub          ' Quit if error occurs.
        End If
        MSG = "Choose OK to clear the bitmap from the form."
        MsgBox MSG
        Set Picture = LoadPicture()    ' Clear form.
End Sub
```

14.5 : Coordinate systems

bars.vbp

There is a tutorial program available that explains the constructs, explained in this topic, by example.

So far, I have covered the basic drawing operations you can perform. When making drawing you always are doing this relative to a coordinate system. I have shown you how to specify where you want to draw in the coordinate system, but I have not explained you how to set it up.

You can impose your own coordinate system using the *Scale, ScaleMode, ScaleHeight, ScaleWidth, ScaleLeft* and *ScaleTop* properties of the object you are drawing on.

14.5.1 : Scale

Using the *Scale* method, you can redefine the coordinate system for a Form, PictureBox or Printer.

```
object.Scale (x1, y1) - (x2, y2)
```

object	An object where the method will be applied. If none is specified the Form object that has the current focus will be used as output.
x1, y1	Single-precision values that indicate the horizontal and vertical coordinates that define the upper-left corner of object.
x2, y2	Two optional single-precision values that specify the horizontal and vertical coordinates that define the lower-right corner of object.

The *Scale* method allows you to set the coordinate system to any scale of your liking. *Scale* affects the coordinate system for both run-time graphics statements and the placement of controls. If you use *Scale* with no arguments (both sets of coordinates omitted), it resets the coordinate system to twips.

You can specify scales as you please. You can also set the scale using the *ScaleLeft, ScaleHeight, ScaleWidth* and *ScaleTop* properties. Sometimes the plain Scale method is easier then setting each of these properties manually. It depends on what you want to do.

14.5.2 : ScaleMode

The *Scalemode* property returns or sets a value that gives the unit of measurement that will be used with when applying graphics methods, or when positioning controls.

```
object.ScaleMode [= value]
```

The possible settings for value are:

vbUser	0	Indicates that one or more of the *ScaleHeight, ScaleWidth, ScaleLeft* and *ScaleTop* properties are set to custom values.
VbTwips	1	(Default) Twips: (1440 twips per logical inch; 567 twips per logical centimeter).
VbPoints	2	Point (72 points per logical inch).
VbPixels	3	A Pixel is the smallest unit of monitor or printer resolution.

vbCharacters	4	Character (horizontal = 120 twips per unit; vertical = 240 twips per unit).
VbInches	5	Inch
VbMillimeters	6	Millimeter
VbCentimeters	7	Centimeter

Using a combination of **ScaleHeight**, **ScaleWidth**, **ScaleLeft** and **ScaleTop** properties you can create a coordinate system completely at will, even including both positive and negative coordinates.

Setting the value of any of these automatically switches **ScaleMode** to vbUser. By setting the **ScaleMode** property to a number larger than 0, the **ScaleHeight** and **ScaleWidth** will automatically be set to the new unit of measurement. **ScaleLeft** and **ScaleTop** will be set to 0 at the same time. The **CurrentX** and **CurrentY** property settings change to reflect the new coordinates of the current point.

14.5.3 : ScaleHeight, ScaleWidth

The properties return or set the scale size for the horizontal (**ScaleWidth**) and vertical (**ScaleHeight**) measurement of an object.

```
object.ScaleHeight [= value]
object.ScaleWidth [= value]
```

Using the **Scalewidth** and **Scaleheight** you can create your own, custom, measurement system. The scale increases from top to bottom and left to right. Setting **Scalewidth** and **ScaleHeight** to negative values makes coordinates increase from bottom to top and right to left.

Using these properties in conjunction with the **ScaleLeft** and **ScaleTop** properties, you can create a full coordinate system with both positive and negative coordinates to your liking.

Note The **ScaleHeight** and **ScaleWidth** properties are not the same as the **Height** and **Width** properties. **Height** and **Width** **set** the width on the screen while **Scaleheigt** and **scalewidth** set the graphics scaling inside the object

14.5.4 : ScaleLeft and ScaleTop

The properties return or set the horizontal (**ScaleLeft**) and vertical (**ScaleTop**) coordinates for the left and top edges of an object.

```
object.ScaleLeft [= value]
object.ScaleTop [= value]
```

Using these properties and the related *ScaleHeight* and *ScaleWidth* properties, you can set up a full coordinate system with both positive and negative coordinates.

Note	The *ScaleLeft* and *ScaleTop* properties are not the same as the *Left* and *Top* properties. *Top* and *Left* set the position on the screen while *Scaleleft* and *Scaletop* set the graphics scaling inside the object.

14.6 : The graphics environment in.NET

The graphics environment under NET is completely different from the rather primitive tools found in Visual Basic Classic. Although most of the methods that were available under Visual Basic Classic are still valid, some have been replaced with a different approach. One notable difference is the unification of coordinates. Every operation is now pixel-related and all the old measurement units like pixels and twips are gone.

One major difference is, that you have to perform operations in the paint event of a control. You cannot simply execute drawing methods anywhere in code. Whereas this seems a drawback at first, it is actually an advantage, since now all controls are automatically refreshed when the display changes.

14.6.1 : Point object

The Point object acts as a carrier for an x/y-coordinate.

Example:

```
Dim pnt as new drawing.point (100,100)
```

14.6.2 : Size object

The *size* object represents the size of an object.

Example:

```
Dim my_size as new Size (100,150)
```

The above code defines an area of 100 pixels across and 150 pixels up. You can manipulate width and height of this object by manipulating its *width* and *height* properties

Example:

```
Dim my_size as new drawing.point (100,100)
My_size.width =200
My_size.heigth =200
```

14.6.3 : Rectangle object

A rectangle is the next step in the elementary drawing of objects. It is defined by a left and top coordinate and a height and width.

Example:

```
Dim my_rectangle as new drawing.rectangle(10,10,20,30)
```

This defines a new rectangle at 10, 10 with a width of 20 pixels and a height of 30 pixels. You can retrieve or set this information from the object by manipulating the **Left**, **Top**, **Width** and **Height** properties.

Example:

```
Dim my_rectangle as new drawing.rectangle(10,10,20,30)
My_rectangle.left=100
My_rectangle.top = 100
My_rectangle.width=200
My_rectangle.height=300
```

This would inflate the rectangle 10-fold.

14.6.4 : Colors

Any graphics object can have color specified. The net framework has a colors collection that is defined by names. You can access this collection using the **Drawing.Color** enumeration.

Example:

```
Dim My_color as drawing.color
My_color = drawing.color.aquamarine
```

The Visual Basic Help system has a complete list of all available colors.

It is also possible to create your own custom color by using **the Color.FromARGB** method.

ARGB is a format that specifies an alpha channel and RGB are the values for red green and blue. The alpha Channel specifies the level of transparency from 0 to 255 and each of the color channels red, green and blue define the palette position of the color. The values are supplied as a comma limited list or can be directly coded into an integer value.

Example:

```
Dim My_color as drawing.color
My_color = color.fromARGB (50,255,255,255)
My_color = &h80FFFFFF
```

The above code does twice the same: it sets a color value at 50% transparency and wiht maximum red green and blue. This will result in 50% white. It is equally possible to directly specify the color, if you know how to work with hexadecimal numbers as shown in the last line of code.

It is also possible to retrieve directly the current windows template color using the **Drawing.SystemColors** collection.

Example:

```
Dim My_color as drawing.color
My_color = drawing.systembrushes.activeborder
```

This will return the color that is currently assigned for an active border n the windows system.

14.6.5 : Brushes

Besides working with simple solid colors, you can also work directly with complex colors like gradients, hatches and more.

Example:

```
Dim brush1 as new drawing.solidbrush(color.red)
Dim brush2 as new drawing.solidbrush(color.fromARGB(50,255,255,255))

Dim my_bitmap as new drawing.bitmap("texture.bmp")
Dim my_hatch as new drawing.Texturebrush (mybitmap)
```

The first line defines a brush and assigns it a standard color belonging to the color collection, while the second line defines directly a custom color.

The last two lines load a bitmap and assign it to the brush. The **Drawing.Bitmap** loads a bitmap from file and stores it in the my_bitmap object, and this is assigned to the brush using the **Drawing.TextureBrush** method.

Just as with the color selection, there are a number of defined system brushes.

Example:

```
Dim My_color as drawing.color
My_color = drawing.systembrush.HighlightText
```

It is also possible to make a brush that contains a gradient. The **LineargradientBrush** in the **Drawing2d** namespace can create this structure for you. You define a drawing canvas as a rectangle construction, specify begin and end color and the angle that needs to be used to create the flood.

Example:

```
Dim mybrush new Drawing2d.LineargradientBrush(_
        New rectangle (0,0,100,100),color.white,color.blue,45)
    e.graphics.fillrectangle(my_brush,0,0,100,100)
```

This gives the following result when used to fill a rectangle:

If the brush surface is smaller than the area that needs to be filled the brush will be repeated:

Example:

```
Dim mybrush new Drawing2d.LineargradientBrush(_
        New rectangle (0,0,50,50),color.white,color.blue,45)

    e.graphics.fillrectangle(my_brush,0,0,100,100)
```

This renders the following image:

14.6.6 : Pens

A pen is used to draw lines and curves.

Example:

```
Dim My_pen as new drawing.pen(color.blue)
```

The pen object has a number of properties that allow you to fine-tune its appearance. **StartCap** and **EndCap** specify how a line should begin and end when drawn using the pen. You can select a number of predefined endings from the **LineCap** enumerations. There are caps styles from rounded, pointed, arrows and many more.

Further properties like **LineJoin** allow you to specify how lines will be joined together and **DashStyle** allows you to create all sorts of dashed lines.

You can also specify a pen width by providing an optional parameter.

Example:

```
Dim My_pen as new drawing.pen(color.blue,4)
```

This will create blue pen that is three pixels wide.

14.6.7 : DrawLine and DrawLines

Drawing a simple line using a pen is not harder then drawing a line in Visual Basic Classic.

Example:

```
e.graphics.drawline(my_pen,from_x,from_y,to_x,to_y)
```

The e object needs to be of the type **Painteventargs**.

14.6.8 : Drawing shapes

If you have read the previous topics, you should have acquired a good idea of the basic concepts and methods involved in performing graphics operations. From here on drawing more complex shapes is nothing more than providing additional parameters of the point, rectangle pen and brush type.

14.6.8.1 : Rectangles:

The **DrawRectangle** method requires you to provide a pen and two coordinate pairs, either as integers or as two points.

Example:

```
Dim green_pen as new pen(color.green)
Dim red_pen as new pen(color.red)
e.graphics.drawrectangle(green_pen,10,10,100,100)
e.grahiccs.drawrectangle(red_pen, _
                         drawing.point(100,100), _
                         drawing.point(110,110))
```

This draws the following image:

14.6.8.2 : Polygons

Just like a rectangle, a polygon requires you to provide a drawing pen, but this time you have to specify an array of points. The shape will automatically be closed.

```
Dim red_pen as new pen(color.red)
Dim p1 as new point(1,1)
Dim p2 as new point(10,15)
Dim p3 as new point(129,107)
Dim p4 as new point(55,14)
Dim p5 as new point(19,12)
Dim polygon as point() = {p1, p2, p3, p4, p5}
e.graphics.drawpolygon (red_pen,polygon)
```

An array of the type point I defined and filled with coordinate information. The array is then passed to the *DrawPolygon* method.

This renders the following image:

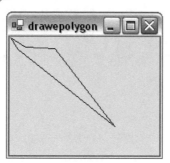

14.6.8.3 : Circles, ellipses, arcs and pies

Circles and ellipses are drawn using the same command. All that differs is the aspect ratio between the x and y dimension:

Example:

```
Dim my_pen as new pen(color.blue)
Dim from_x,from_y,horizontal,vertical as integer
From_x = 10
From_y=10
Horizontal = 100
Vertical = 50
e.graphics.drawellipse(my_pen,from_x,from_y,horizontal,vertical)
```

The above code draws an ellipse on the screen that looks like this:

In order to draw circles just make the horizontal equal to the vertical size.

The **DrawArc** method allows you to draw part of an ellipse. Its arguments define the pen, a center coordinate followed by horizontal and vertical size and finally the start angle and end angle. Drawing is performed in a clockwise motion.

Example:

```
Dim my_pen as new pen(color.blue)
Dim from_x,from_y,hor,vert,start_a,stop_a as integer
From_x = 10
From_y = 10
Hor = 50
Vert = 100
Start_a = 10
Stop_a = 100
e.graphics.drawarc(my_pen, from_x, from_y, hor, vert, start_a,
stop_a)
```

There are a couple of important thing to note about the Arc command.

- Drawing is done in a clockwise fashion. Therefore, if you draw from zero to 90 degrees you get the fourth quadrant of the circle!

- The stop angle must be higher than the start angle. If not, then a segment equal to start angle + stop angle is drawn beginning at the start angle.

You can also create Pies directly. The difference between an arc and a pie is that the pie has two fly-lines from the corners of the arc to the centre coordinate.

Example:

```
Dim my_pen as new pen(color.blue)
Dim from_x,from_y,hor,vert,start_a,stop_a as integer
From_x = 100
From_y=100
Hor = 50
Ver = 100
Start_a = 10
Stop_a = 100
e.graphics.drawpie(my_pen, from_x, from_y, hor, _
                   vert, start_a, stop_a)
```

This gives the following result:

14.6.8.4 : Curves

Previously I have explained the polygon construction that creates a closed trace based on the corner points specified as an array of points. The **DrawCurve** and **DrawClosedCurve** methods allow you to draw smooth curves. A curve-fitting algorithm will automatically render a flowing curve through the corner points specified.

Example:

```
Dim my_pen As New Pen(Color.Blue)
    Dim my_curve(7) As System.Drawing.Point
    my_curve(0) = New Point(20, 50)
    my_curve(1) = New Point(40, 100)
    my_curve(2) = New Point(60, 50)
    my_curve(3) = New Point(80, 100)
    my_curve(4) = New Point(100, 10)
    my_curve(5) = New Point(120, 100)
    my_curve(6) = New Point(140, 50)
    my_curve(7) = New Point(160, 100)
    ' for an open curve:
    e.Graphics.DrawCurve(my_pen, my_curve)
    ' for a closed curve:
    e.Graphics.DrawClosedCurve(my_pen, my_curve)
```

This would produce the following result:

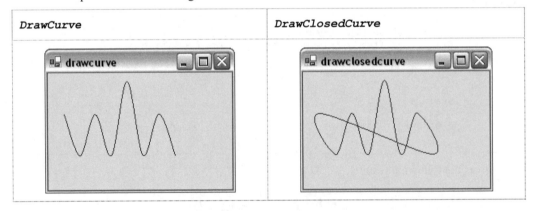

14.6.9 : Filling shapes

Any closed shape can be filled either with a solid color or with a pattern.

For each of the presented drawing methods a complementary filling function is available.

FillRectangle, **FillEllipse**, **FillPie**, **FillCurve** and **FillPolygon** are all used in a similar fashion ad their counterparts, except, instead of specifying a pen this time, you specify a brush.

Example:

```
Dim my_brush as drawing.solidbrush = system.drawing.brushes.blue
e.graphics.fillrectangle (my_brush,10,10,100,100)
```

This gives the following result:

14.6.10 : Drawing Graphics

In order to load directly a graphics file onto the screen you can use the **DrawImage** method and pass it an object of the type **Drawing.Bitmap**.

Example:

```
Dim my_bmp as new drawing.bitmap ("test.bmp")
e.graphics.drawimage (my_bmp, new drawing.point (50,50))
```

The above code will load an image and store it in **my_bmp**. The **DrawImage** method renders the image at coordinates **50, 50** on the screen. The coordinates need to be passed as a point so we have to invoke the **Drawing.Point** method.

It is possible to warp an image by specifying more points, or scale an image by passing a rectangle as the second parameter.

For a full detailed explanation of the **Drawimage** method, please consult the Visual Basic Help.

14.6.11 : Drawing Text

You can render text on the screen if you want to create special effects that are not possible using standard objects such as label and textboxes. Text can be drawn in any available font and be filled with a specific brush that can be a solid color, a flood or even a bitmap image.

You need to define a new variable of the type font and retrieve the font and size required. You can modify additional properties such as the font style by passing an argument form the *FontStyle* enumeration.

Example:

```
Dim my_brush as new drawing2d.Lineargradientbrush(_
              New rectangle(0,0,100,100),
              Color.white, _
              Color.blue, _
              45)
Dim my_font as new drawing.font("Arial Black",36, fontstyle.italic)
e.graphics.drawString("Visual Basic Rulez !",my_font,my_brush,10,10)
```

This renders the following result:

14.6.12 : Paths

Because the previously presented drawing methods might not create the desired effect when it comes to complex shapes, it is possible to create a complex shape called a path.

The *GraphicsPath* accepts any previously explained drawing method and will combine this to one object.

Example:

```
Dim mypath As New Drawing2D.GraphicsPath
mypath.StartFigure()
mypath.AddLine(10, 10, 10, 100)
mypath.AddLine(10, 10, 100, 10)
mypath.AddLine(100, 10, 100, 100)
mypath.AddArc(10, 54, 90, 90, 0, 180)
e.Graphics.DrawPath(blackPen, mypath)
```

This renders the following image:

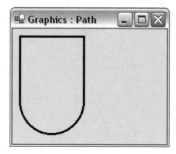

A graphics path can both be painted and filled, depending on whether you call the **DrawPath** method and passing a pen or call the **FillPath** method and pass a brush as argument.

14.6.12.1 : ClosePath

It is also possible to close a path automatically using the **ClosePath** method. This traces a line from he very first coordinate specified to the very last coordinate specified.

Example:

```
Dim mypath As New Drawing2D.GraphicsPath
mypath.StartFigure()
mypath.AddLine(10, 10, 10, 100)
mypath.AddLine(10, 10, 100, 10)
mypath.closepath
e.Graphics.DrawPath(blackPen, mypath)
```

Will connect a line from point 100, 10 to point 10, 10 creating a triangle.

14.6.13 : Regions

You have probably seen programs that do not use rectangular windows but circular or even completely odd-shapen windows. This is possible with any object in windows but involves interacting directly with the GDI of windows. In NET, this is far easier to accomplish.

A region is an area that acts as a clipping surface. It defines the visible part of a control that can act as parent to other controls, such as a form for instance. This can be used to shape existing forms in any arbitrary form. The region property takes a path as input.

When using the path we created in the previous example and applying it to our window, we actually cut out a visible area.

Example:

```
Dim mypath As New Drawing2D.GraphicsPath
mypath.StartFigure()
mypath.AddLine(10, 10, 10, 100)
mypath.AddLine(10, 10, 100, 10)
mypath.AddLine(100, 10, 100, 100)
mypath.AddArc(10, 54, 90, 90, 0, 180)
Dim my_region As New Region(mypath)
Me.Region = my_region
```

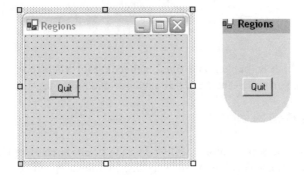

Chapter 15 : Creating console applications (NET)

So far, all our programs have really been using the graphical user interface to interact with the user. It is possible in Visual Basic NET to make a console application that uses a text-based command line interface much like in the old DOS days.

You might wonder what the use of such programs could possibly still be, but there are cases where this comes in handy. A tool that performs a specific operation but uses command line arguments to perform its command input / output is such a case. Examples could be a background program or a program that is called from batch files.

15.1.1 : Standard I/O

You can perform I/O from and to the console using the **Write**, **WriteLine**, **Read** and **ReadLine** commands.

15.1.1.1 : *Writing something to the command line:*

To send text output to the screen, you can use the **Write** or **WriteLine** methods of the console object.

Example:

```
        Console.writeline ("Type your name")
```

This will write the message to the console and move to the next line. If you do not want to move to the next line, you can either use the **Write** method or specify modifiers. Check for a detailed explanation of the **Write** and **WriteLine** methods in the section on File I/O.

15.1.1.2 : *Getting input from the command line*

Besides sending output to the console, it is equally possible to retrieve information form the console such as user input.

Example:

```
        User_input = Console.readline ()
```

Anything the user types will be returned into the variable **user_input** the moment the user hits the enter key. Program execution is halted until this actually happens. It is possible to create this as a separate process so that other parts of your program can continue running. After all we are still writing in the NET platform, and can use all functionality including multitasking and threading.

15.1.2 : Redirecting IO

It is possible to redirect the I/O from the console window to for instance a file. The **SetIn** and **SetOut** methods allow you to redirect program input and output to other streams than the default screen and keyboard.

For instance, you can redirect all output to and from a file by simply creating a **StreamReader** and **StreamWriter** and assigning them to the console input and output.

Example:

```
My_output = new streamwriter ("output.txt")
My_input = new streamreader ("input.txt")
Console.setin (my_input)
Console.setout (my_ouput)
```

The above code will open two files: **input.txt** and **output.txt**, and assigns them to the default handlers of the **console** object. All operations such as getting input and printing information would be performed on those files. This allows you to make programs that can manipulate files directly without any user interaction. This is a great way to write a command line tool to perform certain, often used, function. Of course, you might want to be able to specify optional parameters, which brings us to our next topics: retrieving the command line arguments or parameters.

15.1.3 : Retrieving command line parameters

Console applications are often passed so-called command line arguments, information that is required for the program to do its work. In order to retrieve the command line parameters you can use the **Environment.CommandLine** property or, alternately, invoke the **Environment.GetCommandLineArgs** function that will split the command line into an array.

Example:

```
Dim parameters as string
Paramters = Environment.CommandLine
```

This would return the entire command line as a string, to split it for you, the **CommandLineArgs** function can help you.

Example:

```
Dim parameters as string () = Environment.CcommandLineArgs
```

If the arguments were A B C then the string would be split an A would reside in location 0, B in location 1 and C in location 2 of the parameter array.

Chapter 16 : Communicating to the world around us

What good is a program, if it cannot communicate to the outside world? So far we have concentrated on communicating with the user of the program. Maybe it is time to have a look at what other things we could possibly want communicate with.

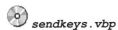 *sendkeys.vbp*   There is a tutorial program available that explains the constructs, explained in this topic, by example.

16.1 : SendKeys: a simple way of communicating

Yes, you can emulate sending keystrokes to another program. This is perhaps the simplest way of talking to other applications. **SendKeys** can send one or more keystrokes just like you would be typing on the keyboard.

```
SendKeys string [, wait]
```

String	The string expression holding the keystrokes to send.
Wait	An Optional Boolean value that specifies the wait mode. The default False returns control to the calling procedure immediately after the keys are sent. If set to True the keystrokes must be processed before control is returned to the procedure. You can use this to wait for the target program to complete its operation before sending more information.

A key is represented by its name. For the normal letters, numbers and punctuation this is the key itself. Special keys such as Shift Ctrl and the function keys have a specific name assigned to them. For example, to send the letter A you just use "A" as string. To send multiple characters you write them together in the string. For example sending the test "Hello World" would require you just to pass that string to the **sendkeys** method. The string will be split and each character will be sent as a keystroke.

The plus (+), caret (^), percent sign (%), tilde (~), and parentheses () are used to combine specific keys and will not be sent as output but processed internally. If you want to send any of these character you need to enclose them within accolades {}. For example, to send "**A+B**" as a string you need to pass "**A{+}B**" to the **sendkeys** method. The same is true for square brackets. These need to be enclosed in accolades as well. Then the question remains how do you send an accolade? Well, simply by enclosing it in an accolade as well: *{{}* and *{}}*. The **sendkeys** interpreter will know how to handle this.

In order to send special control keys such as Enter and Tab, you have to use specific pre-defined key names. The following table gives an overview of the available key names:

Key	Code
BACKSPACE	{BACKSPACE}, {BS}, or {BKSP}
BREAK	{BREAK}
CAPS LOCK	{CAPSLOCK}
DEL or DELETE	{DELETE} or {DEL}
DOWN ARROW	{DOWN}
END	{END}
ENTER	{ENTER} or ~
ESC	{ESC}
HELP	{HELP}
HOME	{HOME}
INS or INSERT	{INSERT} or {INS}
LEFT ARROW	{LEFT}
NUM LOCK	{NUMLOCK}
PAGE DOWN	{PGDN}
PAGE UP	{PGUP}
PRINT SCREEN	{PRTSC}
RIGHT ARROW	{RIGHT}
SCROLL LOCK	{SCROLLLOCK}
TAB	{TAB}
UP ARROW	{UP}
FUNCTION KEYS (F1.. F16)	{F1}{F2}{F3} … etc

To specify a combination of keys with SHIFT, CTRL or ALT, you can precede the key code with one or more of the following codes:

Key	Code
SHIFT	+
CTRL	^
ALT	%

It is possible to make the SHIFT, CTRL and ALT 'sticky'. This means they should be held down while several other keys are pressed. For example, to specify to hold down SHIFT while AB and C are pressed, use "+(ABC)". In order to hold down ALT while D is pressed, followed by E without ALT, use "%DE".

To specify repeating keys, use the form {key number}. You must put a space between key and number. For example, {LEFT 10} means press the LEFT ARROW key 10 times; {X 5} means press X 5 times.

Note	You cannot use **SendKeys** to send keystrokes to an application that is not designed to run in Microsoft Windows. **Sendkeys** also cannot send the PRINT SCREEN key {PRTSC} to any application.

The following example uses the **Shell** function to run the Calculator application included with Microsoft Windows. It uses **SendKeys** to send keystrokes to add some numbers, and then quit the Calculator. (To see the example, paste it into a procedure, then run the procedure. Because **AppActivate** changes the focus to the Calculator application, you cannot single step through the code.)

```
Dim ReturnValue, I
ReturnValue = Shell("CALC.EXE", 1)    ' Run Calculator.
AppActivate ReturnValue         ' Activate the Calculator.
For I = 1 To 100      ' Set up counting loop.
      SendKeys I & "{+}", True
   ' Send keystrokes to Calculator
Next I ' to add each value of I.
SendKeys "=", True     ' Get grand total.
SendKeys "%{F4}", True        ' Send ALT+F4 to close Calculator.
```

16.1.1 : AppActivate

This activates the application window specified by its window name.

> AppActivate title[, wait]

Title	This is a string expression, which specifies the title in the title bar of the application window you want to activate. When you launched the other program from your code you can use the task ID returned by the Shell function to activate the application. This is actually a better way, since some programs change their caption depending on the files they have open.
Wait	An optional Boolean that specifies whether the calling application has the focus before activating another. If set to False (default), the specified application is immediately activated. If True, the calling window waits until it receives the focus and then activates the target application.

The **AppActivate** statement passes the focus to the given application but it does not alter the window state of the program, e.g.: a minimized window will remain minimized. If you want to change this, you can use the **Shell** function to start an application and set the window style.

When Windows is trying to find the application to activate, the specified title is compared to the title string of each running application. The first application that matches the given string will be activated. If multiple applications are running with the same title, there is no telling which one will be activated. This depends on their internal process ID.

16.1.2 : Shell

The **Shell** command allows you to runs an executable program from your code. The function returns the program's task ID if successful, or zero if the shell execute fails.

```
Shell(pathname[,windowstyle])
```

pathname	This specifies the filename and optional location of the program to execute and any required arguments or command-line switches.
windowstyle	An optional Integer, which sets the style of the window in which the program is to be run. If no **windowstyle** is given, the program is started minimized but with the focus set to it.

The **windowstyle** can have any of these values:

vbHide	0	The Window is hidden and the focus is passed to the window.
vbNormalFocus	1	The Window has the focus but it is restored to its original size and position.
vbMinimizedFocus	2	The Window is displayed as an icon with the focus.
vbMaximizedFocus	3	The Window is maximized and has the focus.
vbNormalNoFocus	4	The Window is restored to its last size and position. The focus does not move.
vbMinimizedNoFocus	6	The Window is displayed as an icon. The currently active window remains active.

If the **Shell** function succeeds in executing the given program file, it will return the ID of the started program. The ID is a unique number that identifies the running program to Windows; see this as the 'handle' to the program If the Shell function can't start the named program, an error occurs.

	The Shell function runs other programs asynchronously. This means that a program started with Shell might not finish executing before the statements following the Shell function are executed.
Note	

16.2 : DDE: another means of inter-program communication

You might wonder: what is DDE? Well, this is one of the cornerstones of Windows and Windows programming. DDE stands for Dynamic Data Exchange. In short, it allows you to send information across programs.

You can actually write programs that talk to each other. This is an interesting feature, which allows you to write programs that exchange not only data, but also commands between programs. A DDE session can be set up with virtually any Windows application. Most programs support it in one way or another. The only problem is finding out the command set for that particular program you want to communicate with.

First of all, we need to set up the communication. This requires specifying the application and target of the DDE conversation.

16.2.1 : LinkMode:

The *LinkMode* retrieves or sets the type of link used for a DDE session and it activates the connection.

Syntax:
```
object.LinkMode = [number]
```

If a control is used as the source or target in a DDE conversation, the possible link modes are the any of the following:

Constant	Setting	Description
vbLinkNone	0	(Default) None — No DDE interaction.
vbLinkAutomatic	1	Automatic — the Destination control is updated each time the linked data changes.
vbLinkManual	2	Manual — the Destination control is updated only when the *LinkRequest* method is invoked.
vbLinkNotify	3	Notify — An event (*linkNotify*) occurs whenever the data changes, but the target control is updated only when the *LinkRequest* method is invoked.

An entire form can be set as the source or target of a DE conversation as well. In that case the settings for number are:

Constant	Setting	Description
vbLinkNone	0	(Default) None — No DDE interaction. There is no on-going DDE conversation. There is a possible pitfall here: if you set this to 0 (None) at design time, it will be stuck since you will not be able to change it 1 (Source) at run time. This has to do with the code generation. The necessary code will not be present in the program to toggle this on. Instead, set it to 1 at design time and call it to 0 as the first thing you do from code.
vbLinkSource	1	Source — Allows any child Label, PictureBox, or TextBox control on the form to supply data to any requestor that wants to perform DDE. The event generating code and updating is handled by the Visual Basic compiler. So you do not need to bother with that.

Note   Setting a data link at design time with the Paste Link command from the Edit menu will automatically set the **LinkMode**, **LinkTopic** and **LinkItem** properties. The link will be saved and compiled into the project and the resulting code will attempt to re-establish the conversation as soon as it executes.

16.2.2 : LinkTopic

The **LinkTopic** property allows you to specify the application and data group used in the DDE conversation. **LinkTopic** is used in conjunction with the **LinkItem** property to define the complete DDE link.

```
object.LinkTopic = [value]
```

The **LinkTopic** property provides the necessary information to the target to set up the destination or source link. The string provides one or more elements of the applications DDE syntax, which include application, topic and item.

Note   The actual syntax can be slightly different from application to application. Always check the documentation of the application you want to create a DDE link to for details.

For example, within Microsoft Excel, you use the syntax:

```
application|topic!item
```

While with Microsoft Word, you would omit the pipe character and use:

```
application topic item
```

A Visual Basic application uses the Excel convention:

```
application|topic
```

The exclamation mark for topic is implicit.

Note The same note as for the *LinkMode* applies here: if you save the *LinkTopic* with the project then each time the form is reloaded an attempt will be made to re-establish the connection.

16.2.3 : LinkItem

The *LinkItem* will retrieve or post the data from and to the destination control.

```
object.LinkItem = [string]
```

For instance, a *LinkItem* in a DDE conversation with Microsoft Excel could be "R1C1".

If you are interacting with a Visual Basic application, you can simply use the complete reference of an object, for example: myprogram|form1|label1.

Example:

```
Private Sub form_load()
        Text1.LinkMode = 0
        Text1.LinkTopic = "Excel|Sheet1"
        Text1.LinkItem = "R1C1"
        Text1.LinkMode = 1
        Text2.text="1"
        Text3.text="1"
End sub

Private Sub fetch_Click ()
        Dim cell As String
        CurRow = "R" & text2.text & "C" & text3.text
        Text1.LinkItem = CurRow
End Sub
```

The above example is attached to a form with 3 textboxes. Textbox1 will contain the information from the excel file, textbox 2 alloys you to specify a row and textbox 3 allows you to specify a column.

Here is a view of the form in design mode:

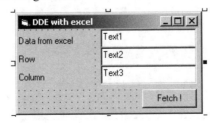

When clicking the button, a DDE request will be sent to the paired application (in this case Excel) and the contents of the specified cell will be retrieved.

16.3 : Serial IO: Talking to world beyond the port.

This is probably one of the most obscure parts of windows. Most people still regard to this as a tricky thing. Well it is not. Windows includes a standard object called MSCOMM that handles all the down-to-earth stuff for you. From programming the serial interface card over controlling the handshaking process up to actually exchanging data: all you have to do is set it up correctly.

16.3.1 : Inserting the object

First of all you should insert the MSCOMM object into your program.

NET	It is possible to use the MSCOMM control from the NET platform through the COM accessing layer. The problem is that you need to have Visual Basic 6.0 installed on your machine in order to have a correct license in the registry for this to work. The NET 2.0 framework has serial port access built in.

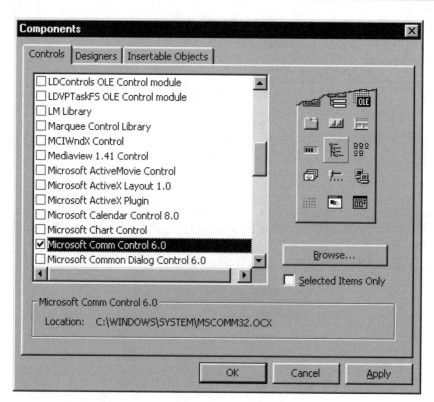

To do this, right click on the object browser and select Add-Component. Then browse for the MSCOMM Object, and make sure it is checked. It will then appear on the object browser.

You can put up to 16 of these in a project (Windows directly supports up to 16 Serial ports). If you need more ports, you will have to install additional drivers into the operating system. Unfortunately, there is no direct and easy way to detect the number of serial ports in a computer system. There are some API calls that allow you to extract the so-called system-metrics. However, this leads us too far. There are dedicated books to API programming (Check the suggested reading list at the back of this book).

Simple communications can be set up in a snap. All we have to do is select the comport, specify its operating parameters and finally open it. So let us have a look at the most used parameters.

16.3.2 : PortOpen

The **PortOpen** method allows you to set the state of the communications port. This property is only available at runtime.

```
object.PortOpen =[value]
```

The value parameter is of the **Boolean** type and can thus be true or false.

By assigning a **True** value to the **PortOpen** property, an attempt will be made to obtain control over the port specified in the **Commport** property. By assigning a false value, all buffers will be flushed and once communication is completed, the port will be closed. Any information in the output buffer will be sent before the port is closed. Incoming information will be available in the receive buffer up until the point the port actually closes down.

MSCOMM will automatically close the assigned serial port upon termination of your program.

Before opening the port make sure the **CommPort** property is set to a valid port number, or a 'device not available' error will occur (error code 69). When attempting to open a port with settings that it will not support, the port will go open but might not function as intended. Port control settings are specified using the **Settings** property.

Note	Never-ever attempt to close or open a port two times in a row. This yields an error. You should first check the state of the port.

You can only change its state. You cannot set it to the state it already has for an error will occur. You can make a construction like this to avoid the problem:

```
If comport.portopen=true then
   Comport.portopen=false
Else
   Comport.portopen=true
End if
```

16.3.3 : Handshaking

The **Handshaking** property defines the protocol to be used with the connected device.

```
object.Handshaking = [value]
```

The following settings are possible:

Setting	Value	Description
comNone	0	(Default) No handshaking.
comXOnXOff	1	XON/XOFF handshaking.
comRTS	2	RTS/CTS (Request To Send/Clear To Send) handshaking.
comRTSXOnXOff	3	Both Request To Send and XON/XOFF handshaking.

Handshaking determines the communications protocol that will be used to govern the flow of information between your computer and the other side of the cable.

Originally, serial ports used handshaking to signal to the sending device that it was OK to send more information. As computers have substantially increased in speed, they can easily outrun even the fastest serial communication. However, many devices do require correct handshaking since they might not be able to follow the stream of information correctly.

Several methods are possible:

The hardware (RTS/CTS) handshaking is handled by the electronics in the serial port. An additional set of control signals (Ready To Send and Clear to Send) are used to signal when it is OK to transmit more information. MSCOMM is aware of these lines and can set the UART in the correct mode.

Software handshaking is a protocol that uses two reserved characters for handshaking. One character (XON) enables transmission and the other (XOFF) disables it. Whenever the slave is ready for data it sends XON to the master, and if its input buffer is full, it sends XOFF and processes the buffer.

16.3.4 : Settings

The settings property controls the communication parameters that will be used for data transport.

```
object.Settings = [value]
```

The settings are passed as comma delimited string. Invalid parameters will create a runtime error.

There are four elements in the string: the baud rate, the Parity, the number of data bits and the number of stop bits. The default value of value is: "9600,N,8,1" which translates to 9600 Baud, no parity, 8 data bits and 1 stop bit.

The following table lists the valid settings.

Baud Setting	Parity setting		Data bits	Stop bits
110	E	Even	4	1
300	M	Mark	5	1.5
600	N	None	6	2
1200	O	Odd	7	
2400	S	Space	8 (Default)	
9600 (Default)				
14400				
19200				
28800				
38400 (reserved)				
56000 (reserved)				
128000 (reserved)				
256000 (reserved)				

A reserved value may not work on all computers. Only newer fast machines actually support these baud rates. Attempting to open a comport that does not support these settings, may or may not result in a runtime error.

16.3.5 : Outbuffersize, Inbuffersize

Because of the inherent problems with serial communications in terms of being fast enough to catch the incoming data and buffer the outgoing data, MSCOMM provides a mechanism to increase the reliability. The *Outbuffersize* and *Inbuffersize* allow you to specify a software buffer to hold incoming and outgoing data.

```
object.OutBufferSize  = number
object.InBufferSize   = number
```

Outbuffersize and *Inbuffersize* set the total size of the transmit and receive buffers. By default, this is set to 512 bytes.

Note	Keep in mind that these buffers require memory and processing time from the computer. In general, leave the setting at 512 and increase it only when absolutely necessary. With a modern computer there rarely should be a case, except when using the fastest UARTS at 10 Mega baud) where this becomes an issue.

16.3.6 : OutbufferCount, Inbuffercount

These properties allow you to retrieve the number of bytes that are still in the input buffer ,waiting to be processed by you and how many are still in the output buffer waiting to be sent by the UART. These properties are not available at design time.

```
object.OutBufferCount = [value]
waitingchars = object.OutBufferCount
receivedchars= object.InBufferCount
```

You can also clear the transmit buffer by setting the *OutbufferCount* property to 0.

Note	Do not confuse the *OutbufferCount* property with the *Outbuffersize* property which reflects the total size of the transmit buffer.

16.3.7 : Parityreplace

A parity code is a simple mechanism to detect a transmission error caused by electrical disturbance on the signal received. The UART can detect this and raises a flag if a received byte contains a detectably error using this mechanism. MSCOMM can automatically replace such a 'corrupt' byte with a user specifiable character.

```
object.ParityReplace = [value]
```

By default, the *ParityReplace* character is a question mark (?).If you set *ParityReplace* to an empty string ("") this disables replacement of the character where the parity error occurs and information is returned as received leaving the error handling up to you.

In any case, the *OnComm* event is still fired and the *CommEvent* property is set to *comEventRXParity*.

16.3.8 : DTRenable

The *DTRenable* property controls whether the Data Terminal Ready (DTR) line will be asserted during communications. The Data Terminal Ready signal is used by a computer to signal to an attached device that it is ready to accept data.

```
object.DTREnable = [boolean]
```

When set to true, the Data Terminal Ready line is made logical high upon opening the port by setting the **PortOpen** property to true, and made low again upon closing the port by setting **PortOpen** to **False**. If **DTREnable** is set to **False**, the Data Terminal Ready will always remain low.

Note	When talking to a modem, in most cases setting the Data Terminal Ready line to low will disconnect the phone line and thus end the call.

16.3.9 : OnComm Event

The **OnComm** event is raised whenever the value of the **CommEvent** property changes. Anything that is happening to the port generates an **OnComm** event

```
Private Sub object_OnComm ()
End sub
```

The **CommEvent** property contains a numeric code indication the cause of the event.

16.3.10 : CommEvent

The **CommEvent** property returns the most recent communication event or error. This is a runtime only property.

```
X = object.CommEvent
```

Whenever **OnComm** fires, the **CommEvent** contains updated information on the cause of the event. This can be a communication error or simply a character incoming or outgoing. To determine the actual cause you need to evaluate the value.

Possible values that are actually error codes:

Constant	Value	Description
ComEventBreak	1001	A Break signal was received.
ComEventCTSTO	1002	The Clear To Send line was low for longer then normal for the given communication settings. The other side might be stuck or unable to cope with the dataflow.
ComEventDSRTO	1003	The Data Set Ready line was low for too long. The other side might not be able to follow your communication speed.
ComEventFrame	1004	The hardware detected a framing error. Information was corrupted and may need re-sending.
ComEventOverrun	1006	A character was not read from the hardware before the next character arrived and was lost.

ComEventCDTO	1007	The Carrier Detect line was low for the system specified amount of time while trying to transmit a character. Carrier Detect is also known as the Receive Line Signal Detect (RLSD).
ComEventRxOver	1008	There is no room in the receive buffer. Information has been lost.
ComEventRxParity	1009	The hardware detected a parity error and information integrity has been compromised. You might want to request a resend.
ComEventTxFull	1010	Transmit Buffer Full. The transmit buffer was full while trying to queue a character. Information is lost.
ComEventDCB	1011	An unexpected error occurred retrieving Device Control Block (DCB) for the port. This can occur if another program attempts to grab control of the port and succeeds, or if the port is no longer controllable (Serial port over USB: the port was unplugged). This is a very rare event.

Values that are normal events:

Constant	Value	Description
ComEvSend	1	There are fewer than *SThreshold* number of characters in the transmit buffer. You can now send the next chunk of information. This can be used to make a high-level packet-processing algorithm.
ComEvReceive	2	Received the number of characters specified by **Rthreshold**. This event is generated continuously until you use the Input property to remove the data from the receive buffer.
ComEvCTS	3	A change in Clear To Send line occurred.
ComEvDSR	4	A change in Data Set Ready line occurred. This event is only fired when DSR changes from 1 to 0.
ComEvCD	5	A change in Carrier Detect line occurred.
ComEvRing	6	Ring detected. Some UARTS (universal asynchronous receiver-transmitters) may not support this event. This line is typically asserted by a modem to indicate an incoming call.
ComEvEOF	7	End Of File (ASCII character 26) character received.

16.3.11 : Rthreshold, SThreshold

The **Rthreshold** and **SThreshold** properties govern the number of characters actually sent or received before MSCOMM asserts the **OnComm** event.

```
object.Rthreshold = [value]
```

Setting the **Rthreshold** property to 0 (the default) disables the **OnComm** event from firing upon reception of characters. By setting **Rthreshold** to 1, the MSCOMM control will raise the **OnComm** event for every character received.

So that's about it concerning serial communications. A simple program is available that allows you to send and receive character over a serial port. An in depth hardware approach to serial programming will be handled later on in this book. The examples on how to make use of this powerful object will be explained there.

16.4 : Serial IO under NET

Serial communication under NET is a task that appears to be not easy. But then again, appearances have proved to be wrong.

It is possible to use the MSCOMM OCX in Visual Basic NET by importing it. The drawback is that you are required to have Visual Basic 6.0 installed on your machine as well, and when distributing an application you need to register the OCX on the new machine as well.

Registering the OCX is a matter of launching regsvr32 and specifying the mscomm.dll and OCX file.

It is possible though to access the serial port as an I/O stream through the kernel of windows. API programming is explained later in this book but don't worry about the details for the moment

16.4.1 : The control structures definition

In order to interface with the kernel of windows a number of data structures need to be defined as all interaction is done using so-called Device Control Blocks (DCB's). The entire structure is passed as one block of data to and from the kernel. The kernel knows the order and type of data it will receive from the DCB.

```
Public Structure DCB
        Public DCBlength As Int32
        Public BaudRate As Int32
        Public fBitFields As Int32
        Public wReserved As Int16
        Public XonLim As Int16
        Public XoffLim As Int16
        Public ByteSize As Byte
```

```
        Public Parity As Byte
        Public StopBits As Byte
        Public XonChar As Byte
        Public XoffChar As Byte
        Public ErrorChar As Byte
        Public EofChar As Byte
        Public EvtChar As Byte
        Public wReserved1 As Int16
End Structure
Public Structure COMMTIMEOUTS
        Public ReadIntervalTimeout As Int32
        Public ReadTotalTimeoutMultiplier As Int32
        Public ReadTotalTimeoutConstant As Int32
        Public WriteTotalTimeoutMultiplier As Int32
        Public WriteTotalTimeoutConstant As Int32
End Structure
Public Const GENERIC_READ As Int32 = &H80000000
Public Const GENERIC_WRITE As Int32 = &H40000000
Public Const OPEN_EXISTING As Int32 = 3
Public Const FILE_ATTRIBUTE_NORMAL As Int32 = &H80
Public Const NOPARITY As Int32 = 0
Public Const ONESTOPBIT As Int32 = 0
```

16.4.2 : The IO prototypes

The next thing we need to do is, define the prototypes for the functions in the kernel. Prototypes are empty subroutines that actually reference the real functions in an external library, which in this case is the windows kernel.

```
Public Declare Auto Function CreateFile Lib "kernel32.dll" _
        (ByVal lpFileName As String, _
        ByVal dwDesiredAccess As Int32, _
        ByVal dwShareMode As Int32, _
        ByVal lpSecurityAttributes As IntPtr, _
        ByVal dwCreationDisposition As Int32, _
        ByVal dwFlagsAndAttributes As Int32, _
        ByVal hTemplateFile As IntPtr) As IntPtr

Public Declare Auto Function GetCommState Lib "kernel32.dll" _
        (ByVal nCid As IntPtr, _
        ByRef lpDCB As DCB) As Boolean

Public Declare Auto Function SetCommState Lib "kernel32.dll" _
        (ByVal nCid As IntPtr, _
        ByRef lpDCB As DCB) As Boolean

Public Declare Auto Function GetCommTimeouts Lib "kernel32.dll" _
        (ByVal hFile As IntPtr, _
        ByRef lpCommTimeouts As COMMTIMEOUTS) As Boolean

Public Declare Auto Function SetCommTimeouts Lib "kernel32.dll" _
        (ByVal hFile As IntPtr, _
        ByRef lpCommTimeouts As COMMTIMEOUTS) As Boolean

Public Declare Auto Function WriteFile Lib "kernel32.dll" _
```

```
                (ByVal hFile As IntPtr, _
                ByVal lpBuffer As Byte(), _
                ByVal nNumberOfBytesToWrite As Int32, _
                ByRef lpNumberOfBytesWritten As Int32, _
                ByVal lpOverlapped As IntPtr) As Boolean

        Public Declare Auto Function ReadFile Lib "kernel32.dll" _
                (ByVal hFile As IntPtr, _
                ByVal lpBuffer As Byte(), _
                ByVal nNumberOfBytesToRead As Int32, _
                ByRef lpNumberOfBytesRead As Int32, _
                ByVal lpOverlapped As IntPtr) As Boolean

        Public Declare Auto Function CloseHandle Lib "kernel32.dll" _
                (ByVal hObject As IntPtr) As Boolean
```

The **CreateFile** function creates a file much in the similar way the regular file creation functions of NET work with the exception that it returns a different data type and allows you access to a so called device file. Device files are logical names associated with hardware devices such as COM1, COM2 and LPT1 etcetera. For people remembering DOS style basic, such as QuickBasic or PowerBasic, you accessed the serial port in exactly the same way as accessing a file: open "com1:" for output as #1. This can be done since the ports exist as device files.

Getcommstate retrieves the flags associated with the communication interface. I will explain the flags later on in this chapter.

Setcommstate allows you to change the state flags.

The **Getcomtimeouts** and **SetComTimeouts** allow you to modify the timeout parameters associated with the interface. In order to prevent your program from stalling until data is actually arriving, you can set a timeout. If this timeout expires, control is returned to your program and you can check what is going on by checking the state flags using the **GetCommState** function.

WriteFile and **ReadFile** allow you to read and write to the device file.

In order to make the code manageable, we will declare some local variables:

```
        Dim Serial_handle As IntPtr
        Dim Success As Boolean
        Dim My_DCB As DCB
        Dim My_CommTimeouts As COMMTIMEOUTS
        Dim BytesWritten, BytesRead As Int32
        Dim Buffer() As Byte ' Declare variables to use for encoding.
        Dim oEncoder As New System.Text.ASCIIEncoding
        Dim oEnc As System.Text.Encoding = oEncoder.GetEncoding(1252)
        Buffer = oEnc.GetBytes("Test")
```

The **Serial_handle** is the handle to be used when manipulating the port. They act just like a filehandle. **My_DCB** is an instantiation of the DCB structure we defined earlier while the actual bytes read and written is stored in the **BytesWritten** and **BytesRead** integers. A buffer array is defined to hold incoming and outgoing data.

The encoder function is there to convert Visual Basic type strings to an array of bytes and strip off the string size.

16.4.3 : Obtaining a Device handle to the serial port

Just like when opening a file you need to open the Comport. This is done by passing the correct information to the *CreateFile* routine in the kernel.

Example:

```
Serial_handle = CreateFile("COM1", _
                           GENERIC_READ Or GENERIC_WRITE, _
                           0,
                           IntPtr.Zero, _
                           OPEN_EXISTING, _
                           FILE_ATTRIBUTE_NORMAL, _
                           IntPtr.Zero)
```

16.4.4 : Controlling the port settings

Since we have defined a device control block, we can manipulate the individual settings of the port through this mechanism. Since the DCB is empty after creation, it is a good idea to retrieve the current settings and use this as a template to modify and write back.

Example:

```
Success = GetCommState(Serial_handle, My_DCB)
My_DCB.BaudRate = 9600
My_DCB.ByteSize = 8
My_DCB.Parity = NOPARITY
My_DCB.StopBits = ONESTOPBIT
Success = SetCommState(Serial_handle, My_DCB)
```

Take care to manipulate only the settings pertaining to the port, and to only set them to allowed values. As with all API calls you are dealing with the kernel and you need to be exact. Passing erroneous information or modifying parameters you do not know will crash your application faster than you can blink your eyes.

16.4.5 : Timeouts

To avoid your program waiting endlessly for something to happen on the serial port you can set the timeout parameters for the port. The *CommTimeOuts* structure we defined earlier allows you to retrieve and set this information. Just as with the device control block this structure is not initialized after start, so the easiest way is to retrieve it, modify what you want and write it back.

Example:

```
Success = GetCommTimeouts(Serial_handle, MyCommTimeouts)

MyCommTimeouts.ReadIntervalTimeout = 0
MyCommTimeouts.ReadTotalTimeoutConstant = 0
MyCommTimeouts.ReadTotalTimeoutMultiplier = 0
MyCommTimeouts.WriteTotalTimeoutConstant = 0
MyCommTimeouts.WriteTotalTimeoutMultiplier = 0

Success = SetCommTimeouts(Serial_handle, MyCommTimeouts)
```

16.4.6 : Writing something to the port

The *WriteFile* method provides the data path to the I/O port. By providing the buffer, the size of the buffer and the number of bytes that need to be written, the kernel has enough information to perform the actual IO operation.

```
Success = WriteFile(Serial_handle, Buffer, Buffer.Length,
BytesWritten, IntPtr.Zero)
```

16.4.7 : Reading Data from the Port

To read data from the serial port you can use the *ReadFile* function. The function requires the handle of the port, the buffer, the size of the buffer and a variable to store the number of bytes written and retrieved.

Example:

```
Success = ReadFile(Serial_handle, Buffer, BytesWritten, BytesRead,
IntPtr.Zero)
```

16.4.8 : Closing the port

Since this communication system considers the comport to be a device file, you need to close the file once operations are finished, just as you would do with a real file. The *CloseHandle* function informs the kernel that the port is no longer required and closes it down.

Example:

```
Success = CloseHandle(hSerialPort)
```

16.4.9 : Sample program

This sample program will open a Comport and send out a string. It will then wait indefinitely for reception of something. Upon reception, it will dump the received information and exit.

```
Console.WriteLine("Opening Com1")
My_port = CreateFile("COM1", GENERIC_READ Or GENERIC_WRITE, 0, _
                     IntPtr.Zero, OPEN_EXISTING, _
                     FILE_ATTRIBUTE_NORMAL, IntPtr.Zero)
Success = GetCommState(My_port, My_DCB)
My_DCB.BaudRate = 9600
My_DCB.ByteSize = 8
My_DCB.Parity = NOPARITY
My_DCB.StopBits = ONESTOPBIT
Success = SetCommState(My_port, My_DCB)
Success = GetCommTimeouts(My_port, MyCommTimeouts)
MyCommTimeouts.ReadIntervalTimeout = 0
MyCommTimeouts.ReadTotalTimeoutConstant = 0
MyCommTimeouts.ReadTotalTimeoutMultiplier = 0
MyCommTimeouts.WriteTotalTimeoutConstant = 0
MyCommTimeouts.WriteTotalTimeoutMultiplier = 0
Success = SetCommTimeouts(My_port, MyCommTimeouts)

Success = WriteFile(My_port, Buffer, Buffer.Length, _
                    BytesWritten, IntPtr.Zero)

Success = ReadFile(hSerialPort, Buffer, BytesWritten, BytesRead,
IntPtr.Zero)

Success = CloseHandle(my_port)
```

16.5 : Serial IO under Visual Basic 2005 (NET2.0)

Visual Basic 2005 will have native support for Serial communications, a feature that was requested by many users of Visual Basic NET. Currently little information is available on the specifics but in general all functionality that was present in the MSCOMM object will now reside inside the NET platform itself. Even though Serial ports are a disappearing kind, they are still used and supported.

16.6 : TCP/IP for VB Classic: Windows Sockets with Winsock

The Winsock control, invisible to the user, provides easy access to TCP and UDP network services. Using this control, you do not need to understand the details of TCP or to call low-level Winsock functions. By setting properties and invoking methods of the control, you can easily connect to a remote machine and exchange data in both directions.

16.6.1 : TCP Basics

TCP, which is short for Transfer Control Protocol, enables you to create and maintain a session between your computer and a remote machine on a network supporting the TCP protocol. TCP encompasses a whole collection of different protocols such as Telnet, HTTP, FTP Ping, SMTP and many more.

Any device on a network that uses the TCP protocols has a unique identifier called the IP address. To determine which of the protocols is to be used when actually transmitting information a port number is defined. A standard list of port numbers can be found by searching on the internet for the so-called RFC's. The RFC's are a collection of documents that details on the available protocols on a network governed by TCP.

Setting up a connection is a matter of specifying the remote and local port that need to talk to each other, the IP address of the machine you want to talk to and asserting the Connect Property.

In case you are providing a server function, you can invoke the **Listen** method, which will accept incoming calls.

Once a connection has been established, data can be transferred freely between the two computers. Sending data is as simple as using the **SendData** method, and whenever data is received from the remote machine the **DataArrival** event will occur. By using the **GetData** method you can retrieve the information waiting in the receive buffer.

16.6.1.1 : Some Background on TCP

TCP is a sophisticated control mechanism that chops data into packets and sends them over a network. Since it is hard to establish the exact route each packet will follow on beforehand, a sequence number is assigned to the packet. Upon reception, the sequence numbers are compared and packets are automatically resorted. A powerful error detection and correction mechanism using Cyclic Redundancy Check (CRC) secures every packet. Reception of an erroneous packet will automatically trigger a request to resend.

Most people think that TCP is a pure internet or Ethernet protocol but that is not the case. Although TCP supports multiple users on a network and can even send messages to more than one user at the same time, by using so called multicast packets, it is perfectly possible to use TCP over a closed loop network or point-to-point network. Some devices even use TCP over a serial port. While this adds a substantial overhead, it brings along many advantages in the error detection and correction mechanism. Another nice advantage is that from a programmer's perspective the actual Medium does not tend to matter. All the programmer does is using the **SendData** and **ReceiveData** methods. Everything else is handled in the so-called protocol driver. The ultimate medium chosen, whether serial port, Ethernet, radio link or anything else, does not matter to the programmer.

16.6.2 : UDP Basics

The User Datagram Protocol (UDP) is an older protocol that does not have the technical capabilities of TCP. For instance there is no session number or sequence number. A packet sent on UDP is a 'best effort' trial to get information through. If a packet is lost, or information arrives out of sequence, there is no way to detect this. The integrity of a packet is guaranteed by a CRC but the relation between packets is simple not there. You will need to devise a handshaking mechanism to make this protocol more robust. Nevertheless, many devices that are handling less critical communication prefer UDP over TCP since the actual code behind is a lot smaller and requires a lot less memory to run. UDP is therefore ideal on small devices running on a small CPU.

TO create a link using UDP you set up the **LocalPort** and **RemotePort** properties and give a connect command. The major difference is that the Protocol property is switched to UDP.

16.6.3 : RemoteHost and RemoteHostIP

The **RemoteHost** property specifies the network identifier of the machine you want to establish a connection with. Any acceptable hostname can be provided as string to this property, for example URL like www.elektuur.nl or IP address such as 127.0.0.1 are acceptable.

```
object.RemoteHost = [string]
```

Changing this value while a connection is open, has no effect. You will need to close the session before changing the **RemoteHost**.

RemoteHostIP allows you to retrieve the real IP address behind a URL. It can be interesting to find out the true IP address instead of attempting to use a URL. Keep in mind that the link between a URL and IP address is governed by a domain controller and can change at any time. Try to use the URLs as much as possible as they provide a more manageable way of controlling a network.

16.6.4 : LocalHostname and LocalIP

These properties are read only and allow you to retrieve your own hostname and IP name on the network. You can use this for instance to send a message to the user with the information on how to connect to your machine.

Example:

```
Label1.Caption = "Hostname   : " & Winsock1.LocalHostName
label2.Caption = "IP Address: " & Winsock1.LocalIP
```

16.6.5 : Protocol

The **protocol** property allows specifying whether to use UDP or TCP as a transport protocol.

```
object.Protocol = [protocol]
```

Where: 0 = TCP protocol and 1 = UDP protocol. Note that control must be closed before this property can be changed. Changes only go into effect upon opening a session.

16.6.6 : State

The State property returns the state of the communication setting. This is a read only property.

```
X = object.State
```

These are the possible results for the State property:

Constant	Value	Description
SckClosed	0	The default state, the socket is closed.
SckOpen	1	The socket is open.
SckListening	2	The socket is Listening.
SckConnectionPending	3	A Connection is pending
SckResolvingHost	4	The socket is trying to resolve a URL to an IP address.
SckHostResolved	5	The socket has found the IP address for the given URL.
SckConnecting	6	The socket is handshaking with the remote machine and establishing the connection.
SckConnected	7	You are Connected: the socket can now send and received data.
SckClosing	8	The Remote side is closing the connection: the other machine has terminated the link.
SckError	9	An Error has occurred.

16.6.7 : ConnectionRequest and Accept

The **ConnectionRequest** event is generated by the Winsock control whenever a remote machine requests a connection.

This is valid for TCP server applications only since UDP does not really require a connection in order to transmit data. The event fires for an incoming connection request. The **RemoteHostIP** and **RemotePort** properties allow you to retrieve who exactly is attempting to communicate.

```
object_ConnectionRequest (requestID As Long)
```

The **requestID** is the identifier for this particular connection request. As you will know by now, you can have any number of connections open simultaneously. The ID allows you to discriminate between sessions; much like a filehandle allows you to manipulate a specific file.

You can decide whether or not to accept the connection. If the incoming connection is not accepted, the remote machine peer will receive a *Close* event.

The *Accept* method is use to accept an incoming connection request from a remote machine. Upon receiving a *ConnectionRequest* event, you can execute the *Accept* method to complete the handshaking and open a link to the remote machine. In this case, you act as the Host or server for the connection.

```
object.Accept requestID
```

The *Accept* method is used in the *ConnectionRequest* event. The *ConnectionRequest* event has a corresponding argument, the *RequestID* parameter that should be passed to the *Accept* method. An example is shown below:

```
Private Sub Winsock1_ConnectionRequest (ByVal requestID As Long)
        ' Close the connection if it is currently open
        ' by testing the State property.
        If Winsock1.State <> sckClosed Then Winsock1.Close

        ' Pass the value of the requestID parameter to the
        ' Accept method.
        Winsock1.Accept requestID
End Sub
```

When accepting an incoming connection the socket will change from listen state to connect state and will not further handle other incoming connections, until the current session is closed and switched to listening mode again. In order to accept multiple incoming connections you need to instantiate a new instance of the Winsock control, and allow that one to handle the connection. This will be explained in detail in the examples.

16.6.8 : DataArrival and GetData

The *DataArrival* event is generated when new data arrives.

```
Sub object_DataArrival (bytesTotal As Long)
End sub
```

This event will only occur on the reception of new data. If you do not read all data in on shot out of the receive buffer, the event will not re-fire because of data that was left behind. Furthermore, the remaining data may be overwritten upon arrival of new data.

The *GetData* method retrieves the current received data and stores it in a variant. You will need to know the format of the data in order to be able to process it correctly.

```
object.GetData data, [type,] [maxLen]
```

The optional *Type* and *Maxlen* variables allow you to fine-tune the data type and data size:

Type	An optional parameter that can specify the type of data to be retrieved, as shown in the table below.
MaxLen	An Optional parameter that specifies the desired size when receiving a byte array or a string. If omitted for byte arrays or strings, the entire block of data will be returned. For other data types, this parameter is ignored.

The Type of data can be set to any of the following:

Byte	*vbByte*
Integer	*vbInteger*
Long	*vbLong*
Single	*vbSingle*
Double	*vbDouble*
Currency	*vbCurrency*
Date	*vbDate*
Boolean	*vbBoolean*
SCODE	*vbError*
String	*vbString*
Byte Array	*vbArray* + *vbByte*

Normally you should only invoke a *GetData* method as a response to a *DataArrival* event generated by the WinSock control. The *DataArrival* event will provide you the exact number of bytes that was received so you can use that immediately with the *GetData* method to retrieve the data as a string. Always read the entire data chunk. If you do not retrieve all information, the remainder will be overwritten upon arrival of a new block of data.

In the appendix of this part examples will be given be given on how to set up a little Telnet server. This is a program you can log into over the internet, and that can accept commands and send you data. You can use this to make a remote controlled system that can run over the Ethernet, intranet or even the internet.

16.7 : TCP/IP Net style

The NET platform would not be worthy that name if it could not provide access to a network. After all, the whole intention of the NET platform is to make developing network aware programs easier.

The CLR has a number of built in functions that allow you to connect to remote machines and services in an easy way. It even provides high-level protocol interpreters such as HTTP parsers, things you had to write yourself in Visual Basic Classic.

16.7.1 : Accessing a web server

Suppose a web server holds a file called test.txt that contains the text 'hello world'. The server is, for instance, located at www.elektuur.nl.

Accessing a web server can be done using the **Net.WebClient** class.

Example:

```
Dim my_client as new net.webclient()
Dim my_webstream as IO.stream = my_client.openread _
                   ("http://www.elektuur.nl/test.txt")
Dim my_reader as new IO.streamreader(my_webstream)
Dim my_text as string = my_reader.ReadToEnd()
My_reader.close()
Console.writeline(my_text)
```

This example starts out by defining an object of the **net.webclient** class. It then invokes the **openread** method of the newly created **net.webclient** object and passes it the URL to the file. The resulting handle is stored **in my_webstream**.

The second big step is to create a **streamreader** that will read the resulting data block and store it in a string.

Finally, the stream is closed and the string simply dumped to the console.

16.7.2 : Downloading a file from a web server

It is equally easy to download a file directly for a server and drop it onto the local storage device. The **DownloadFile** method will directly grab a file and save it into a specified file.

Example:

```
Dim my_client as new net.webclient()
my_client.DownloadFile ("http://www.elektuur.nl/test.txt","grab.txt")
```

The above piece of code will grab the file directly and store it as 'grab.txt' on our machine.

16.7.3 : Accessing a TCP/IP based service

You do not always have the convenience of accessing a HTTP based server. Fortunately, Net provides generic commands that allow you to perform basic I/O on a network. The *TCPClient* class provides just this capability. The *TCPClient* returns a stream that can be operated upon using the standard *StreamReader* and *StreamWriter* class objects. The *TCPClient* requires as arguments the address, as either an IP address or resolvable URL, and the port number it needs to connect to.

Example:

```
Dim my_network as new Net.Sockets.TCPClient("127.0.0.1",90)
Dim network_stream as IO.Stream = my_network.GetStream()
```

The above code opens a connection to port 90 on a machine with address 127.0.0.1 (our own machine).

Now that we have access to a network stream, we can defines stream readers and writers

Example:

```
Dim net_reader As New IO.StreamReader(network_stream)
Dim netdata As String = net_reader.ReadToEnd()
Console.WriteLine (netdata)
```

16.7.4 : Serving data to the network

It is equally possible to create your own server applications to handle incoming requests from within Visual Basic NET. Instead of creating a *TCPClient* you simply create a *TCPListener* and wait for an incoming connection.

Example:

```
Dim my_server As New NET.Sockets.TcpListener(23)  ' telnet port
my_server.start()
Dim my_socket As Net.Sockets.socket = my_server.Acceptsocket()
' we are waiting for a connection here
Dim welcome As String = "Welcome to the VB NET server"
Dim buffer as byte() = Text.Encoding.ASCII.GetBytes(welcome)
my_socket.Send(welcome)
my_server.Stop
```

The above code opens a *TCPlistener* on our machine that will monitor port 90 for traffic. As soon as a connection attempt is made, the *AcceptSocket* will resolve and the program will continue its flow. The Send method will give the user a welcome message. Note that we need to convert our strings to an array of bytes. Windows represents text as Unicode characters and those may not necessarily be compatible on the other side. Sending pure ASCII will resolve this problem. The **Text.Encoding.ASCII** class allows you to convert strings to and from ASCII code.

Finally the Server is stopped. Of course, you will need to add code to interact with the user to make this interactive.

To retrieve information from the user you can use the Receive function. This will read the incoming buffer.

```
Dim my_server As New NET.Sockets.TcpListener(23)  'telnet port
my_server.start()
Dim my_socket As Net.Sockets.socket = my_server.Acceptsocket()
' we are waiting for a connection here
Dim welcome As String = "Welcome to the VB NET server" & _
                        ControlChars.CrLf & _
                        "Enter your name:"

Dim out_buffer() as byte = Text.Encoding.ASCII.GetBytes(welcome)
my_socket.Send(out_buffer)

Dim in_buffer (100) as byte
Dim logon_name as string
Dim buf_size as integer

' collect input and search for 'enter'
Do until instr(logon_name,controlchars.crlf)>0
   Buf_size = my_socket.receive(in_buffer)
   Logon_name += Text.Encoding.ASCII.Getstring(in_buffer)
Loop
welcome = "Welcome " logon_name" & _
          ", we hope you have a nice stay." _
          ControlChars.CrLf
out_buffer() = Text.Encoding.ASCII.GetBytes(welcome)
my_socket.Send(out_buffer)

my_server.Stop
```

The pre-defined string **vbCRLF** from VB classic is replaced with the **controlchars.crlf** method in NET.

Another thing that may rise eyebrows is the += operator that exists in NET. This is a notation that is borrowed from the C# world and allows a simply method to add information to an existing string.

Ordinarily you would have written **logon_name = logon_name & ...**

This can be simply rewritten as: **logon_name += ...**

The above code shows how you can use the Receive method from the Socket to collect data.

Chapter 17 : Some more case studies

Doodle: A Graphics program

This program demonstrates the use of graphics manipulation routines. Doodle is a simple program that allows you to draw into a PictureBox. You can save the data to a standard BMP file. You can select to draw geometric shapes such as draw lines, circles, ellipses and rectangles, or you can draw freehand. It allows you to select colors for your drawing and specify filled or open shapes.

Miniterm: A simple terminal

This program will allow us to communicate with the outside world in a simple fashion. A number of practical things are given that will show you, besides serial communication, how to implement some data manipulations.

AlphaServer: A Telnet Server application

This program can be started on any machine that has a valid IP address, and is connected into a TCP/IP network (LAN / WAN / Intranet / Internet). You can log on to it and interrogate it. This could be a program that collects data on some remote site, and can be accessed and controlled via remote.

LoanCalc: Using Excel from your program

This example shows yet another way to control other programs. It will derive an object from the 'Excel' program and use it to perform some calculations. Actually, it uses Excel as a 'Server' program to perform its task.

17.1 : Case Study 3: Doodle, A graphics program

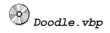 **Doodle.vbp**   There is a tutorial program available that explains the constructs, explained in this topic, by example.

As with any program, we start by creating a new project and adding the standard menu. File – Save / load /quit. The necessary code to quit is written as well.

I inserted a picture box called 'workspace' that will be used as the target of the drawing operations. I created a couple of frames as well. The first frame holds three option buttons. They will allow me to select the kind of shape I want to draw. In this frame is also a checkbox that allows me to select a filled shape.

The other two frames contain each an array of 16 option buttons. These will be used to select the drawing colors.

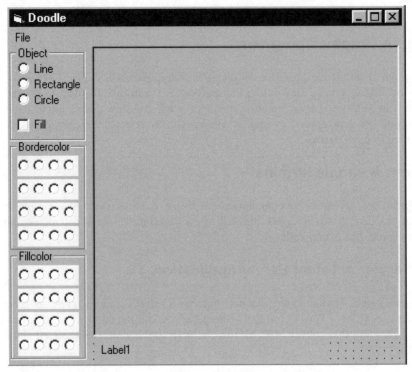

At the bottom, I added a label as well. This will be used to display the cursor coordinates during the drawing operation. As you can see, the option buttons that allow the color selection have a strange appearance. I Set the caption to empty and changed the *backcolor* to light yellow. The actual changing of the *backcolor* has no particular meaning. It is just an indication for me that something will be done with this color from within the code.

The primary code attached to this form looks like this:

```
Dim Sbordercolor
Dim sFillcolor

Private Sub bordercolor_Click(Index As Integer)
    Sbordercolor = Index
End Sub

Private Sub colorfill_Click(Index As Integer)
    sFillcolor = Index
End Sub


Private Sub Form_Load()
    Dim X
```

```
            For X = 0 To 15
                Bordercolor(X).BackColor = QBcolor(X)
                colorfill(X).BackColor = QBcolor(X)
            Next X
        End Sub

        Private Sub quitprogram_Click()
            End
        End Sub
```

In order to have easy access to the selected border color and fill color I created two variables: **Sbordercolor** and **sFillcolor**. One of the option button arrays is called **Bordercolor** while the other is called **colorfill**. Whenever I click on one of these buttons, I store the index of the clicked option button into the appropriate variable.

The form load routine is going to assign the colors to the radio buttons. I perform a sweep from 0 to 15 and ask the corresponding **QBcolor**. That **QBcolor** is then assigned to the **Backcolor** property of the radio button.

Finally, the **Quitprogram_click** simply terminates execution.

In order to display the coordinates I simply attach a small blurb of code to the **MouseMove** event of the workspace.

```
        Private Sub workspace_MouseMove(Button As Integer, _
            Shift As Integer, X As Single, Y As Single)
            Label1.Caption = "X:" + Str$(X) + " Y:" + Str$(Y)
        End Sub
```

This will update the contents of the **label1.caption** property whenever a **MouseMove** is detected on the Workspace PictureBox.

With this out of the way, we can concentrate on the real drawing routines. Depending on the selected shape in the first frame, we need to decide what to do. We can only take action if the user clicks with his mouse to point to the coordinates of the shape he wants to draw.

Logically you would use the **workspace.click** event. But alas, this does not return the coordinates where the user has clicked. Therefore, we need to attach code to the **MouseDown** event. The problem is that the user needs to click twice, the first click designates top left, and second click the bottom right corner. Therefore, I created three static variables to hold this information.

Remember static variables? As static variables are not destroyed upon exiting the subroutine, so the next time I enter the routine, they still exist, and the data in them are still valid.

One of them is going to be used as a **Boolean**. The first time the user clicks the content will be 0. The if-then else clause will then execute the part of the code where X and Y get stored in **StartX** and **StartY**. It also turns the **Firstclick** to 1.

The second time the user clicks, the program flow will run over the **Else** clause.

```
        Private Sub workspace_MouseDown(Button As Integer, _
              Shift As Integer, X As Single, Y As Single)
            Static firstclick
            Static startx, starty

            If Button = 1 Then
                If firstclick = 0 Then
                    ' this is the firstclick
                    ' store the coordinates
                    startx = X
                    starty = Y
                Else
                    ` second click: execute
                End If
                ` toggle firstclick
                If firstclick = 0 Then
                    firstclick = 1
                Else
                    firstclick = 0
                End If
            End If
        End Sub
```

All we need to fill in now is the code to do the drawing. This code goes into the **Else** clause
('second click: execute).

First, we need to decide what the user selected as shape style.

```
        If drawtype(0).Value = True Then
            workspace.Line (startx, starty)-(X, Y) _
                          , QBColor(sbordercolor)
        End If
```

If he selected line, we are simply going to draw a line from the start coordinates to the current
coordinates with the selected border color.

In a similar way, the box can be created. Except that, here the user could have selected to fill
the box. Drawing a filled box with a different border color is not directly possible. Therefore,
what I am going to do is draw two boxes. One full box with the **FillColor**. On top of that, I
am going to draw a second box with the border color.

```
        If drawtype(1).Value = True Then ' rectangle
            ` if required draw a filled box
            If fillit.Value = 1 Then
                workspace.Line (startx, starty)-(X, Y), _
                              QBColor(sfillcolor), BF
            End If
            ` draw the outline
            workspace.Line (startx, starty)-(X, Y), _
                          QBColor(sbordercolor), B
        End If
```

The same is done for the circle command. Except that here the second X coordinate will determine the radius. The circle command does not allow you to create filled circles. Therefore, we have to be a bit creative here. Furthermore we cannot use the x and y coordinates since we need to specify the radius.

The radius is determined by the difference between **startx** and **x**. This can be obtained by calculating the absolute value of **Startx - x**.

To create the filled image I draw a number of circles and change the radius from 1 to the maximum radius.

```
If drawtype(2).Value = True Then
    If fillit.Value = 1 Then
        For z = 1 To Abs(startx - X)
            workspace.Circle (startx, starty), z, QBColor(sfillcolor)
        Next z
    End If
    workspace.Circle (startx, starty), Abs(startx - X), _
                     QBColor(sbordercolor)
End If
```

The result of some doodling could look like this:

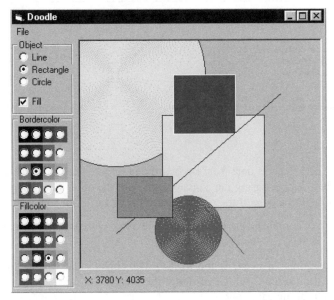

That's it. Now you can create simple drawings. Of course, this is not like a real drawing program but it gives you insight in simple graphics operations.

You could add now the Save command using the **Savepicture** method, and load one using the **Loadpicture** command. However, I leave that up to you to explore.

17.2 : Case Study 4: The data terminal

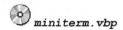

miniterm.vbp

There is a tutorial program available that explains the constructs explained in this topic, by example.

The basics of this program are the same as any program. A form, a menu with a Quit entry and the usual Startup and exit code

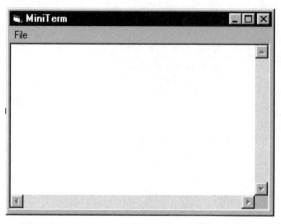

```
Private Sub Form_Load()
    Me.Show
    DoEvents
End Sub

Private Sub quitprogram_Click()
    End
End Sub
```

Since a terminal works accepts data from keyboard and remote site we need a control where we can display this data. Since, during the conversation with the other side, many characters could have been sent, it might be good if there were a scroll back buffer of some sort.

The easiest way to accomplish this is by using a textbox with **Multiline** and **scrollbars** (both) turned on.

Next thing we are going to need, is the MSCOMM object. Just enable this on the control toolbar and insert it onto the form. Never mind the location on the screen. Once the program starts running, it will disappear anyhow.

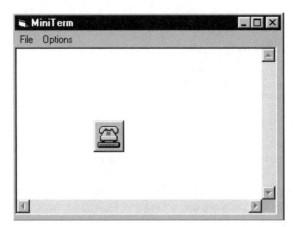

Since we do not always know who is on the other side, it would be nice if we could select the port we want to talk to, and the baud rate setting.

The pitfall here is that, when we attempt to open a non-available port, or try to set it to impossible parameters we get a runtime error. Therefore, we need to tackle these. I know I have not explained you yet how to do that. For now, just ignore this. Error handling will be explained in detail later on in this book.

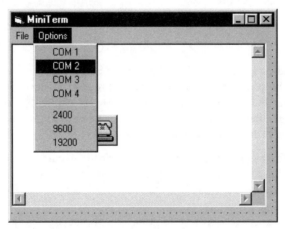

To select comports I added an options menu in which you can click the port and speed. If the port is not accessible, or the speed is invalid, the values will simply be grayed out. When the program starts, I simply activate each of the options to allow this to happen.

```
Private Sub comport1_Click()
    ' switch off the selected ports
    comport1.Checked = True
    comport2.Checked = True
    comport3.Checked = True
    comport4.Checked = True
```

```
                ' make sure the port is closed
                If rs232.PortOpen = True Then rs232.PortOpen = False
                rs232.CommPort = 1
                On Error GoTo openfailed
                rs232.PortOpen = True
                comport1.Checked = True
                Exit Sub
          openfailed:
                comport1.Enabled = False   ' disable menu
          End Sub
```

The above code will treat an occurring error by graying out the appropriate menu entry. During the startup of the program, we simply call each of these routines. This will make sure the user gets to see only the available ports. The code for the four other comports is exactly the same, except that we set the **RS232.comport** clause to the appropriate port, and make sure the correct menu entry is checked.

```
           Private Sub Form_Load()
                Me.Show
                DoEvents
                comport1_Click
                comport2_Click
                comport3_Click
                comport4_Click
                comport1_Click
           End Sub
```

Testing serial ports takes some time. Since the **Form_Load** is executed before the form actually is displayed this might give the impression that the program is slow. So if we apply a small trick we give the user the feeling the program is fast. By explicitly executing the **Me.Show** statement, we force the display of the form. Of course, we need to give Windows the time to do this, so we execute the **DoEvents** command.

The code to control the baud rate is simply going to close the current selected port, change the baud rate and reopen it.

```
            Private Sub baud2400_Click()
                If rs232.PortOpen = True Then rs232.PortOpen = False
                rs232.Settings = "2400,N,8,1"
                rs232.PortOpen = True
            End Sub
```

What we have built so far, is the entire user interface and the options to allow the user to customize the program configuration. Now we have to focus on the real communication.

The MSCOMM object generates an **OnComm** event whenever something happens on the serial port. If we then check if it was an incoming character, we can simply read it from the buffer and send it to the textbox. This would allow us to receive data.

```
Private Sub rs232_OnComm()
    Select Case rs232.CommEvent
    ' Handle each event or error by placing
        Case comEvReceive    ' Received RThreshold # of
                             ' chars.
            Text1.Text = Text1.Text + rs232.Input
            rs232.Input = ""
    End Select
End Sub
```

In order for this to work, you must not forget to set the **Rthreshold** to 1. This makes sure the *OnComm* event is fired for every incoming character.

To transmit data, we need to check when the user types something. Now we cannot use the **Textbox.change** event since it can be changed by the data receiving routine as well. Another problem is that we need to extract the last character of the entire text since that would be the last character typed. This would involve moving a lot of data every time and make the program slow. But fortunately, we have a **Keypress** event. Furthermore, the **keypress** event returns us the ASCII code of the pressed key. So that is exactly what we need.

```
Private Sub Text1_KeyPress(KeyAscii As Integer)
    'ship the character to the comport
    ' here you could first do translation if required
    rs232.Output = Chr$(KeyAscii)
End Sub
```

Of course, the presented program is a simple case. You could improve it considerably by allowing it to a CR/LF translation. Some machines (like UNIX based computers) only use LF to indicate a new line. PC's require CR/LF. So you could add options to translate this. This could be done by checking the ASCII code of the incoming character, or key press, and changing the code to the appropriate code(s).

The following routine would translate an incoming LF to CR/LF.

```
Private Sub rs232_OnComm()
    Select Case rs232.CommEvent
    ' Handle each event or error by placing
        Case comEvReceive    ' Received RThreshold # of
                             ' chars.
            x$ = rs232.Input
            rs232.Input = ""
            If x$ = Chr$(10) Then
                Text1.Text = Text1.Text + vbCrLf
            Else
                Text1.Text = Text1.Text + rs232.Input
            End If
    End Select
End Sub
```

This one will send a CR/LF whenever you hit ENTER.

```
Private Sub Text1_KeyPress(KeyAscii As Integer)
    'ship the character to the comport
    If KeyAscii = 13 Then ' CR to CRLF translate
        rs232.Output vbCrLf
    Else
        rs232.Output = Chr$(KeyAscii)
    End If
End Sub
```

We managed to write a little terminal program in a matter of minutes. You can of course extend this much further, but that is not the job of my book. I have given you the basis of how to do serial communications and how to respond to the events associated with it.

17.3 : Case Study 5: AlphaServer, a Telnet server

aserve.vbp

There is a tutorial program available that explains the constructs, explained in this topic, by example.

The basics of this program are again the same as of any program. On the risk of re-iterating: a form, a menu with a Quit entry and a textbox that will act as a console.

In order to have access to TCP/IP we need to instantiate the MSWinsock control. Since we are building a server, we will need a public and a private object. Why exactly, will become clear later.

In the startup code of the form, we need to specify that the **Public** object (in this case the Public Socket) has to be listening to port 23. Port 23 is the port used for Telnet connections. The definitions of these ports are defined in the TCP/IP protocol.

```
Private Sub Form_Load
    PublicSocket.Localport=23
    PublicSocket.Listen
End sub
```

The above code will make that happen.

Next, we have to attach some code to the **Connectrequest** event of our Public Socket.

```
Private Sub Publicsocket_ConnectionRequest(byval _
            requestid as long)
If privatesocket.state = sckClosed then
    Privatesocket.Localport=0
    Privatesocket.Accept requestid
    Privatesocket.Senddata "Hello there, you just logged on"
End if
End Sub
```

Whenever a **connectionrequest** is occurring, we will check if the **Privatesocket** is free to receive connection. If so, we will pass the connection request to **Privatesocket** and establish the link by sending some data.

Remember in Winsock that you are either a public listener or a connected Talk/Listener. A public listener will accept any data coming from anyone. It can also transmit data to anyone out there. However, if two users are connected, both will receive the data.

The private listener is set up for point to point. Only valid connected users will get to see this.

The **Publicsocket** is listening to anyone transmitting on port 23. The **Privatesocket** sets up a private link to your machine.

That's it. It is that simple.

17.3.1 : A more elaborate server supporting multiple Sessions

The previously described server supports only one session at a time so it is of no real practical use, except where such behavior is desirable such as remote monitoring applications. For most other purposes multiple sessions will be more convenient. Therefore, I will describe how you can do such a thing.

The first section of code contains the variables definition and a command interpreter that can handle commands typed by users. Command interpreters will be handled in detail later on in the book, so do not worry about that yet. Suffice it to say that the command interpreter is a big **Select-Case** structure that evaluates strings and responds depending on the result of the evaluation.

The program contains two instances of the Winsock control. One has been named **publicsocket** and the other is named **privatesocket**.

A generic routine called **Logit** has no other purpose than to write some information to a textbox so that the operator of the server can follow what is going on with the machine.

```
' we support 127 sessions
Dim SessionState(127) As Integer
Dim SessionUser(127) As String

' this adds a string to the textbox to show what is going on.
Private Sub LogIt(s As String)
     Text1.Text = Text1.Text & Time$ & " " & s & vbCrLf
End Sub

' The command interpreter code.
' evaluates the user entry and acts accordingly
Private Sub RunIt(Index As Integer)
    Dim i As Integer
    Dim w As Winsock
    LogIt "Executing (" & Str$(Index) & ") - " & _
          PrivateSocket(Index).Tag
    Select Case UCase(PrivateSocket(Index).Tag)
```

```
Case "TYPE"
    For a = 0 To 255
        PrivateSocket(Index).SendData "a:" + Str$(a)
        PrivateSocket(Index).SendData Chr$(a)
    Next a
Case "EXIT", "QUIT", "BYE"
        PrivateSocket(Index).SendData "Logoff"
        LogIt "Logoff (" & Str$(Index) & ")"
        DoEvents
        PrivateSocket(Index).Close
        SessionState(Index) = 0
Case "TIME", "NOW"
        PrivateSocket(Index).SendData "Time is:" + Time$
Case "DATE", "TODAY"
        PrivateSocket(Index).SendData "Date is:" + Date$
Case "WHOAMI"
        PrivateSocket(Index).SendData _
        "You are:" + SessionUser(Index) + _
        ", session id:" + Trim$(Str$(Index))
Case "WHO"
        PrivateSocket(Index).SendData "Current users" & vbCrLf
        For Each w In PrivateSocket
            If w.State <> sckClosed Then
                PrivateSocket(Index).SendData SessionUser(w.Index) _
                                            & vbCrLf

            End If
        Next w
Case "HELP", "?"
        PrivateSocket(Index).SendData _
        "List of valid commands" & vbCrLf & _
        "--------------------" & vbCrLf & _
        "Date - Display the current date." & vbCrLf & _
        "Exit - End the telnet session." & vbCrLf & _
        "Who  - List all user." & vbCrLf & _
        "Time - Display the current time." & vbCrLf
    Case Else
            PrivateSocket(Index).SendData "Unknown command dude !"
    End Select
End Sub
```

The next chunk of code handles the startup and exit of the program and contains nothing really new, except for the code that initializes the sockets. The public socket is the one that handles the initial contact with the server. Once a connection has been established, a **privatesocket** will be allocated for the user that has been granted access.

The **publicsocket** is initialized as being attached to the telnet protocol using port 23 (port 23 is generally used for the telnet protocol). You will thus be able to connect to the server using the default telnet application that comes with Windows. Once the socket is initialized, it is switched to the listen state and left alone.

Upon exiting the program, the **publicsocket** and all instance of the **privatesocket** will be closed automatically.

```
Private Sub Form_Load()
    Dim i As Integer
    For i = LBound(SessionState) To UBound(SessionState)
        SessionState(i) = 0
    Next i
    PublicSocket.LocalPort = 23
    PublicSocket.Listen
    LogIt "AlphaServer started on " & _
        PublicSocket.LocalHostName & _
        "(" & PublicSocket.LocalIP & ")"
End Sub

Private Sub Form_Unload(Cancel As Integer)
    Dim p As Winsock
    If PublicSocket.State <> sckClosed Then
        PublicSocket.Close
    End If
    For Each p In PrivateSocket
        If p.State <> sckClosed Then
            p.Close
        End If
    Next p
    LogIt "Server stopped"
End Sub
```

The primary control code is attached to the **ConnectionRequest** handler for **publicsocket**. Whenever an attempt to connect is made, this event will fire.

The code attached to it will first look for a free instance of **privatesocket**. After all, users may have logged off already so there is no need to instantiate a new copy of the **privatesocket**. If none is found a new copy of **privatesocket** is instantiated. Its parameters are set to the current requestID and **Localport** is set to 0. By doing this you actually transfer the current session to the newly instantiated, or previously instantiated but free, **privatehandler**. Setting the **localport** to 0 allows the instance to take over the correct port from the **publicsocket** object. The last thing the **publicsocket** code does, is send a welcome message to the other side and request a login name. It also creates an entry in the log window that a new connection was created.

```
Private Sub PublicSocket_ConnectionRequest(ByVal requestID As Long)
    Dim Found As Boolean
    Dim i As Integer
    Dim s As String
    found = False
    i = PrivateSocket.LBound
    Do While Not Found
        If PrivateSocket(i).State = sckClosed Then
            Found = True
        ElseIf i < PrivateSocket.UBound Then
            i = i + 1
        Else
            i = i + 1
```

```
                    Load PrivateSocket(i)
                    Found = True
                End If
            Loop
            PrivateSocket(i).LocalPort = 0
            PrivateSocket(i).Accept requestID
            PrivateSocket(i).SendData _
            "------------------------------------------------" + vbCrLf
            PrivateSocket(i).SendData _
            "|                    Alphaserver                |" + vbCrLf
            PrivateSocket(i).SendData _
            "|             Driven by Visual Basic 5.0        |" + vbCrLf
            PrivateSocket(i).SendData _
            "------------------------------------------------" + vbCrLf
            PrivateSocket(i).SendData "Identify yourself: "

            LogIt "Connection Request from " & PublicSocket.RemoteHost & _
                "(" & PublicSocket.RemoteHostIP & ") Session - " & _
                Str$(i)
        End Sub

        Private Sub PublicSocket_Error(ByVal Number As Integer, _
                                    Description As String, _
                                    ByVal Scode As Long, _
                                    ByVal Source As String, _
                                    ByVal HelpFile As String, _
                                    ByVal HelpContext As Long, _
                                    CancelDisplay As Boolean)
            LogIt "Error " & Str$(Number) & ": " & Description
        End Sub
```

The **publicsocket** error handler simply logs the error number and associated text but does not attempt to resolve the error.

The **privatesocket** handler looks a bit weird at first but it actually contains a bit of clever program logic. Since there is only one handler that will actually handle many different instances, things could get messy in terms of memory allocation. I opted to use a different technique. Since every instance of the **privatesocket** has an associated **tag** property, I am using that one to pass information between the object and the handling code. The code will therefore always receive the correct information without the requirement to manage an array with information that could possibly be overwritten by other instances.

Whenever a character arrives, the **dataarrival** event will fire and the string will be retrieved. The string, which is actually a single character, is evaluated. If it is the backspace character (**chr**$(8)), the already received information is decremented by one character. If it is a carriage return (enter) the entered information will be processed by the **processinput** routine. And if it is neither backspace or enter, then the string is simply added to whatever we already received as input, except if we are receiving the password fro the other side in which case a * is returned for every key hit. The **sessionstate** variable lets us know whether we are still in logon mode or not. More detail about the **sessionstate** will follow later on when we deal with the dispatching logic.

```
Private Sub PrivateSocket_DataArrival(Index As Integer, _
                                  ByVal bytesTotal As Long)
    Dim s As String
    PrivateSocket(Index).GetData s, vbString
    Select Case s
    Case Chr$(8)
        If Len(PrivateSocket(Index).Tag) > 0 Then
            PrivateSocket(Index).Tag = _
                Left$(PrivateSocket(Index).Tag, _
                    Len(PrivateSocket(Index).Tag) - 1)
            PrivateSocket(Index).SendData s + " " + s
        End If
    Case vbCrLf
        PrivateSocket(Index).SendData vbCrLf
        ProcessInput Index
        PrivateSocket(Index).Tag = ""
        If SessionState(Index) = 2 Then
            PrivateSocket(Index).SendData vbCrLf & ">"
        End If
    Case Else
        PrivateSocket(Index).Tag = PrivateSocket(Index).Tag & s
        If SessionState(Index) = 1 Then
            PrivateSocket(Index).SendData "*"
        Else
            PrivateSocket(Index).SendData s
        End If
    End Select
End Sub

Private Sub PrivateSocket_Error(Index As Integer, _
                            ByVal Number As Integer, _
                            Description As String, _
                            ByVal Scode As Long, _
                            ByVal Source As String, _
                            ByVal HelpFile As String, _
                            ByVal HelpContext As Long, _
                            CancelDisplay As Boolean)
    LogIt "Error(" & Str$(Index) & ") " & _
        Str$(Number) & ": " & Description
End Sub
```

The **privatesocket** error-handler again does nothing else but logging the error and continue. No attempt is made to resolve the error.

The final chunk of code is the **processinput** dispatcher. It takes the received string and decides if the user has a valid logon before attempting to execute the users command. If no valid logon is found for the current session it will go through the logon sequence. A piece of code has been foreseen to check a password.

The **sessionstate** variable holds the current point in the session. If it is set to zero, the logon process has not been completed yet. If the logon is successfully evaluated by the **validlogon** function, then the welcome message is displayed, if not a bailout message is displayed and the session is terminated. Upon success the ***sessionstate*** is augmented to 2, which means that subsequent data will be processed using the ***runit*** function we defined previously.

```
Private Sub ProcessInput(Index As Integer)
    Select Case SessionState(Index)
    Case 0
        SessionUser(Index) = UCase(Trim(PrivateSocket(Index).Tag))
        PrivateSocket(Index).SendData "Enter password: "
        SessionState(Index) = 1
    Case 1
        X = Validlogon (sessionuser(index), PrivateSocket(Index).Tag)
        If x = true then
            PrivateSocket(Index).SendData _
            "Welcome to Alpha-One " & SessionUser(Index) & vbCrLf & _
            "Local date is:" & Date$ & vbCrLf & _
            "Local time is:" & Time$ & vbCrLf & vbCrLf & _
            "--------------------------------" & vbCrLf
            LogIt "Logon (" & Str$(Index) & ") " & SessionUser(Index)
            SessionState(Index) = 2
        Else
            PrivateSocket(Index).SendData _
            "Login incorrect. Bye!" & vbCrLf
            SessionState(Index) = 0
            Privatesocket_close (index)
        End if
    Case Else
        RunIt Index
    End Select
End Sub

' handler to terminate a session
Private Sub PrivateSocket_Close(Index As Integer)
    PrivateSocket(Index).Close
    LogIt "Connection closed (" & Str$(Index) & ")"
End Sub

' possible password checker. Now everyone is allowed
Private Function ValidLogon(user As String, password As String) _
        As Boolean
        ValidLogon = True
End Function
```

What looks to be a complex task, actually turned out to be a piece of cake. Getting the logic down to handle the multiple sessions was the hardest part but with some careful planning turns out to be an easily manageable chunk of code as well. Of course, you still might want to add password checking and more commands to this basic server. For instance, the DIR command could be easily implemented using a shell command.

Example:

```
Case "DIR"
    Shell "dir >t.t"
    Open "t.t" for input as #1
    While not eof(1)
```

```
                  Line input #1,a$
                  Privatesocket.send a$ & vbcrlf
            Wend
            Close #1
            Kill "t.t"
```

This code would make a directory snapshot using the shell command into a file, subsequently read the file line by line and return its contents to the user on the other side.

It would also be possible to define groups of users by manipulating the *sessionstate* parameter. For instance, you could define more levels in there and then decide, depending on the *sessionstate* what commands are allowed and which not. Doing this you could create guests, users, super-users and administrators easily.

17.4 : Case Study 6: AlphaServer under NET

When the guts of TCP connections using the NET framework have been explained earlier, I actually built an AlphaServer-like program. So there is no need to re-iterate this here.

17.5 : Case Study 7: LoanCalc: Using Excel in your applications

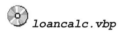
loancalc.vbp

There is a tutorial program available that explains the constructs, explained in this topic, by example.

This program demonstrates how to access functions in other programs. The basics of this program are the same as of any program. Some new concepts will be introduced here.

The basis of the program is a couple of textboxes and a button to start the calculation.

The three textboxes are designated *txtAmount*, *txtYears* and *txtInterest* respectively. The button is simply called *cmdCalc*.

The *cmsCalc* routine is pretty straightforward and self-explanatory. Let's focus on the actual *Calcpay* routine. First of all, we need to declare a variable to access the external object 'excel'. For easiness sake, let us simply call it Excel.

The second line will assign the *excel.application* to this variable. Actually what we are doing here is obtaining a so-called 'handle' to excel. Once we have a handle to an object, we can manipulate it.

That is exactly what happens in line three. We access the PMT function of the excel object, pass it variables just as we would to any other object, and retrieve the result.

```
            Private Sub cmdCalc_Click()
                Amount = Val(txtAmount.Text)
                Years = Val(txtYears.Text)
                Interest = Val(txtInterest.Text)
                Payment = CalcPay(Amount, Years, Interest)
                Label3.Caption = Payment
```

```
End Sub

Public Function CalcPay(Amount, Years, Interest)
    Dim excel As Object
    Const ExcelObject = "Excel.Application"
    Set excel = CreateObject(ExcelObject)  ' grab excel
      CalcPay = excel.Pmt
                ((Interest / 100) / 12, Years * 12, -1 * Amount)
    excel.Quit
    Set excel = Nothing   ' release excel
End Function
```

If you no longer need the object, you can simply destroy it. This normally happens automatically. For instance if you close a form, the objects contained in the form are automatically destroyed.

Since we created the object during runtime, we are responsible to destroy the object again. The pitfall in this case is that excel is an external program. While it was launched automatically upon creating the handle, it is not terminated automatically. Therefore, we first ask Excel to terminate itself and then release the handle to excel by setting the handle of the 'excel' variable to *Nothing*.

Unfortunately, not every program allows you to derive objects from it. In general, all Office products allow you to do this.

Introduction to Part III: Master Programming with Visual Basic

In the previous parts we have seen what Visual Basic is and what we can do with it. This ranges from simple applications to full-blown programs that can be communicating to the outer world.

Visual Basic brings a vast amount of routines and procedures with it. These can exist either inside the compiled code or externally in libraries. Microsoft ships many extra libraries with Visual Basic. You can also find on the market a lot of third party libraries and objects to use with Visual Basic. However, we have been neglecting the biggest library of them all: The Windows core itself.

So far, we still have only scratched the surface of what you can do with the Windows operating system. While Visual Basic unleashes most of it, you will sometimes find yourself in a situation where you ask yourself: how do they do that? You might have been trying to create a program that acts in a similar way as a program you have seen. Yet it seems close to impossible to do it. Well maybe you are not looking in the right place. While Visual Basic brings a wealth of procedures, functions, routines and objects, there is a tremendous amount of stuff dormant in any system, waiting for someone to open the lid on it.

Windows itself is to be considered one huge collection of functions and routines that you too, as a Visual Basic programmer, can exploit to your benefit. This part of the manual will plunge into this matter and explain you how to take a lead start on creating very impressive applications.

In the next part, we are going to dig deeper into this amazing system and explore it. I am also going to show you how to build your own libraries and controls. This will definitely extend the capabilities even further.

Chapter 18 : Digging into Windows

This chapter will take you deeper into the operating system. You will learn how to exploit the embedded functions of the operating system for the benefit of your programs.

18.1 : DLL's

What are DLL's? Simply said: a Library of routines. The name itself: 'Dynamic Linkable Library' might be scary at first, but really it is nothing more than a library that you can attach to your code and use the routines from, just as these were routines you wrote yourself.

A DLL, however, is not like an ordinary program library. In a normal programming style, a library is glued or 'linked' into a program during compile time. Suppose you create 50 applications using the same library and you load them all into memory at once. You would have 50 copies of your library loaded in your computers memory. What a waste of space. This is where the concept of DLL kicks in. The library is not embedded into an application. It is merely distributed with it. Whenever an application that needs the library is started, the operating system loads the library into memory. Any application that needs it can use this library. Upon termination of the last application that uses one particular library it is automatically unload.

Well, this is all nice but what can you do with them? Well, most Windows programs are built out of two parts: a user interface and a DLL that contains the real workings of the program. Let us take Excel as an example. The user interface is nothing more than a data manipulator. The real calculation routines are stored in a DLL library. This library is referenced whenever the GUI part of excel calls for it.

Since you can access DLL's from Visual Basic, you can use the Excel routines inside your program directly. Why write a complex math routine or graphic display routine, if someone else already has done this?

Actually, the example of excel is poorly chosen. There is no need to access the DLL since you can access the whole of Excel as an object.

You cannot do some things directly in Visual Basic, since there are no built in methods. Actually, the same goes for any programming language. For instance, in a DOS based environment you could read and write memory locations at will using Peek and Poke. The same was true for I/O operations.

Since Windows manages all these things now, it does not like you to fiddle around with them. That is the main reason why Microsoft has left these operations out of Visual Basic. In fact, they are gone in most programming languages. However, in assembler you are still king of the system. There you can do whatever you want. Therefore, if you could create a routine that accesses hardware, compile it into a DLL and then use it in your program. This used to be the case up and until windows 2000 and XP came along. These operating systems are actually built on a different engine that no longer allows hardware access from even DLL's. You will need to write a so-called kernel mode VXD or SYS driver. Fortunately, these things exist and can be found for free on the internet. A couple of references will be given in the appendixes to this book.

Visual Basic provides a mechanism to access any DLL library. All you need to know is the name of the library, the function name and the arguments it takes. When a function in a DLL is a reserved keyword for Visual Basic, you can use the **ALIAS** statement to specify a different name for it.

You have to think of the operating system as a layered structure. Deep buried inside it are the lowest level functions. While moving to the outer layers the operations become internally more complex but to the programmer easier to use. Visual Basic, and any other programming language for that matter, exposes only the top layer of this structure directly. If you want to access the layers below, you need to do an API access. Every part of the operating system resides somewhere as a function you can access. Sometimes these DLL's are disguised as drivers or whatever. However, you can still reach them.

18.1.1 : Accessing DLL routines

Accessing DLL routines requires you to define the routine to the Visual Basic compiler. This is similar to what you would do if you were to create the routine yourself except that you precede the Sub or Function with the Declare keyword. This indicates to the compiler that you are going to specify an already existing routine that belongs to a DLL library.

Syntax:
```
Public Declare Sub <name> Lib "<file>" [Alias "<aliasname>"] [args]
Private Declare Sub  <name> Lib "<file>" [Alias "<aliasname>"] [args]

Public Declare Function <name> Lib "<file>" [Alias "aliasname"] _
                             [args] [As type]
Private Declare Function <name> Lib "<file>" [Alias "aliasname"] _
                             [argls] [As type]
```

Name	Any valid procedure name. Note that DLL entry points are case sensitive and you should take care to use the exact name, case and all. Routines are searched inside the DLL using the given name and the search is case sensitive.
file	The name of the DLL, including the extension DLL, which contains the declared procedure.
Alias	The Alias allows you to Indicate that the procedure being called has actually a different name in the DLL. It might so happen that a routine exists with a name that is a reserved keyword or already defined variable or function name in Visual Basic or your code. This allows you to 'rename' the function for your purposes. This does not modify the DLL itself but merely gives the

	function a different name towards your program. The Visual Basic compiler makes a wrapper function to perform the translation.
	Alias is also to be used if no symbolic names are present in the DLL but you can only call procedures by their number. In that case, you can assign names to each function using the **Alias** keyword.
Aliasname	Used in conjunction with the **Alias** keyword. A string that gives the true name of the library function. Note that this is again case sensitive.
args	The arguments that are required to be passed to the function or subroutine. Note that the type declarations must match with what the function expects.
type	This specifies the type of the return value in case the called routine is a function. This can be a Byte, Boolean, Integer, Long, Currency, Single, Double, Date, String (variable length only), Variant, a user-defined type, or even an object type.
	Always be careful when passing and or receiving strings to DLL routines.

For functions, the given data type determines the type of data it returns. If the parentheses are empty, Visual Basic will make sure that nothing is passed.

Note	You cannot pass fixed-length strings to functions or subroutines in DLL's. In case you pass a fixed length string to a DLL routine, it will be converted to a variable length string automatically.

Note	If the external routine needs an empty string, you should pass the pre-defined **vbNullString** constant. A string under Visual Basic consists always of 2 bytes specifying its length. The **vbNullString** is really an empty string that does not have a length specifier.

18.2 : On Passing parameters to procedures and functions

In the previous section we have briefly seen the **ByVal** and **Byref** keywords. So let us take a closer look at them, and what can be done with them.

First, we need to understand the concept of a 'Pointer'. This is something often used the 'C' language. Most beginning programmers find this a very difficult concept. Well it is not. The problem is that most books explain it either poorly or in an awkward way.

Then what is Pointer? Well the name really says it all. It is something that points to something else. Suppose I am an office clerk and you are my chief. You come in and ask for a business report A534. As a good clerk, I jump up from my chair, go to the filing cabinet, pop out the report and hand it to you. Of course, you are very pleased with my swift response and my neatly organized filing cabinets. The next day I am not at my desk (I am ill and at home). You come and ask for the same report. But where is it? Now if only I had given you a reference to where it was you could have located it. That is exactly the definition of a pointer: a reference to where the data is stored no as much as the data itself. Accessing a variable by Value is the first case. You asked for information and you got the information without knowing where exactly it was stored. Accessing by reference allows you to manipulate the information.

Now this comparison is not exactly one to one. You can either pass a variable **ByVal** (By value: content) or **ByRef** (By reference: pointer). Passing something **ByVal** means that you will pass the contents of the variable. If I pass you the variable X **ByVal**, and X = 5 then I am passing you 5.

On the other hand, if I pass it **ByRef** (By reference) I am passing you the locations of where X is stored. Then you can retrieve the contents of X.

Now what good is this? Well very simple: if I pass you what is stored in the variable you can use this data. End of line. If I pass you where it is stored, you can retrieve it but you can also MODIFY it! This can be very dangerous. Especially, when something goes wrong in a program, and it contains a pointer, then that is the first place to look at. Another big problem is that most programmers, which assume they understand pointers completely, use pointers whenever they like.

A pointer is something you only use when you want to give the 'demanding' side the privilege to modify the contents of the location (variable) it points to.

Now there is a very tricky part here. Unless you explicitly state that some variable is to be passed by value, it is passed by reference. The reason is that it saves both time and memory to do this. So be careful never to change the contents of passed variables inside a procedure unless you want to do this!

Where can you use this? In any case, where you have functions and procedures that need to return more then one result.

Suppose you have a Procedure called **SwapVariables**. This procedure will swap the contents of two variables. You cannot do it with a function, because it can only return you one of the two passed arguments. Furthermore, you would need extra storage space to temporarily hold the data. This consumes memory and CPU time.

If you give that function access to the passed variables, you can do it.

```
Sub SwapVariables (ByRef X, ByRef Y)
    Dim Tmp
    Tmp = Y
    Y = X
    X = Tmp
End sub
Sub Form1_Load()
    X = 5
    Y = 3
    Debug.print X,Y
```

```
            SwapVariables x,y
            Debug.print X,Y
      End sub
```

18.3 : API programming

What is this API?

API is short for Application Programming Interface. It is an interface between your applications and the computer's operating system. In a complex system like Windows, you cannot just fiddle around with whatever you want. Low-level stuff like disk access, screen update etc. is handled by the operating system. It is a very bad idea to mess with these when you are not absolutely sure about what you are doing. Windows exposes the entire underlying code through this API. Even the most primitive operations can be done using this interface. Not only Windows, but also every windows program, can have an API. The same goes for windows components like network interfaces, Database engines etc.

The Windows API is a very rich set of commands (over 5000 routines) that can enable you to perform task which are not normally possible. As explained in the section about DLL's, with a normal programming language you scratch only the surface of Windows.

Explaining all of the functions in the Windows API would take a course of a couple of months and a book a couple of thousand pages long. Someone has done this however. The best source is the technical documentation Microsoft provides through its Developers Network. This is to be considered the 'bible'. However, due to the very technical nature of this information, it is not always clear to understand. There is a very good book by Dan Aplleman that describes the Windows API functions and how you can use them with Visual Basic. Visual Basic itself has already an include file that predefines most of the API calls you can perform inside Windows.

18.3.1 : A simple API example

Suppose you want to make the computer emit a simple Beep. Well, you cannot. Fortunately the API of Windows has this function because it needs it to allow command.com emit beeps. When you launch a DOS window then the beeps generated there are translated into a call to a kernel function of Windows.

All you have to do is simply expose this function to Visual Basic.

```
Declare Function Beep& Lib "kernel32" (ByVal defer_
            As Long, ByVal depuration As Long)
```

And there you have it: your first DLL access! Now you can make Windows emit simple beeps and sounds. Check out the **Beepdemo.vbp** file to learn more.

Note	The Win95 platform no longer supports the parameters Frequency and Duration. They are simply denied.

NET 2005	The Net platform has a beep command. Therefore, there is no need to perform this using a kernel call anymore.

So what resides where in this huge Windows library? Actually, there is more than one library inside Windows. The operating system itself is a layered construction of processes that communicate amongst them. It is neatly organized in chunks that have a certain, well-specified task.

Windows kernel modules

Kernel32.DLL	Low level operating functions, Memory management, task management, resource handling and related operations.
User32.DLL	Windows management, Messages, Menu's, cursors, carets, timers, communication etc.
GDI32.DLL	Graphics device interface: device output, all graphics manipulations, display content, metafiles, coordinate handling and font management.
COMDLG32.DLL	Additional stuff for common dialogs,
LZ32.DLL	file compression .

Extension libraries

COMCTL32.DLL	New windows control like tree list and richtext edit.
MAPI32.DLL	Mail interface. Allows you to read, create and send messages via e-mail systems.
NETapi32.DLL	Control and accessing of networks.
ODBC32.DLL	Open Database Connectivity Allows you to interface with a number of common database formats.
WINMM.DLL	Multimedia stuff, sound, video etc.

Most functions in the additional libraries are accessible via the built-in objects and controls of Visual Basic. The same goes for the things contained inside Windows. After all, a simple button is contained in USER32.DLL.

To show you the power of these API calls a little example. Suppose you want to restrict the user's cursor to certain boundaries. This is against standard Windows user interface programming rules. Still you can do this. After all Windows calls these routines every time you resize the desktop of your computer.

You can do an API call to *ClipCursor*.

```
DIM myrect as RECT, mypoint as POINTAPI
DIM DL&
Mypoint.x = 0
Mypoint.y = 0
Dl& = clienttoscreen&(pctcursor.hwnd,mypoint)
Meyrect.top = mypoint.y
Myrect.left = mypoint.x
Myrect.right = myrect.left + pctcursor.scalewidth
Myrect.bottom = myrect.top + pctcursor.scaleheight
Dl& = clipcursor&(myrect)
```

Now all of the above might seem mumbo-jumbo to you and to be honest it is to most of us. API programming requires you to know a big deal on how Windows works internally. You have to know how to obtain handles, create rectangles (not simple rectangles, a rectangle is the basic internal object that windows uses to do graphics manipulations.

A more practical use of the windows API is to get environment information. Suppose you want to check who is using the computer. You can do this by asking for the name of the user who logged into the system.

```
Declare Function GetUserName Lib "advapi32.dll" Alias _
    "GetUserNameA" (ByVal lpBuffer As String, _
    nSize As Long) As Long

Public Sub Main()
    Dim Buffer As String
    Dim BufferSize As Long
    Dim ReturnVal As Boolean
    'Create Buffer
    Buffer = Space(255)
    BufferSize = Len(Buffer)
    ReturnVal = GetUserName(Buffer, BufferSize)
    MsgBox "User name is " & UCase(Trim(Buffer))
End Sub
```

If you want to know more about API accessing you should read the book by Dan Aplleman: Visual Basic 5 programmers guide to the WIN95 API. This is the bible on Windows functions: 1541 pages no-nonsense reference material but well worth the effort!

18.4 : API programming under NET

While the entire Windows API is still available to the programmer, the NET platform builds a nice wrapper around it. One reason is to give more structure to the API and provide a uniform way of dealing with the 'guts' of Windows. A second reason is that, in the course of history, the internal workings of Windows have changed substantially. Every change required the creation of a compatibility layer in order to be able to support older programs. The NET platform takes this problem away. Windows provides the engine, NET provides all the controls to the engine and your program drives the engine through the controls. If the engine changes at a certain point in time, there is no problem. The intermediate layer (NET) is updated to reflect these changes.

Before you start accessing the API's directly, you should check if there is no existing class that exposes the same functionality. One exception in NET 1.1 is the access to the serial ports. Since no class is provided there, you need to access the API directly. NET 2.0 does include that support. Accessing the API directly is a trade-off between re-usability and power but not flexibility.

Chapter 19 : ActiveX Control Creation

This is a new, catchy name to disguise OLE. Actually, ActiveX is OLE. Now that does not exactly answer the question. Then what is OLE (or ActiveX for that matter).

It is a mechanism that allows you to 'embed' other programs inside your program. OLE literally means Object Linking and Embedding.

A practical example of this is the following: When you create a document in Microsoft Word, you can embed tables inside this document. Word however does not know how to handle a table. After all, it was designed to be a word processor, not a spreadsheet. However, there is a program that masters tables: Excel. Well that is exactly what Word is going to do. It will store the physical data, which it does not know how to handle inside the document. Upon opening the document, it will read as much as it can and then ship the chunks of mystery data off to somebody else: Excel. Excel will then visualize this part of the data on screen.

This is a very practical system. After all, we are not here to reinvent the wheel all the time. Now this thing has drawbacks too. You need the other application to be able to interpret the data. If you would make a little Visual Basic program, and embedded excel into it (which is perfectly possible), you would end up with a tremendously big executable. Fortunately, there is another possibility.

Programs are written in a layered way. You have the so-called core libraries. These are the real routines that perform the operations with the data. There is an API interface built into this. A user interface then reacts to the users command and calls the appropriate functions.

When doing OLE, you are actually going to bypass the User interface and talk to the core of the system itself. This is of course a very cumbersome task. It means browsing through a list with thousands of calls. So this is not done very often.

The first method (embedding the entire system, including API and all) is called Document embedding (or ActiveX document embedding). The latter method is the real Object embedding.

Now what are the ActiveX objects then? Well, they are simply small programs that are really embedded on Document style. However, they are so small that you can consider them as objects. They have properties, methods and events. Actually, Excel could be thought of as an ActiveX object too, but since that can be used as a standalone program it is not considered an object.

And there you have it. An ActiveX object is a program that has no real use when used stand-alone. Consider a round button. What good would it do to write a program that creates a round button? You could click it … and then what? However, if you embed it into your program you can design a nice user interface to the world's most astonishing program (written in Visual Basic of course).

You can, using Visual Basic create your own ActiveX objects. You can compile them into OCX files and distribute the ActiveX object as a standalone entity. Even other programming languages such as C++ and C# can use the ActiveX object! Actually, any programming language for windows can call the object and use it.

19.1 : Creating an ActiveX Object

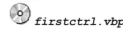 *firstctrl.vbp*

There is a tutorial program available that explains the constructs, explained in this topic, by example.

This is really quite simple. The basic process is similar to creating a regular project. Start a new project and select ActiveX Control. You will get an empty screen. Notice that there is no title bar or control box present.

This is typical for a control object. After all, you are going to place this on another form, so there is no need for title bars or control boxes.

Now you can insert standard Windows objects. Take care to use only the objects that are available inside Windows. Avoid using additional objects and or pluggable components. It will work, but the problem is transporting your object to other computers. You will need to transport the embedded objects as well. Now this works fine as long as you can create a setup program for it. Nevertheless, since an ActiveX object gets compiled to an Object this information is lost in the process.

So let's add a small button (button1) and a textbox (text1).

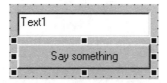

We will attach code that displays a string into the textbox. In the **Control_Load** procedure we assign a certain text to this string.

```
Dim atext$

Private Sub button1_Click()
   Text1.Text = atext$
End Sub

Private Sub UserControl_Initialize()
    atext$ = "Hello world"
End Sub
```

Note Similar to a projects startup code (***Form_Load***) there is a ***Control_load*** that marks the entry into the control. This is executed whenever a control is loaded. If you load multiple copies this code will execute each time. But do not worry each copy (or instance) has a life of it own.

The next thing we have to do now is add a project to the existing one in order to be able to test our control. I have not told you this before but you can compile multiple projects at once. This is called creating a group.

So first, rename the current project to ***MyHello.VBP*** and the control file to ***MyHello.ctl***.

Now let us add a project <File><Add project>. Save this project as ***ctrltest.vbp*** and ctrltest.frm. No finally save the project group as ***Myhello.grp***.

First, we need to make sure that the Form window for the control is closed (minimized is NOT good). The reason for this is that a control leads a life of its own. Once you insert a control it automatically starts running. As long as you have the user-interface designer open for this control, it cannot be initialized properly.

You will notice that on the control browser there is no a new symbol (the last one inserted here displayed with a gray box around it). This is actually our control. Therefore, you do not really need to compile it first to make it run.

If we now insert this control twice, we should get a screen like the following.

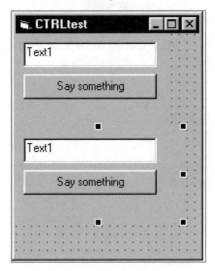

Now if you hit the Run button (F5) you can try clicking on the two buttons and you will see that you have two really independent controls. It is that easy.

You might have noticed that you can size the control when putting it on the form. But alas, it does not really size. You merely 'cut' it.

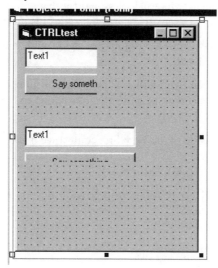

You can control this by attaching code to the **form_resize** event of your control. Let's force it to a fixed size. Simply attach this code to the control.

```
Private Sub UserControl_Resize()
    UserControl.Width = 2295
    UserControl.Height = 1125
End Sub
```

To do this: reopen the form of the control. You will now notice that the controls already on the screen will be come grayed out with diagonal lines.

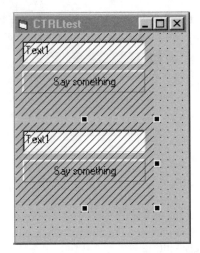

This is your indication that the user interface designer for that control is open and that what you see on the screen is no longer representative since the control is under modification.

After insertion, you close the control design form again and you will immediately see the control on the screen being updated.

If you try to select and size them, you will see that they will jump to a fixed size and that you cannot stretch them anymore. This is because the *Usercontrol_resize* event 'glues' their size stuck.

The next page shows the full code of the very first control we made.

```
Dim atext$

Private Sub button1_Click()
   Text1.Text = atext$
End Sub

Private Sub UserControl_Initialize()
    atext$ = "Hello world"
End Sub

Private Sub UserControl_Resize()
   UserControl.Width = 2295
   UserControl.Height = 1125
End Sub
```

19.2 : Adding properties and events

But what good is a control, if you cannot communicate with it? As you have seen, standard controls like buttons have properties and events. All we have made so far is a dumb box we can insert and play with, but which is not interacting with the programs we are writing.

Therefore, we need to add some properties and events. Visual Basic has a plug-in that will assist you in doing this. You have to insert this in the Add-Ins menu.

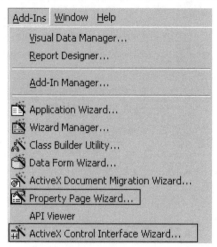

Start the Add-In Manager and select the Property Page and ActiveX Control Interface Wizard. Once you have done this, you can launch the ActiveX control Interface wizard.

You will get a nice screen that you should read the first time in order to get a better understanding of what we are going to do now.

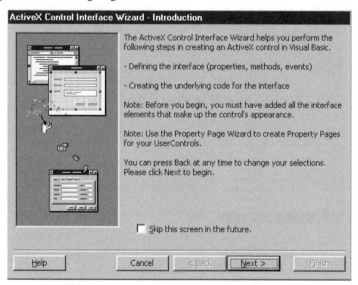

For now, you can just click on Next. The next screen shows you the available STANDARD properties, methods and events you can attach to your control.

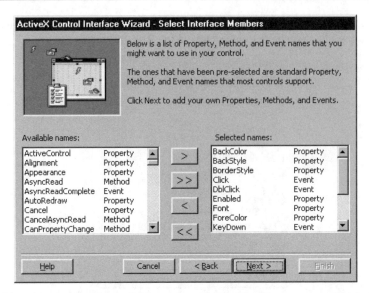

On the left side you see what is available and on the rights side you see what is implemented for now. Since we are building a very simple control, we do not need these. So let's make this list empty by clicking on the double arrow button which points left (<<). This makes the list empty. We are only interested in a Click event. So search for the Click event in the left listbox, select it and click on the single arrow right (>) button.

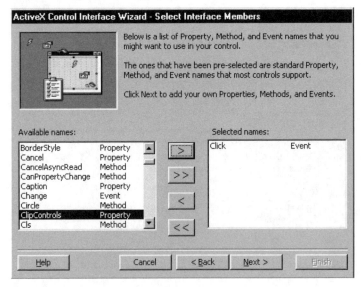

When that is done, we can move on to the next screen: Inserting our own custom properties, methods and events. So go ahead, click next.

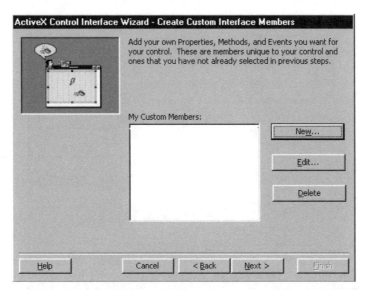

This screen shows you the display to enter your own items. So go ahead and click New.

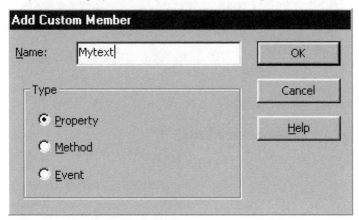

Simply type the name you want to give it and the class it belongs to. In our case, this is a property called **MyText**. Click OK when finished.

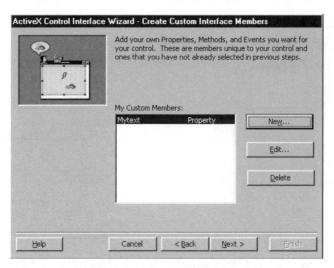

Since this is all for now, we click next to continue. If you would like to add more things, you could just go on here.

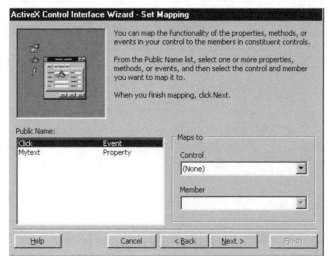

The next window is the so-called Set mapping. This allows us to map the things we selected directly to existing controls in the object.

In our case, we want to map the **Click** event of my control to the **Click** event of the button1 object in my control. This means that, whenever I click the button, the click event will be fired for my control. The user of my control can then take action. If I would have defined a custom event, I could map it as well. Mapping is done by selecting the item of desire and specifying the object in the 'Maps To' frame. When you select a control, you will be able to select the event, property or method in the Member list.

For now, I only want to map this click event.

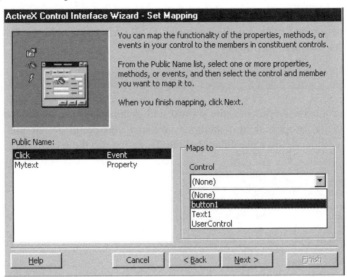

Therefore, I select Button1 as the target control, and the **Click** event as the target member. Finally, we click on next.

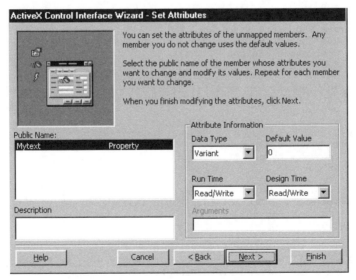

The last screen we need to fill out is the attribute definition. This allows us to define the type of attributes of the properties defined. In our case, the **Mytext** property has to be set to variant. In the attribute information, you can also specify if the attributes need to be available at runtime, or design time or both. You can also select if they have to be read, write or read/write. In addition, you even give them a default value.

The default value is the value that will be shown on the properties browser, when we are manipulating our control. For now, we will not use that feature.

So now, we can click on Finish. Finally, the wizard will update the code you have written so far with the additions you have just made

19.3 : What the wizard came up with …

After completing the above process, the wizard will generate all necessary code to implement the specified events, properties and methods. Wheras you could do all this manually, it is handier and faster to have the wizard handle it all. But what did the wizard generate?

```
Dim atext$
Const m_def_Mytext = 0
Dim m_Mytext As Variant
Event Click() 'MappingInfo=button1,button1,-1,Click

Private Sub button1_Click()
    RaiseEvent Click
    Text1.Text = atext$
End Sub

Private Sub UserControl_Initialize()
    atext$ = "Hello world"
End Sub

Private Sub UserControl_Resize()
    UserControl.Width = 2295
    UserControl.Height = 1125
End Sub

Public Property Get Mytext() As Variant
    Mytext = m_Mytext
End Property

Public Property Let Mytext(ByVal New_Mytext As Variant)
    m_Mytext = New_Mytext
    PropertyChanged "Mytext"
End Property

'Initialize Properties for User Control
Private Sub UserControl_InitProperties()
    m_Mytext = m_def_Mytext
End Sub

'Load property values from storage
Private Sub UserControl_ReadProperties(PropBag As PropertyBag)
    m_Mytext = PropBag.ReadProperty("Mytext", m_def_Mytext)
End Sub

'Write property values to storage
Private Sub UserControl_WriteProperties (PropBag As PropertyBag)
    Call PropBag.WriteProperty("Mytext", m_Mytext, m_def_Mytext)
End Sub
```

Now the above piece of code will probably look very confusing. You will see references to property bags, Get, Let etc .... What is all this you might ask?

The property-bag is a storage space that an object uses to store the name references to its internal workings. The real names of the properties it allows you to manipulate are stored there. Get and Let are functions that are called whenever a property changes. If, during design time, you change one of the objects properties, the Let function will be called and take appropriate action. The same will happen, if during the run of your program you change this property. If you read the property, the GET function will kick in. The availability of these functions depends directly on the parameters you have given in the 'set Attributes' form of the ActiveX control interface wizard.

19.4 : A closer look at the final code

Let us take a look at the code generated by the wizard.

```
Dim atext$
'Default Property Values:
Const m_def_Mytext = 0
'Property Variables:
Dim m_Mytext As Variant
'Event Declarations:
Event Click() 'MappingInfo=button1,button1,-1,Click
```

The first line of code is still the same as we wrote. Then the wizard has inserted a constant to specify a default value for a parameter. This parameter is the *MyText*. When an object initializes, it cannot do this with un-initialized variables. Then, in order to have clean code, the wizard has defined the *m_Mytext* variant. *M_MyText* is a temporary holding pace for the data of the *MyText* property.

Last, it has declared the click event. This event is followed by what appears to be remark. THIS IS NOT A REMARK! Do not remove this. The compiler reads this information, and will use it to find where to map the event. Actually, this is the place, as you can see, where my Click event is mapped to the Button1 Click event. The default value is -1; this means the button is initially not clicked.

```
Private Sub button1_Click()
    RaiseEvent Click
  Text1.Text = atext$
End Sub
```

The next procedure that has been modified, is the Button1_click event handler. The wizard has inserted a line that will trigger the Click event we defined. *RaiseEvent* triggers will trigger whatever code the user of our object has attached to our objects Click event.

Finally, the wizard has inserted the necessary code that will allow the user of our events to change and retrieve properties.

```
Public Property Get Mytext() As Variant
    Mytext = m_Mytext
End Property
```

This procedure allows the user to retrieve the *Mytext* property. It copies the contents of the temporary information (***m_Mytext***) to the users calling code.

```
Public Property Let Mytext(ByVal New_Mytext As Variant)
    m_Mytext = New_Mytext
    PropertyChanged "Mytext"
End Property
```

Same story goes here. Except now, this code can change the *Mytext* property. Whenever the user assigns a new value to the *Mytext* property this code is executed. It sets the ***m_mytext*** variable to the new value.

The ***Propertychanged*** event is going to update the property bag. This makes sure that the Property browser window during design time is updated as well.

```
'Initialize Properties for User Control
Private Sub UserControl_InitProperties()
    m_Mytext = m_def_Mytext
End Sub
```

The ***initproperties*** code is called whenever a new instance of the object gets loaded. Just as the ***object_Initialize*** procedure initializes the user interface, this code will initialize all variables. The final pieces of code allow Windows and Visual Basic to store and retrieve the settings to and from the property bag. As explained above this is the placeholder that explains windows the available properties, and their respective names, from an object.

```
'Load property values from storage
Private Sub UserControl_ReadProperties(PropBag As PropertyBag)
    m_Mytext = PropBag.ReadProperty("Mytext", m_def_Mytext)
End Sub

'Write property values to storage
Private Sub UserControl_WriteProperties(PropBag As PropertyBag)
    Call PropBag.WriteProperty("Mytext", m_Mytext, m_def_Mytext)
End Sub
```

And that's it. The only thing left is the piece of code that makes the object do what it was intended for: sending a message to the textbox

In order to make it work fully, we should now send the ***m_Mytext*** contents to the textbox upon clicking.

```
        Private Sub button1_Click()
            RaiseEvent Click
            Text1.Text = m_Mytext
            'used to be     Text1.Text = atext$
        End Sub
```

And there you have it. A fully operational object you can use in your programs. If you close the editor for the object, you will see that the objects on the other projects form remain grayed out; this indicates that the object has been modified so much that the IDE cannot recover. You should select and delete the objects and replace them with fresh copies.

If you now look in the object browser, you will see that there is a property called **MyClick**. Simply type there 'Yo dude'.

In addition, if you double-click on our object, you will get code for the Click event. There we attach a message box.

```
        Private Sub Form_Load()
            Myhello1.Mytext = "Yo dude"
        End Sub

        Private Sub Myhello1_Click()
            MsgBox " You clicked me "
        End Sub
```

And then: le moment supreme. Make it all work by hitting F5 …

Of course, this is only a simple and not so useful example, but it gives you an overview of how to create your own controls. It is just as easy as creating a normal program. We only have to launch the wizard to assist us in building the necessary links.

Finally, you can ask Visual Basic to create the OCX for the object and then you can distribute it to anyone.

NET ActiveX has been removed from the NET environment since it was only an intermediate solution and is not compatible with the concept of NET. Not to despair, however, since it is possible to create native controls directly inside NET, although it is not so straightforward to upgrade existing code.

19.5 : A custom control in the NET framework

Custom controls in the NET framework are a different animal then under Visual Basic Classic. Besides their name change to Components, they also are essentially Classes with an attached user interface. The way you define events, properties and methods has changed substantially from VB classic as well.

19.5.1 : Starting a Component project

The easiest way to create a new component is to add it to an existing new project. Of course, you can create standalone components directly, but the addition to an existing blank project has the advantage that you can instantiate the component directly.

19.5.2 : Adding Properties

Properties are declared in a similar way as regular functions and procedures except they are preceded by the **Property** keyword.

Example:

```
Public Property message() as string
```

The Code generator will automatically create all necessary code for you. This results in the following output:

```
Public Property message () as string
    Get
    End Get
    Set (Byval Value as String)
    End Set
End Property
```

Here is already a big difference between the NET style and the VB classic style: the Get and Set sections are contained inside one definition. The parameter passing code is automatically created and cast to the same type as the property's type. In the above case, the Value variable will contain the information that is passed tot the property from the calling code.

Now we can start adding code to actually manipulate information from within our custom control. Suppose we have a label added to our form that is called *label1*. The property *message* will update the Text property of the label. We need to add the appropriate code to the property handler for the *message* property.

Example:

```
Public Property message () as string
    Get
          Return label1.text
    End Get
    Set (Byval Value as String)
          Label1.text = value
    End Set
End Property
```

Note the difference in passing parameters. The **Return** keyword is used to pass information to the calling program, just like with any ordinary function.

There is no more **Propertybag** as in Visual Basic Classic, because there is no longer a need to have that mechanism.

Any Public property is automatically accessible to the external world.

19.5.3 : Adding Methods

Adding methods is as simple as defining you own functions and procedures and exposing them as Public.

Example:

```
Public Function addup (x as integer,y as integer) as integer
    Return x+y
End Function
```

Adding public functions will automatically add them to the list of keywords in the IDE. Keep in mind that you need to build your control before updates to the code will take effect.

19.5.4 : Adding Events

The last thing we might need to do is provide events to notify the users program of certain activity that is going on inside our control.

Example:

```
Public Event my_event (byval message as string)
```

In order to fire this event we just call the **RaiseEvent** function.

Example:

```
Private Sub fire_event
    RaiseEvent my_event("This is an event")
End Sub
```

19.5.5 : Adding Variables and Enumerations

It is equally possible to add publicly available variables and Enumerations, so that users of your custom control can access these directly from their code.

Example:

```
        Public Enum DaysOfTheWeek
             Monday
             Tuesday
             Wednesday
             Thursday
             Friday
             Saturday
             Sunday
        End Enum

        Public version as string()

        Public Property today as DaysOfTheweek
        End Property
```

19.5.6 : Interacting with the VB IDE

The interaction between the custom control and the VB IDE is instantaneous. As explained before, there is no longer the need for a **propertybag**.

Visual Basic NET does add a mechanism to fine-tune the interaction with the IDE. You can specify additional information for a property that will determine how it interacts with the IDE environment. Additional information is enclosed between angle brackets (< and>) just prior to the definition of the property. The information belongs to the **System.ComponentModel** class.

19.5.6.1 : Setting the Description

You can set the description that will appear on the property navigator inside the Visual Basic IDE by specifying a **Description** clause in the additional information for the property.

Example:

```
        <System.ComponentModel.Description ("The Message To Be displayed")> _
        Public Property message () as string
             Get
             End Get
             Set (Byval Value as String)
             End Set
        End Property
```

19.5.6.2 : Showing or hiding properties

It is equally possible to hide a property from the IDE by modifying the **Browsable** clause in the definition header.

Example:

```
<System.Componentmodel.Browsable (false)> _
Public Property message () as string
    Get
    End Get
    Set (Byval Value as String)
    End Set
End Property
```

19.5.6.3 : Setting Default Values

You can use the *System.Componentmodel.Defaultvalue* parameter to set a default value for the property.

Example:

```
<System.Componentmodel.DefaultValue ("My_Label")> _
Public Property message () as string
    Get
    End Get
    Set (Byval Value as String)
    End Set
End Property
```

19.5.6.4 : Setting the Category

You can also define your own categories in the property browser. This makes it easier to locate your own added properties later on

Example:

```
<System.Componentmodel.Category ("My Properties")> _
Public Property message () as string
    Get
    End Get
    Set (Byval Value as String)
    End Set
End Property
```

Of course, you can combine all these parameters into one definition clause by separating them by a comma.

Note	It is important to note that you need to rebuild you component in order to accurately reflect the changes. In Visual Basic Classic, the code would run immediately as soon as the focus jumped to the form that had custom controls instantiated. This is not the case in Visual Basic NET.

Chapter 20 : Building better programs

What is a better program? That strongly depends on the definition of a good program. How can you classify a program as good? If it is better then a bad program. So it all comes down to defining bad programs. Then what are bad programs?

Well, I can give you many examples:

⇒ A program that crashes very often;

⇒ eats memory and does practically nothing;

⇒ is terribly slow;

⇒ looks awfully ugly (depends strongly on personal taste, though);

⇒ behaves strangely some times;

⇒ corrupts and wastes your data.

I think we can all largely agree on the above. Well except maybe the 'Looks awfully ugly'. This depends on personal taste. And I am not going into that one. After all this is a book on programming, not on style.

So what can we do to make faster, smaller, more stable programs?

The very first step is taken during coding process. Write clean source code! Do not make constructions that you yourself hardly understand. Insert comments. It does not hurt and will not waste memory or speed once compiled. And most of all: adhere to the KISS principle.

20.1 : The KISS Way

No, I am not asking you to kiss your computer. KISS is the abbreviation for 'Keep It Simple Stupid'. It means you need to write code that is as simple to understand as possible. Do not write 'complex' things like:

```
X=0
Doagain:
IF x < 4 then x=x+1 else x=x-1 ; If X=4 then goto stopit else goto _
Doagain; Stopit: End
```

Any clue what this is doing? Let's have a look at this. First, let us write it out so that it becomes clearer.

```
X=0
Doagain:
   IF X<4 then
       X=x+1
```

```
        Else
            X=x-1
        End if
        If x = 4 then
            goto Stopit
        Else
            Goto Doagain
        End if
      Stopit:
        End
```

Well, at least it has turned out a bit better. But still, what does it do? Let's analyze.

If **x** is smaller than four, it gets incremented with one. If it is equal or larger, it is decremented with one. Next, **x** is compared against four. If it is four, we jump to the label **Stopit**. If it is different from four we do it all over again. If you think a bit more about this code then you will see that the decrementing part never is executed. When you start at zero the first **if-then-else** will be executed while **x** is smaller than 4. When X is 3 the decision of the **If-Then-else** will increment **X** to 4 and the next **If-then-else** will jump to **Stopit**. Therefore, **X** will never be decremented. We just found our first piece of DEAD code. Dead code is code that consumes memory but does absolutely nothing. It does not even get executed! Now the optimizer in the compiler can catch and eliminate dead code as long as we are talking about entire procedures or functions that are never called. However, it cannot eliminate the above case of dead code.

Therefore, we could rewrite the code as follows:

```
        X=0
      Doagain:
        IF X<4 then
            X=x+1
        End if
        If x = 4 then
            goto stopit.
        Else
            Goto doagain
        End if
      Stopit:
        End
```

If we now look again, we will see that all we are doing here is incrementing X until it reaches 4. So why not use a **While-Wend** construction?

```
        X=0
      While x <4
          X = x+1
      Wend
      End
```

Now isn't that a quite a bit more readable?

This demonstrates a number of basic KISS principles:

- One line = One command

- Avoid *Goto's* and *Gosubs* (except of course for error handling)

- Don't write dead code

- Use brackets when writing mathematical expressions. That way, you are at least sure how they will evaluate and you do not have to remember if it was multiply before subtraction or after subtraction.

The advantage of KISS is not only easy readable code. It will run faster and, most importantly, compile to smaller executables. If you or someone else has to review this program months or years from now, he will understand what it is doing! So by thinking a little longer about implementing a piece of code, you can save yourself a lot of time, both during execution of the program, and during your work to maintain and update the program.

Adhering KISS rules will also lead you to using variable names with a meaning. Instead of Simply Using X and Y, you should use names that have a meaning. After all, it has no impact on the speed of the program.

Another big point in KISS is: do not re-invent the wheel! Use as much of the existing things as possible. Do not create every the same routines over and over again.

So, how can this be done? Well: Comment your code and partition it. This means that you divide your program in small manageable chunks and transform them into a routine. Then save this routine in a module. Later on, maybe in a different project, you can simply re-use this routine. Also make sure that the routines you write are well documented.

If you want to create re-usable code, the two things that you should adopt is indenting your code and use CamelWriting for your variable and procedure names. Stop laughing. I am dead serious here.

Indenting is the process where you indent lines of code depending on where they belong.

```
If x=5 Then
B=4
Else
Open "myfile" for output as #1
Print #1,x
Close #1
X=0
If b= 10 then
Open "myfile" for input as #1
Line input #1,a$
B=val(a$)
Close #1
End if
End if
```

Well? Where do the 'end ifs' belong? If you would indent it, you could immediately see.

```
        If x=5 Then
           B=4
        Else
           Open "myfile" for output as #1
           Print #1,x
           Close #1
           X=0

           If b= 10 then
              Open "myfile" for input as #1
              Line input #1,a$
              B=val(a$)
              Close #1
           End if
        End if
```

Now you have to agree that this looks a lot more readable. You immediately see the *If B=10 then else* block and the main *If-Then-Else* block. Now let us look at CamelWriting. When writing good and clean code, you create names for functions, procedure or variables that are descriptive of their nature. Often this name will consist of more then one word. To make these names more readable for humans, you should adopt this CamelWriting thing.

The name ***thisisavariable*** becomes more readable if you write it as ***ThisIsAVariable***. This style of writing, where you capitalize every first letter of a word is known a CamelWriting.

20.2 : Atomic Programming

This is a derivative of the KISS principle that dictates the following.

Break your program in the smallest possible routines. (Atoms)

Suppose you have a program that contains a number of routines that all need to access a certain file. Depending on the procedure, some will need to open it in read mode, some in write mode. Some routines even need to do both. If inside this routine you will frequently open and close this file, it might be a good idea to eliminate all these lines of code and replace them with two custom procedures: *OpenFile* and *CloseFile*.

```
        Sub streamout (text$)
           Open "mystream" for output as #1
           Print #1,text$
           Close #1
        End sub
        Sub Streamin (message$)
           Open "mystream" for output as #1
              Print #1,message$
           Close #1
           Open "mystream" for input as #1
              Line input #1,text$
           Close #1
        End  sub
```

Suppose this is a big program that uses this stream to communicate with another program. Practically you would need to implement a lot more error handling since the other person might have it open.

These routines (and others) that access the stream could be floating around anywhere. If you rewrite this to the following:

```
Sub streamout (text$)
    OpenStream
    Print #1,text$
    CloseStream
End sub

Sub Streamin (message$)
    OpenStream
    Print #1,message$
    OpenStreamRead
    Line input #1,text$
    CloseStream
End   sub
Sub OpenStream
    Close #1
    Open "mystream" for output as #1
End sub
Sub CloseStream()
    Close #1
End sub
Sub OpenStreamReadmode()
    Close #1
    Open "mystream" for input as #1
End sub
```

You end up with something far more readable and maintainable. If the file changes or you want to implement error handling now, you can simply modify the **OpenStream**, **CloseStream** and **OpenStreamReadmode** procedures.

You do not need to go digging in thousands of lines of code to patch all of the open and close commands.

20.3 : Naming objects

Another rule of thumb is, just like with variables, to give object and controls meaningful names. Do not keep the default things like **button1** and **button2** or **text3** and **text5**. Give them a real name. And even better: Precede their name with a 3-letter abbreviation that describes their nature.

For a button you could use **btnHelloWorld**, the matching textbox could be **txtHelloWorld**. You would then write a procedure like this:

```
Private sub btnHelloWorld_Click()
    TxtHelloWorld.text="Hello World"
End Sub
```

Years from now you will read this code, and you will be able to find out what it does and what it refers to.

Note	To find a variable declaration quickly, simply right click it and select the Definition option. The code editor will jump to the definition of the variable or procedure. To return, right click again and select Last Position.

20.4 : Error handling in Visual Basic Classic

Even when you have been programming perfectly clean code, and have a fully bug free program, something can crew up. Something stupid, like running out of disk space, can crash even the most perfect program. Fortunately, there are ways to deal with what is called 'externally invoked errors'. System failure, invalid filenames and more can be intercepted and handled by writing a bit of code.

Visual Basic has a built in object that provides an easy interface to handling errors. All you have to do is enable it inside your code.

When developing an application and an error occurs, you get a message that something went wrong and the debugger asks you to either terminate the execution of jump you to the line where it occurred. Once the program is compiled, this is no longer the case. If an error occurs, then you simply are kicked out of execution. You will be notified that an error of some type has been detected.

20.4.1 : The On Error Goto clause

The *On-Error-Goto* clause enables an error-handling routine and specifies the location of the routine within a procedure; can also be used to disable an error-handling routine. Error handling is always done inside a routine. You have to enable an *On error Goto* clause in the beginning of the routine. The target of the *Goto* has to be inside the same routine.

```
On Error GoTo < label >
On Error Resume Next
On Error GoTo 0
```

The *On Error* statement syntax can take on any of the following formats:

On Error GoTo <label>	The On Error Goto clause enables the error-handler routine that is defined at the specified label. The label needs to be defined inside the procedure where the On Error Goto clause is defined. If an error occurs during runtime and the error handler is defined then program execution will branch to your specified code where countermeasures can be taken.
On Error Resume Next	This clause forces program execution at the line after the

	offending one. You can use this to skip over code that may not be executable in certain occasions, notably when relating to objects. This is mostly used in code that handles the manipulations of passed objects to a procedure.
On Error GoTo 0	This re-instates the default error handler of the Visual Basic compiler and shuts down your custom error handlers for the remainder of the procedure or until you define a new error handler.

By default, any runtime error is fatal and will result in program abortion unless you define an error handler. Writing error handlers is the most difficult task since they too can be prone to errors, and that's the last thing you want: an error inside an error handler. In that case the current procedure is aborted, and control is returned to the calling code. If there is an error handler present, that one can take countermeasures. If none is present at a higher level the error will be fatal again and program execution will cease.

Once an error has been resolved, the normal execution can be restored using the Resume Next or Resume keywords.

Note	Error-handlers are not separate routines but they belong integrally to a procedure.

Your error handler can retrieve additional information on the nature and cause of the error by checking the contents of the **Number** property of the **Err** object. This value only reflects the most recent error. Additionally a message can be retrieved from the **Err.Description** parameter. This may be used to inform the user of the program what exactly went wrong, or write this information to a debugging log for instance.

Since the error handler is an integral part of your code, you will need to skip it prior to exiting the code normally. You can use the **Exit Sub**, **Exit Function** or **Exit Property** statement to signal the end of normal executable code.

Example:

```
Sub Buggy_code()
        On Error GoTo ErrorHandler
        ...
        Exit Sub
ErrorHandler:
        ...
        Resume Next
End Sub
```

The above code will normally run until the **Exit Sub** clause is encountered and then exit to the calling code. Should an error occur in the mean time the specified error handler **errorhandler** will execute, attempt to resolve and force a resume next.

Note An error occurring during a call to a dynamic-link library (DLL) will not raise an exception and thus cannot be trapped with Visual Basic error handling code. Always check the return values of DLL functions for a success or failure. You may need to consult the API specifications to find out what is returned and how. It is possible to retrieve the **Err.LastDLLError** property for more information in case an error occurred inside the DLL.

20.4.2 : The Err object

This object contains information about run-time errors. It tells you which error happened and can also give you a description of it. You can use it to simulate errors as well. This is very useful to test your error handlers when writing software.

Whatever generated the error will set the properties of the **Err** object. By default, this is simply the number associated with a particular error. When an error occurs, all properties of the **Err** object are assigned information on the nature and cause of the problem so that it can be resolved by the error handler.

It is possible to generate errors on purpose to test your error handler. You can use the **Err.Raise** method to force an error occurring. The **Err** object's properties are automatically cleared whenever a Resume, **Exit Sub**, **Exit Function** or **Exit Property** statement is encountered. You can use the Clear method explicitly reset the **Err** object.

The Err object has a collection of properties that assist you in identifying and handling the error.

Number	The unique identification number of an error.
Source	The name of the current Visual Basic project.
Description	A textual description of the error in cause. If no description is available then the message "Application-defined or object-defined error" is returned.
HelpFile	The location of the file where more information can be found.
HelpContext	The Help File context ID for the error.
LastDLLError	This contains the error code for the last call to a dynamic-link library (DLL). This is a read only property.

Example:

```
Dim Msg
On Error Resume Next
Err.Clear
Err.Raise 5
If Err.Number <> 0 Then
```

```
        Msg = "Error # " & Str(Err.Number) & _
               " was generated by " _
               & Err.Source & Chr(13) & Err.Description
        MsgBox Msg,, "Error", Err.Helpfile, Err.HelpContext
    End If
```

The above example generates an 'invalid procedure call' error and displays all information available in the **Err** object to the user.

20.4.3 : Resuming execution after handling the error

The **Resume** clause can resume execution after an error-handling routine is finished.

```
        Resume [0]
        Resume Next
        Resume <label>
```

The Resume statement syntax can have any of the following forms:

Resume	If the error has been handled then execution will be returned to the offending statement. The statement will attempt to execute again and, upon success, the program will resume normal operation. In case the error fires again the error handler will again be triggered.
Resume Next	Execution will resume with the statement immediately following the offending statement.
Resume label	Execution will resume at the given label. Note that the label must be defined inside the procedure where the error handler is defined. You cannot jump out of a function of procedure.

The **Resume** statement is valid only inside an error-handling routine. If used elsewhere it will cause an error itself.

```
        Sub ResumeStatementDemo()
                On Error GoTo ErrorHandler    ' Enable error-handling
                Open "TESTFILE" For Output As #1    ' Open file
                Kill "TESTFILE"        ' Attempt to delete open file.
                Exit Sub        ' Exit Sub to avoid error handler.
        ErrorHandler: ' Error-handling routine.
                Select Case Err.Number ' Evaluate error number.
                        Case 55 ' "File already open" error.
                                Close #1        ' Close open file.
                        Case Else
                                ' Handle other situations here....
                End Select
                Resume 'Resume execution at same line that caused the error.
        End Sub
```

20.4.4 : Trappable errors

Any error occurring during run-time can be trapped by an error handler, unless it is a system error of the operating system itself. The following sections give you an overview of errors that can occur. For ease of use, they are categorized by cause. Note that I am not going to discuss all errors. Most of the possible error codes you will probably never get. I am only giving the ones that pop up occasionally.

20.4.5 : Syntax Errors (errors against the Basic syntax)

These typical errors occur when starting the program inside the IDE for the first time.

3	Return without GoSub	The cause is clear; there is nothing to return to. Avoiding *Gosubs* altogether solves this problem.
5	Invalid procedure call	You attempted to call a procedure but forgot to pass some parameters.
13	Type mismatch	You tried to assign data to a variable of the wrong type like a string to an integer.
20	Resume without error	You error handler contains an error!
92	For loop not initialized	You have a Next without a for.
35	Sub, Function, or Property not defined	You are accessing something which does not exist.

20.4.6 : Runtime errors

These occur during the run of the program. They are mostly due to flawed programming logic or memory problems.

6	Overflow	The result of a calculation is too big to store in the given variable type, or is simply too big to be calculated at all.
7	Out of memory	Now how did that happen?
11	Division by zero	A typical calculation error. There is no mathematical solution for dividing by zero.
14	Out of string space	You tried to cram more data into a too small string.
28	Out of stack space	Have you been programming recursive stuff?

20.4.7 : Flawed Programming logic errors.

9	Subscript out of range	This occurs when trying to access an inexistent array element. If you defined an array of 10 elements and try to read or write element 11 you will get this
10	This array is fixed or temporarily locked	You tried to **Redim** a static array
16	Expression too complex	Try breaking it down in simpler parts

20.4.8 : File handling errors

These errors occur when handling files.

52	Bad file name or number	There is a problem creating the handle
53	File not found	The file does not exist.
54	Bad file mode	You tried to read from a file opened for output or vice versa.
55	File already open	You tried to open an already open file.
57	Device I/O error	Ouch! Serious one. The device where the file resists is not ready. Typical for floppy drives.
61	Disk full!	Disk Space. The final frontier … or get a bigger disk
62	Input past end of file	You tried to read beyond the end of the file.
63	Bad record number	Can occur when reading records from files.
67	Too many files	You attempted to store too many files in a directory.
68	Device unavailable	The target where the file exists went offline. typical for removable media.
70	Permission denied	You cannot do that. The file is in use by someone else.
71	Disk not ready	A timeout on disk operations. Can happen on floppy drives or virtual file drivers.
74	Can't rename with different drive	You can rename a file across drives.
75	Path/File access error	The path or file does not exist.
76	Path not found	The path is invalid.

The above-mentioned errors are the most common. There are lots more possible errors, but you should consult the on-line help for Visual Basic when those occur.

Note	Any error occurring during the run of the executable, that is not handled properly, is FATAL. This means bye-bye program. Therefore, it is a good idea to start writing error handlers.

20.5 : Error handling in the NET framework

The NET framework has a different error handling methodology. There is no more need for **on error goto** and **resume** and all the other jumping through hoops. The NET environment replaces all these constructions with a simply try-catch clause.

Whenever a risky section of code is being executed, such as accessing potentially non-existent files, you may want to enclose these in a try-catch clause.

The **Try** section contains the risky statements. As soon as an error is encountered, the **Catch** block comes into effect. The **catch** section should try to create a remedy for the problem at hand. Once the **Catch** clause has ended, the program will retry to execute the offending section of code. Once the code no longer produces an error the code contained in the **finally** block will be executed.

Example:

```
Procedure get_config()
    Dim file as io.filestream
    Try
        File = new io.filestream("test.txt", _
            Io.FileMode.Open, Io.FileAccess.Read)
    Catch ex as exception
        IO.File.Create("test.txt")
        File = new io.filestream("test.txt", _
            Io.FileMode.Open, Io.FileAccess.Read)
    Finally
        Dim content as string = new io.streamreader(file).ReadToEnd()
    End Try
End sub
```

If the opening of the given file fails, it will be created and then the file will be attempted to re-open. It is possible to find out the problem by checking the ex variable in the above code.

Items that can be retrieved from the exception class go from a textual representation of the problem to a complete stack trace. You can also have multiple catch clauses appended to one Try.

Example:

```
Procedure get_config()
    Dim file as io.filestream
    Try
        File = new io.filestream("test.txt", _
            Io.FileMode.Open, Io.FileAccess.Read)
        Dim X = 100 / 0
    Catch ex as exception
        IO.File.Create("test.txt")
        File = new io.filestream("test.txt", _
            Io.FileMode.Open, Io.FileAccess.Read)
    Catch ex as ArithmeticException
        Console.writeline (e.tostring)
    Finally
        Dim content as string = new io.streamreader(file).ReadToEnd()
    End Try
End sub
```

The above code has a dedicated error handler for any arithmetic operators and a general error handler for any other error occurring.

Try-catch clauses can be nested, so it is possible to provide further error handling within the error handler.

Example:

```
Procedure get_config()
    Dim file as io.filestream
    Try
        File = new io.filestream("test.txt", _
            Io.FileMode.Open, Io.FileAccess.Read)
    Catch ex as exception ' file does not exist : create it
        try
            IO.File.Create("test.txt")
            File = new io.filestream("test.txt", _
                Io.FileMode.Open, Io.FileAccess.Read)
        Catch e as exception ' file could not be created
            Console.writeline ("could not create file")
        End try
    Finally
        Dim content as string = new io.streamreader(file).ReadToEnd()
    End Try
End sub
```

Chapter 21 : The Windows registry

You can consider this as advanced digging into Windows. The Registry is probably the most obscure part of Windows. Most people still regard to this as the mythical place where Windows stores the data needed for its internal operation. Well it is more then that. You can use it too. Under the older Windows version, you would store configurations for your program in separate INI files. Now you can use the Registry. However, you cannot manipulate the registry directly. The reason for this is that the registry is managed by Windows and you cannot just start changing this file. In addition, it is a very complex structure where a lot of information is stored. A simple screw-up could result in a total system crash.

Fortunately, Visual Basic has a command set that allows us to store and retrieve data using the registry.

21.1 : Digging into the registry

You can have a look at the registry by launching the Regedit program. This is a hidden program inside Windows that allows you to view and manipulate the registry. In order start it, you have to follow the following procedure:

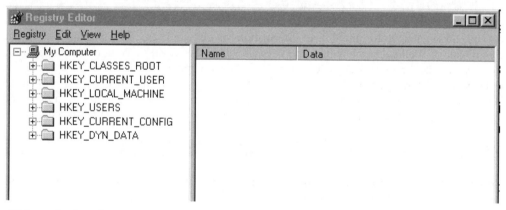

Click on the Start button.

Select Run.

Type Regedit and click OK.

This starts up the Registry editor. You will get the basic screen from Regedit.

If you want to find something, you need to know the key name for the entry. The registered user of the operating system can be found using the **RegisteredOwner** key. If you click on <Edit> <Find> and type **RegisteredOwner** it will jump you to the location where this information is stored.

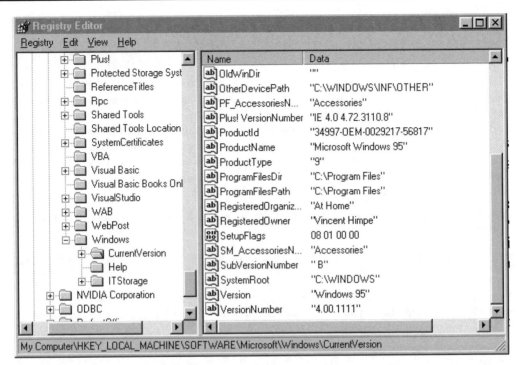

As you can see, numerous other bits of information can be found here. The question is what can we do with it? Well not much really. The keys already in the registry belong to other programs. You can check for certain keys to verify if certain programs are installed. You could for instance create a program that requires you to have Excel installed on the computer. During installation you could check for the registry key for Excel. If it was not found in the registry then you could prompt the user that your program explicitly needs Excel in order to run.

21.2 : Data mining in the registry

Now that we have a basic understanding of the registry, it is time to start sniffing around. So far, we have used the Regedit program, but we can do this from Visual Basic as well.

The registry operators can use named arguments that must be passed accordingly. The order in which they are passed, is of no consequence. You have the choice of using regular parameters or named arguments. The example below does 3 times exactly the same, except the first two lines use named arguments.

Example:

```
Somefunction argument1 :="hello, argument2 := "world"
Somefunction argument2 :="world, argument1 := "hello"
Somefunction "hello" , "world"
```

21.2.1 : GetSetting

The *Getsetting* method returns the value of an entry in the registry.

```
GetSetting(appname, section, key[, default])
```

Appname	A string expression that contains the name of the application or project we are looking for.
Section	A string expression that contains the section where the key is found.
Key	A string expression containing the name of the key information to return.
Default	An optional expression that specifies the value to return if the given key is not found in the registry This is by default a zero-length string ("") but this can be overridden this way.

In order for the *Getsetting* method to function properly, all passed information needs to match. If no correct match is found the default value will be returned.

Example:

```
GetSetting "MyApp","MyCategory", "WindowLeft", 0
```

The above code will retrieve the setting **windowleftleft** for an application called **Myapp** and filed in the category **Mycategory** for that application

21.2.2 : SaveSetting

The *SaveSetting* method allows you to save or create an application entry in the Windows registry.

```
SaveSetting appname, section, key, setting
```

Appname	A string expression specifying the name of the application or project that defines the setting.
Section	A string expression that contains the name of the section where the key will be saved.
Key	A string expression that contains the name of the key itself.
Setting	The value that the key is being set to.

If the key cannot be saved, an error will be raised.

Example:

```
' example using named arguments
SaveSetting appname := "MyApp", section := "my_category", _
            key := "WindowTop", setting := 75
' example using direct access
SaveSetting "MyApp","my_category", "Windowtop", 75
```

21.2.3 : DeleteSetting

The *DeleteSetting* can delete a section or key setting from the Windows registry.

```
DeleteSetting appname, section[, key]
```

Appname	A required String that contains the name of the application to which the key applies.
Section	A required string expression containing the name of the section where the key setting is being deleted. If the appname and section are the only parameters supplied then the entire section is deleted together with all key settings classified under them.
Key	An optional string expression that containing the name of the individual key setting to be deleted.

All given parameters must correctly evaluate in order for the key to be deleted. If one or more arguments do not match, nothing will happen.

 Use this command with extreme caution. Do not start deleting at random, or you could soon be faced with the blue screen of death (General protection failure) and an inoperative computer.

```
DeleteSetting "MyApp","my_category", "Windowtop"
```

21.2.4 : GetAllSettings

This convenient routine allows you to retrieve directly all registry key entries that belong to your program. All you need to do is, pass a two dimensional array to the method and it will return you the entire chunk of data.

Example:

```
Dim my_settings ( , ) as string ' 2 dimension array
My_settings = GetAllSettings ("My_application","my_category")
Dim x as integer
For x = lbound(my_settings,1) to lbound(my_settings,1)
    Debug.Print ("key:" & my_settings(x,0));
    Debug.Print (", value:" & my_settings(x,1))
Next x
```

The above chunk of code retrieves the entire list of settings for the *my_category* section of *my_application* registry entry and dumps it to the console.

21.3 : Make use of the registry

You can store your own program settings inside the registry. This can be useful to store user settings, last accessed file lists etc. Another useful thing is the window size and position last used. When the program is restarted later, it will always appear at the last coordinates. Since you can specify a default value, it will work even the first time the program is started.

```
Private Sub Form_Load()
    Me.Left   = GetSetting(App.Title, "Settings", "MainLeft", 1000)
    Me.Top    = GetSetting(App.Title, "Settings", "MainTop", 1000)
    Me.Width  = GetSetting(App.Title, "Settings", "MainWidth", 6500)
    Me.Height = GetSetting(App.Title, "Settings", "MainHeight", 6500)
End Sub
```

The above code will store the relevant information into the windows registry.

You will note that it makes use of the **App** object. The **App** object is an object that returns relevant information about the program. You can retrieve the application name, path to the program, check if another copy of it is running etc. For more information about it, you should check the Visual Basic Help File about the **App** object.

The following code takes care of saving the information upon exiting the program. If the program is currently minimized it does not store the information.

```
Private Sub Form_Unload(Cancel As Integer)
    Dim i As Integer
    If Me.WindowState <> vbMinimized Then
        SaveSetting App.Title, "Settings", "MainLeft", Me.Left
        SaveSetting App.Title, "Settings", "MainTop", Me.Top
        SaveSetting App.Title, "Settings", "MainWidth", Me.Width
        SaveSetting App.Title, "Settings", "MainHeight", Me.Height
    End If
End Sub
```

One last warning might be in place here. Never ever, fiddle with the Registry when you do not exactly know what you are doing.

When developing program that access the registry it is a good idea to make sure you have a safe copy of the registry. To create this simply fire up the registry editor and Select <File><Export>. Typically, I call this regback.txt and put it in the root directory of my boot disk. When something goes wrong and the registry is corrupted, you can reinstall this safe copy. To do this you have to run the Regedit program under DOS. There you can specify it to import this data and recover the registry.

Note	Anything installed or modified to this registry after you took the backup, will be lost.

21.4 : The Registry and NET

Access to the registry from the NET platform is unchanged with the exception of added security. An alternate mechanism is provided using the Registry class from the *Microsoft.Win32* namespace.

21.4.1 : The Microsoft.Win32 namespace

The NET platform has an entire class devoted to registry access. By importing the *Microsoft.Win32* namespace into your project, you have direct access to a number of methods that make registry management possible.

Example:

```
Imports microsoft.win32

Dim my_key as registrykey = Registry.CurrentUser.OpenSubKey _
                ("Software",true)
Dim new_key as registrykey = my_key.createsubkey ("my_program")
New_key.setvalue ("owner","vincent")
New_key.Flush
```

The above code opens the Software section of the user that is currently logged on to the machine. It goes on to get a hold of the keys for **my_program** and then proceeds to create an entry for the owner of the program.

Later on, we can retrieve this key in the following manner:

Example:

```
Imports microsoft.win32

Dim my_key as registrykey = Registry.CurrentUser.OpenSubKey _
                ("Software\my_program")
Console.writeline my_key.GetValue("Owner")
```

Chapter 22 : Scripting interpreters

Often you will write programs that control a system and you want to give the user some means of further automation. You can do this by writing a script engine or you can even give your user access to the VbScript engine. VbScript is a real programming language not unlike Visual Basic for applications (VBA for short) that can be found in numerous Microsoft programs.

There is a difference between a scripting and a programming language. A script runs top to bottom and has no constructs like loops, subroutines etc.

22.1 : Building a simple script interpreter

When you do not need a programming language but only want to give the user the possibility to record a sequence of actions, and recall them to run the sequence again, you can work with a script interpreter.

Typically, the first thing you need is a place where the user can write and edit a script. You should also provide routines to read and save scripts. You can easily build this based on our little text editor from Part I.

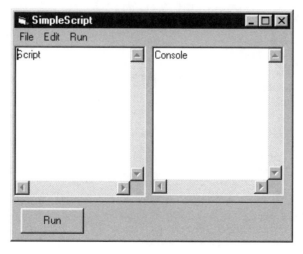

I just added a menu and a button that allows starting the execution of the code. In addition, a second textbox was added. This one will act as the output window for the script engine. Generally, when people are developing scripts, things will go wrong. Therefore, it is a good idea to store the script to a temporary file during execution. The file is deleted upon termination. If your program crashes, you can simply restore this file yourself, or you could make the scripting engine smart enough to do an automatic recovery. So let us attach some code that will create this temporary file and recover for us.

```
Private Sub Form_Load()
    On Error GoTo NoRecovery
    Script.Text = ""
    Open "tmpscript.scr" For Input As #1
    Script.Text = "' Recovered script:" + vbCrLf
    While Not EOF(1)
        Line Input #1, a$
        Script.Text = Script.Text + a$ + vbCrLf
    Wend
NoRecovery:
    Close
End Sub
```

Upon execution of the program it attempts to open the **tmpscript.scr** file if this fails we know that the previous run did not crash. If there is such a file, it will be loaded into the script window.

22.1.1 : Running the script

```
Private Sub Fire_Click()
    tmpfile = FreeFile

    ' store script to temporary file
    Open "tmpscript.scr" For Output As #tmpfile
    Print #tmpfile, Script.Text
    Close #tmpfile

    ' load and start interpreting
    Open "tmpscript.scr" For Input As #tmpfile
    While Not EOF(tmpfile)
        ' read script line by line and interprete
        Line Input #tmpfile, commandline$
        ' clean up the input
        commandline$ = Trim$(commandline$) + "   "
        ` check for comment
        If Left$(commandline$, 1) = "'" Then
        Else
            ` execute command
        End If
    Wend
    Close #tmpfile
    Kill "tmpscript.scr"
End Sub
```

The above code is attached to the Fire button. The command Run from the menu simply calls the **Fire_Click** method to invoke the execution. Upon activating the engine, the script is written to the temporary file. Then the engine reopens the file and, as long as the end has not been reached, reads it line by line.

This is the basis for the interpreter. The next thing we need to do is clean up the read line so that it does not contain any unwanted stuff. After all, the user of the engine might decide to modify it manually with other programs. A good point is to remove all leading and trailing spaces, and that is exactly what the next piece of code does. The script engine will analyze the code and try to extract blocks of text. But suppose we, the users, have entered an empty line! This could lead the script engine to crash. Therefore, we will add two dummy spaces at the end of each command. Later on. it will become clear, why exactly two spaces. The next thing the code does, is check if the line begins with an apostrophe ('). If this is the case, it will not be passed to the script engine, since we defined this character as the comment character.

Upon completion, the temporary file is deleted using the KILL command. If the script engine crashes this file will not be deleted and the recovery routine in the **Form_Load** will pick it up. Now that all this preliminary work has been done, we can concentrate on the real engine: The Parser.

22.1.2 : The script Parser

This is the real engine that will determine what commands and arguments, if any, are present in the line and will invoke the appropriate code. First, we need a way to extract the command. This engine is based on following criteria:

- One command per line.

- Unlimited amount of arguments per line.

- Commands and arguments separated by a fixed character (a space).

- Comment is preceded by an apostrophe (').

We now need to extract the command from the command line. Since our script language dictates that all commands and optional parameter should be separated by a space this is quite easy

```
Ecmd = InStr(commandline$, " ")
cmd$ = Left$(commandline$, Ecmd)

' Now determine the string with arguments
argument$ = Right$(commandline$, Len(commandline) - Ecmd)

' clean up the junk and convert cmd$ to uppercase
cmd$ = trim$(UCase$(cmd$))
' now we are ready to parse the commands
```

Depending on what functions you want to make available, you can modify the script engine. At least you should give the user the possibility to see the script running and that is exactly why I put the second textbox on the screen.

It would be nice if the user could manipulate this console. It would be very useful if the user could, at least, add text to the console and clear the console.

```
Select Case cmd$
    Case "QUIT", "END", "BYE"
        End
    Case "CLS"
        Console.Text = ""
    Case "PRINT"
        Console.Text = Console.Text + argument$ + vbCrLf
End Select
```

A Messagebox would come in handy too. It allows the user to stop the script temporarily.

```
Case "MESSAGE"
    MsgBox argument$,, "Message:"
```

Using the same programming logic, you can add instructions yourself. Since we are using a general *Select Case* system as a parser, it is easy to allow multiple possibilities for one command. As you can see, I already created a command that allows you to terminate the program.

Now that these basic things are out of the way, we can start to implement the real instruction set. Instruction typically requires data input of some sort. So we will need a routine that can extract the relevant parameters from the argument$.

22.1.3 : Parameter extraction

Depending on the command, the user might have passed one or more parameters. In order to cope with this, you would have to write a routine for each possible case. However, there is an easier way. If you make a routine that can extract one parameter at a time from the parameter string, we could call it the number of times we are expecting parameters. Furthermore, the routine could warn the user if he has forgotten one or more of them.

```
Function GetArgument$(ByRef argument$)
    tmp$ = Trim$(argument$)
    If Len(tmp$) = 0 Then
        MsgBox "Error in Script: Missing parameter "
    Else
        tmp$ = tmp$ + " "
        x = InStr(tmp$, " ")
        ' extract argument and return value
        GetArgument$ = Trim$(Left$(argument$, x))
        ' delete argument from argument string
        argument$ = Right$(argument$, Len(argument$) - x)
    End If
End Function
```

Let's make two script commands ADD2 and ADD3. ADD2 will add two arguments together. ADD3 will add three arguments. This will demonstrate the use of the *GetArgument$* function.

```
    Case "ADD2", "ADD"
        a = Val(GetArgument$(argument$))
        b = Val(GetArgument$(argument$))
        c = b + a
        entry "Result = " + Str$(c)
    Case "ADD3"
        a = Val(GetArgument$(argument$))
        b = Val(GetArgument$(argument$))
        c = Val(GetArgument$(argument$))
        d = c + b + a
        entry "Result = " + Str$(d)
```

The Entry routine is a simple routine that can write a string to the console.

```
    Sub entry(txt$)
        Console.Text = Console.Text + txt$ + vbCrLf
    End Sub
```

The above code demonstrates the basic creation of commands and the handling of the arguments. However, this is by far not the end of what is possible. If you want a routine, which can take an undetermined number of arguments, you could do the following:

```
    Case "ADDX"
        While Len(Trim$(argument$)) > 0
            x = x + Val(GetArgument$(argument$))
        Wend
        entry "Result =" + Str$(x)
```

To test all of the above you can try out this little script:

```
    CLS
    PRINT This is my first script
    ADD2 5 6
    ADD2 7 8 9
    ADD3 7 8 9
    PRINT the following command will produce a SCRIPT error
    ADD3 5 6
    ' The following demonstrates the ADDX command
    ADDX 1 2 3 4 5 6 7 8 9
    Message The system will now crash to demonstrate recovery
    crash
    END
```

As you can see, scripting is a very powerful tool to embed in your applications. This allows you to automate frequently use tasks. When I build big test systems, I create a program that allows the user to manipulate every machine and system in it. The sequences that need to be executed to perform the actual measurement, are not hard coded but embedded in scripts. This allows the user of the system to modify at will, without me needing to revise the program over and over again. Moreover, it hides all the down-to earth stuff from the people operating the system. They do not need to know how to set up and acquire data from a certain instrument. No, they simply write in the script READVOLTAGE, and the system will control the appropriate instrument, retrieve the result and dump it to the console.

As state before this home-built script engine is NOT a programming language. If you need features like looping, jumps etc., you will need a real engine.

22.2 : MSScript: A real script interpreter.

Visual Basic allows you to embed the MSScript engine inside your programs. This is a very powerful tool not unlike Visual Basic for Applications (VBA). There is one small problem with this interpreter: It is not installed on every machine. Furthermore, there is No help for it.

It is very well possible that you cannot try out the following. You can install the MSScript engine from the Microsoft Windows SDK toolkit. These tools are standard available in the Professional editions of Visual Studio and Visual Basic. On windows 2000 / XP, this is a standard component of the operating system.

22.2.1 : Scripting language

The language used by MSScript is VbScript. However, not all functionality of Visual Basic is embedded in VbScript.

Variables:

One big difference is, that here there is only the Variant data type. Therefore, there is no need at all for the DIM command except for creating arrays.

Objects:

Only objects exposed to VbScript explicitly are accessible. Besides these VbScript only knows the ERR and dictionary objects. Dictionary is an object that stores key and data values.

When you switch *UseSafeSubset* to *False* then you get access to additional objects that allow you to do file manipulations. However, I strongly suggest that you DO NOT do that. Handle all file manipulations in the program where VbScript has been embedded.

22.2.2 : The MSScript properties

MSScript has a number of properties that allow you to specify its behavior. The most important are listed below.

AllowUI	When set to True MSScript can display objects like Message boxes etc.
CodeObject	Returns you the exposed objects.
Error	Returns the information about the scripting error.

Language	You can set this to either VbScript or Jscript (Java).
Modules	Contains a collection of Modules.
Procedures	Contains a collection of Procedures.
Timeout	Allows you to specify the maximum time the script will run before it aborts.
UseSafeSubset	Prevents access to security critical objects like files and disks.

22.2.3 : Script Control Methods

The following are the Methods embedded in the script control

AddCode	Allows you to send code to the script control.
AddObject	Allows you to expose an object to the Script Control.
Eval	Allows you to evaluate an Expression.
ExecuteStatement	Execute a single statement.
Reset	Reset the script engine.
Run	Execute a subroutine.

The **Eval** method is very interesting. It allows you to evaluate mathematical expressions. If you execute the following code, you will get the result for the calculation.

```
X = ScriptControl.Eval "Sin (1+(3/4))"
```

The script control will return the Sinus of 1 and ¾. You can use this to evaluate user entered mathematical expressions in your program.

22.2.4 : Adding code to the script engine

This is only a matter of calling the **AddCode** method. This method is automatically checking the syntax of the transmitted source code. If there is an error, you will be notified. So make sure you write an error handler. The error handler should check the Script's error object and not the one from the main program.

```
Private Sub Sendcode_Click()
    On Error GoTo scripterror
    ScriptControl1.AddCode Text1.Text
    Exit Sub
scripterror:
    MsgBox "Error line " + Str$(scriptcontroll.Error.Line)_
    + Vbcrlf + ":" + scriptcontroll.Error.Text _
```

```
                + Vbcrlf + "scriptcontroll.Error.Description
            Scriptcontroll.Error.Clear
    End Sub
```

The above code will display the line number, the contents of the line, and the description of the error.

22.2.5 : Exposing Objects

You can give VbScript access to any object inside the program where you use the VbScript. All you have to do is expose this object to VbScript. Suppose you have a Label called Display and you want to be able to control this from the Script.

```
        ScriptControll.AddObject "display", Display
```

The above code will do the trick.

In the script you can then simply write:

```
        Display.Caption="Hello"
```

You can also expose functions and procedures inside your program for activation by the script. However, this is not straightforward. You need to create a Class module and embed the functions in there. Inside the program, you can then create a new object from this class and add this to the objects exposed to the Script engine. This will be explained in detail in the example on VbScript in appendix III.

Chapter 23 : Visual Basic for Applications

23.1 : What is Visual Basic for Applications?

Microsoft Visual Basic for Applications (VBA) is actually the IDE and interpreter that is part of the Visual Basic programming environment itself. It is a strip down of the complete system in the manner that it has no compiler that produces an executable format.

VBA can be embedded in a program to allow the end user extendibility, in exactly the same way that VBA in Excel, Word and numerous other applications provides.

All the familiar elements of the full-blown programming environment are available in VBA: the Project Window, a Properties Window and the debugging tools. You can also create custom forms using the standard windows controls and load ActiveX Controls.

The latest release of the toolkit is Visual Basic for Applications Version 6.4. You need to purchase a license from Microsoft to get access to this toolkit if you want to build your own programs that incorporate VBA.

23.2 : Using VBA from Word or Excel to develop code

Most of the code you write in regular Visual Basic, can be run directly in VBA as it has been implemented in Microsoft office. Actually, the VBA there is exactly what is available in the VBA development kit version 6.3 or 6.4.l.

Whereas you can cut copy and paste code, it is not possible to import the forms associated with a real Visual Basic project. You will have to recreate the forms basically from scratch.

On the other hand, modules (BAS files) containing your own routines can be loaded directly.

The toolbox can be right clicked and most controls on your system can be loaded for usage inside VBA. As an experiment, I recreated the AlphaServer project, from a few chapters back, under VBA in Excel without problems. Right click the toolbox and load the Winsock control. Draw a textbox and two instances of the WinSock control, give them the correct name, paste all code and hit start. This worked first time right without a single hitch.

Chapter 24 : Classes

Since we are working in an OOP environment, we have to know a bit about classes. What exactly is this concept of a Class.?

24.1 : The Class concept

Remember the Controls we put on a form? Well, these are actually instantiated classes. Just like an Object or control has properties, methods and events, a class can have all of these.

Therefore, you could consider a class as an object or vice versa. The nice thing about classes is, that you can treat them as objects. You can even define a new variable based on a class.

If you put a control on the screen, let's say a label. You give this the name 'Display'. From now on, you can access the properties for this object by the name 'display'. You could think of this as a variable. The property 'Caption' is embedded into the Object Label. This means that the variable 'Property' belongs to the Class 'Label'. The same goes for the Move method. You can apply the move method to the label. Well, the 'Move' method belongs to the class 'Label'.

Then what is the difference between Classes and Objects (controls). Simply nothing, except maybe that Classes have no visual substance (user interface on screen). Take for instance the Printer object. This is the perfect example of a Class. It is not visible, has no substance yet you can activate methods, set properties and the printer object can raise events.

Classes are a construction to make programming more structured and augment the manageability of large and complex programs.

24.2 : Creating a Class

You start the process of creating a class by selecting Add class module from the Project menu. This will create a new class in your project.

Once you have this you can start creating properties, methods and events. Creating Methods is nothing else than writing **Public** subroutines and **Functions**. Properties have to be defined using the Property command.

Example:

```
' userfunction class

Private c_msg$ ' internal storage for msg$

Public Sub Dosomething()
    MsgBox "I did it" + c_msg$
End Sub
```

```
Public Property Let message(msg As String)
    c_message$ = msg
End Property
```

The above piece of code shows you how to create a *method* (DoSomething) and a *Property* (Message). Note that for the moment you can only assign something to the property. In order to retrieve the data from the property, we need to write a *Property Get* handler.

```
Public Property Get message() as variant
    Message = c_msg$
End Property
```

You also need to allocate storage space to hold the data assigned to a property internally. As you should remember, once a subroutine exits the internal data is destroyed. Therefore, you need to declare a variable at module, or in this case Class, level. You can also declare private subroutines inside your class. These can be accessed from inside the class but are invisible to the user of the class.

Adding an *Event* is as easy anything else. Just write the appropriate code for it.

```
' Declare the event
Public Event YO(ByVal text as string)

' activate it (this should be in a procedure or function)
RaiseEvent YO(" Yo Dude")
```

That's it. You just created a class.

24.3 : Instantiating objects from a class.

This is equally simple. There are two ways to do this. Only one however will unleash the full potential of the class modules.

You can, firstly, use *DIM* to declare a new object that will be derived from a class. By the way, that is the correct terminology to say that you want to access a class

```
Dim User as New Userclass
Dim SecondUser as New UserClass
Dim Userlist(50) as New userclass
```

The second method is, declare a new variable of type *Object* and then assigning it to a class.

```
Dim User as object
Set User = New UserClass
```

The difference here is that the object is not actually created with the *Dim* statement. Only when it is assigned to the *Userclass* then it is created. This conserves memory.

| Note | You can instantiate as many objects from a class as you want. |

24.4 : A practical example

Below is a practical example of a class.

```
' Class Yelling

Private c_msg$ ' internal storage for msg$

Public Sub YO()
    MsgBox c_msg$, , "Yo dude"
    RaiseEvent Yell(" Yelling completed")
End Sub

Public Property Let message(msg As String)
    c_msg$ = msg
End Property

Public Property Get message()
    message = c_msg$
End Property

Public Event Yell(ByVal text as string)
```

This is the end of the class.

```
Private WithEvents shout As Yelling

Sub Form_Load ()
    Set shout = New Yelling

    ' assign text to property Message
    Shout.Message = "Hello World !"
    ' Activate YO method
    Shout.YO
End sub

Sub shout_Yell(byval txt as string)
    Debug.print txt
End sub
```

And this is the end of the main code. You will notice that here I have used yet syntax to instantiate an object derived from the class. The reason is, that I want to attach to the events generated by the class. If I do not explicitly specify, using **WithEvents**, that I want to have access to the events, then I do not get them.

Furthermore, if I create my object this way, Visual Basic will know all the properties and methods of the class. This means that from then on Visual Basic will assist me during my code writing, just as it would with any other of its objects. It will display the nice listbox with all objects and properties the moment it type the dot.

24.5 : Creating a class in NET

Classes under the net platform are commonplace, as the entire NET environment is built on classes. It takes the initial class concept defined in Visual Basic 5.0 and pushes it all the way.

Creating a Class in NET is no different from creating an entire custom control in NET, except that it lacks the user interface part. You still have the capability to create your own methods, functions, properties and events. For a full explanation on how this works, see the section on building custom controls under NET.

Chapter 25 : Yet More Case studies

This section will show some examples of programs that apply the techniques described in this part.

Shutdown Windows via an API call

This little program shows you how to embed an API call in your program.

The LED ActiveX control

I always wanted a simple indictor on my screen. Well here it is.

The PassBox ActiveX control

A simple control that allows you to enter a password, and that displays start instead of the characters you type.

MiniBasic: A program editor for MSScript

This is the basis for a script interpreter based on VbScript. You can expose objects AND your own procedures to the VbScript engine.

Additional Notes on the use of classes

This is not a case study but a proposal for practical use of classes.

25.1 : Case Study 7: Shutdown Windows via an API call

Suppose you need to build a 'closed' system: a kind of setup where the user can only fire up the computer, do his thing and then only can shutdown the system. It might be neat if you could do this directly from the application.
Since you can do this from the Start button of windows, it means it must be accessible somewhere. And indeed, this is an API call just as any other.

Shutdown.bas:

```
Public const ForceExit = 4
Public const Logoff = 0
Public const reboot = 2
Public const Shutdown = 1
Public declare function exitwindowsex lib "user32" _
(byval uFlags as long, Byval dwReserved as long) as long
```

Main form:

The form is very simple: only one command button and an option selector in the form a 3 RadioButtons.

```
        Private sub Command1.click
            If radio1.value = true then
                X = exitwindowsex (logoff,0)
            End if
            If radio2.value = true then
                X = exitwindowsex (reboot,0)
            End if
            If radio2.value = true then
                X = exitwindowsex (shutdown,0)
            End if
            If radio3.value = true then
                X = exitwindowsex (ForceExit,0)
            End if
        End sub
```

If you hit the button, it will log you off from your current session. If you want to kill the operating system, simply replace logoff with **Forcexit**.

Ehm … Did I forget tell you to save before trying this? Oh, I am Sorry, you were supposed to save it before you shut down the system unconditionally and just lost that little program. Luckily, you have this paper copy.

25.2 : Case Study 8: The LED ActiveX control

This example will show you how to build a simple ActiveX control. You start, as usual, with a normal Project. Now you add a new project of the type ActiveX Control.

To make our life easy, I will use a shape control from the toolbar as indicator for our led. I set the property **backstyle** of the control form to **Transparent**. This will assure that only the shape is visible.

The shape is simply called shape1. The control should look like this:

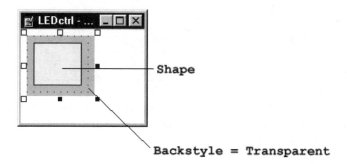

Since I want to allow the user to size the led, I have to attach some code to the resize event.

```
Private Sub UserControl_Resize()
    Shape1.Left = 0
    Shape1.Top = 0
    Shape1.Width = UserControl.Width
    Shape1.Height = UserControl.Height
End Sub
```

Whenever the size of the form changes the shape will resize to fill the entire boundary of the form.

Since I want to start attaching some properties to the Led, it is time to fire up the ActiveX Control Interface Wizard.

In this wizard is took the properties **Shape**, and **Bordercolor** from the standard properties selector.

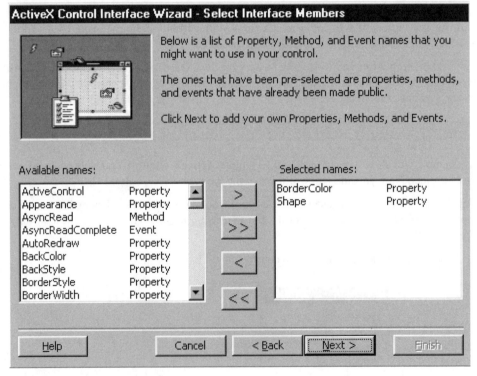

The next step that has to be done, is creating additional properties. I want to specify the **OnColor** and **Offcolor** and the value of the led. A value of 1 means that the led will be **On**, and similar, 0 will be **off**.

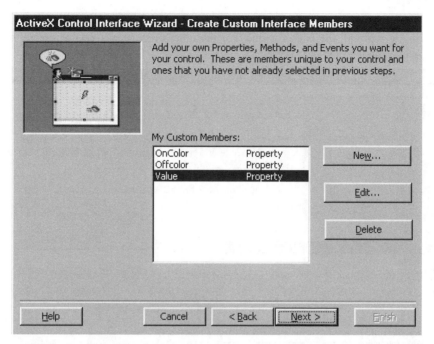

The next thing I have to do is, specify which of my defined properties are mapped to which properties of the existing objects in my control.

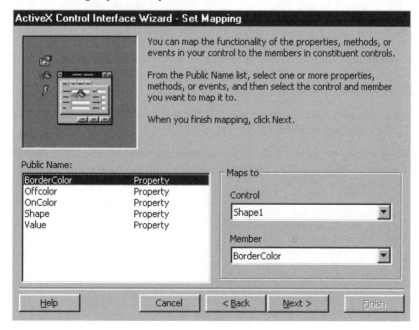

As I can directly map **Bordercolor** and **Shape** to the **Shape1** object, I do so. This saves me from having to write all the code for this. For the other properties, I do not specify anything. This mapping is done in the next screen.

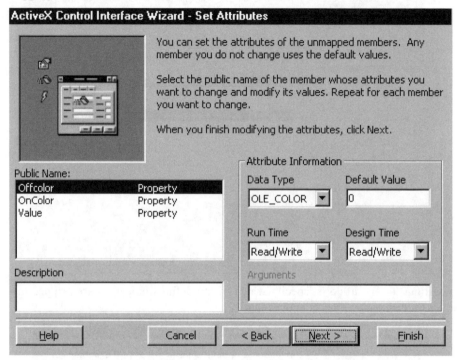

I define the **Offcolor** and **Oncolor** properties as type **OLE_color**. This means that in my property window I will automatically get a color selection tool to specify the appropriate colors. The value is specified as type variant.

Now that all of this user interface stuff is out of the way, I can click on finish and the wizard will write all the necessary code for me.

The only thing I have to write, is the piece of code that changes the color according to the setting of the **Value** property. Therefore, I dig up the correct routine and write the necessary code.

```
Public Property Let Value(ByVal New_Value As Variant)
    m_Value = New_Value
    If m_Value = 1 Then
        Shape1.FillColor = m_OnColor
    Else
        Shape1.FillColor = m_Offcolor
    End If
    PropertyChanged "Value"
End Property
```

The only lines I have to write, is everything between *If* and *End IF*. This is the basic control that will perfectly perform what I intended it to. Nevertheless, we can do better. I will assign a bitmap to the control. This means that this bitmap will appear in the object browser of the Visual Basic. To do this, I select a simple bitmap and assign it to the *ToolboxBitmap* property of my control form.

I can now put some of my objects on the main form of the second project in the group. The next picture shows a screenshot of the control browser with a demo from that contains four copies of my Led control.

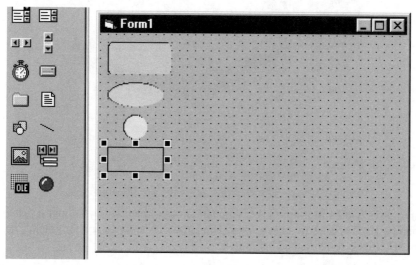

And now you think this is finished? No way! If you take a look at the Shape property, you see that it only contains a numerical field. I would like to see a little pulldown menu there with the possible shapes on it. Enumerating and assigning it to the property variable can do this.

Declaring the variable with the *Enum* keyword does enumerating.

```
Public Enum shapetypes
    rectangle = 0
    Square = 1
    Oval = 2
    Round = 3
    Roundedrectangle = 4
    RoundedSquare = 5
End Enum
```

When this is done, all I have to do, is change the declaration of the *Shape* property. Now it is defined as *Integer*. When I change it to *shapetypes* it will be enumerated according to that list. And presto: a fully working, professional looking control.

So now, I can make a little program with it. You can find this in the LED directory of the CD-ROM. All the program does, is generate a number of random values and display them in bar graphs made from my LED's.

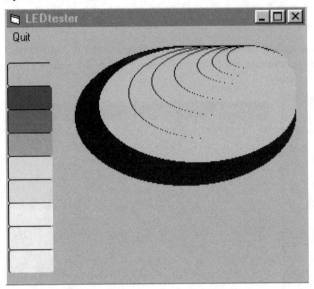

The program uses two control arrays. On an interval basis specified by a timer it generates two random numbers and creates two bar graphs. The left one is an ordinary bar graph. The right on is a Funky 3D elliptic style stacked bar graph.

Once you are satisfied with the look and feel of the control, you can ask Visual Basic to compile it into an appropriate OCX file. From that moment on you can use your control in any program as a separate object. You can even give, or better, sell it to third parties.

25.3 : Case Study 9: A programming environment for MSScript

This is by far not a full-fledged programming environment such as Visual Basic. Nonetheless, it gives an idea on how to embed scripting into your programs.

Let's start with the usual stuff. A form with a textbox called Script, a menu with a File-Quit and a Run Menu. On the run menu, I want to put the Run, Eval and Main entries.

Run will execute the program, *Eval* will prompt me for an expression and evaluate it, and Main will allow me to specify the startup routine for the Script code.

Furthermore, I need to insert the MSScript control as well. Since it is not loaded into the control browser by default, I have to enable it using the right click and selecting Customize. There I will see a reference the MSScript, simply check it and I am up and running.

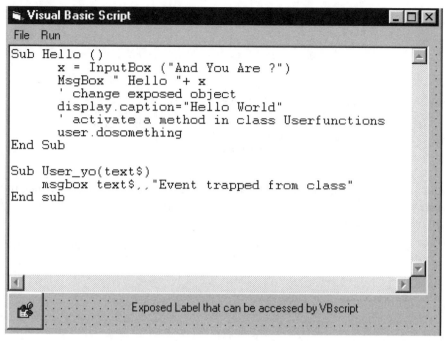

```
Sub Hello ()
        x = InputBox ("And You Are ?")
        MsgBox " Hello "+ x
        ' change exposed object
        display.caption="Hello World"
        ' activate a method in class Userfunctions
        user.dosomething
End Sub

Sub User_yo(text$)
    msgbox text$,,"Event trapped from class"
End sub
```

Exposed Label that can be accessed by VBscript

I also inserted a simple label in order to be able to demonstrate the use of object exposure to the script. As you can see, I set the **Multiline** and **scrollbars** features of the textbox on and already entered a piece of code into the textbox.

The next thing I need to do, is write some code for the user interface.

```
Private Sub Form_Load()
    ScriptControl1.AddObject "display", Display
    Dim userclass As Object
    Set userclass = New Userfunctions
    ScriptControl1.AddObject "User", userclass
End Sub
```

The **Form_load** procedure exposes the label 'Display' to the script engine. This means that from now on the script engine can access all the objects properties, methods and events.

Since I want to give the Script engine access to some routines I have defined in my program, I create a new object of the Class **Userclass** and then add it to the script engine just as I did with the label.

```
Private Sub runprogram_Click()
    On Error GoTo scripterror
    ScriptControl1.AddCode Text1.text
    If Scriptmain <> "" Then
```

```
        ScriptControl1.Run Scriptmain
        Else
        MsgBox "Specify a Main routine first " + vbCrLf + _
               "Doubleclick the routine and select <Run> Set Main"
    End If
    Exit Sub
scripterror:
    MsgBox "Error line " + Str$(ScriptControl1.Error.Line) _
           + vbCrLf + ":" + ScriptControl1.Error.text _
           + vbCrLf + ScriptControl1.Error.Description, _
           vbExclamation, "Script Error !"
    ScriptControl1.Error.Clear
End Sub
```

The **RunProgram** procedure will copy the contents of the textbox to the script engine. If during the syntax check an error occurs, the error handler will retrieve the line number, the string with the error in it and the description.

It will also check whether I have specified the startup routine and if not, the program will not be executed.

```
        Private Sub quitfile_Click()
            End
        End Sub

        Private Sub setmain_Click()
            setmain.Caption = "MAIN:" + Text1.SelText
            Scriptmain = Trim$(Text1.SelText)
        End Sub
```

In order to be able to expose user modules, I created a class called **Userfunctions**. From this class I derived the **Userclass** object in the **Form_Load**. This object is then exposed to the VbScript engine as the User object by issuing the **AddObject** method, as you can see below.

```
        Private Sub Form_Load()
            ScriptControl1.AddObject "display", Display
            Dim userclass As Object
            Set userclass = New Userfunctions
            ScriptControl1.AddObject "User", userclass
        End Sub
```

In this class, I defined some modules that are of general use.

```
        ' userfunction class
        ' put here calls to expose to VBscript

        Dim c_message$
        Dim tmp

        Public Sub Dosomething()
```

```
        MsgBox "I did it" + c_message$,, "Activated Class"
    End Sub

    Public Property Let message(msg As String)
        c_message$ = msg
    End Property
```

The above class contains a property message and a method **Dosomething**. Since they are exposed to VbScript as the User object, you can access these items as **User.DoSomething** and **User.Message**. This code is, of course, expandable as far as you want. Furthermore, you could create as many extra classes as you like. Each of these could be added to the VbScript engine as a new object.

25.4 : Case Study 10: Additional notes on the use of Classes.

Classes can be very useful to define high level blocks of code. The end user need not know what exactly is going on but can work with an abstract object. It is sufficient that he knows the properties, methods and events associated with that class.

Suppose you have, for instance, two machines that have a similar function but a different interface. You could define a class for each. Let's call them Machine1 and Machine2. Both classes contain the same names for the methods, events and properties. However, the internal code is completely different. You could make a program that controls the machines without having to bother about the actual code for the machines. You just use an object created from their class. If you want to use the other machine, all you have to do is derive the object from the other class.

Example:

```
    ' Class for a machine from Vtronix

    Public Event Overrange()

    Private C_x
    Public Property Get Measure() As String
        Measure = "V = " + Str$(C_x) + ":Vtronix"
    End Property

    Public Property Let Range(x As String)
        C_x = x
        If (x > 100) Then RaiseEvent Overrange
    End Property
```

The above class would be the definition of an imaginative machine from the company Vtronix. This machine can be set to a certain range using the **Range** property, and can return Results using the **Measure** property. In case of an over-range, the machine will raise the **Overrange** event.

The next class defines a similar machine from the company Hvsystems.

```
' Class for a machine from VHsystems

Public Event Overrange()

Private C_x
Public Property Get Measure() As String
    Measure = "V = " + Str$(C_x) + ":VHsystems"
End Property

Public Property Let Range(x As String)
    C_x = x
    If (x > 10) Then RaiseEvent Overrange
End Property
```

All we need to do in the program, is instantiate the instruments from the proper class.

```
Private WithEvents voltmeter1 As Vtronix
Private WithEvents voltmeter2 As VHsystems

Private Sub Command1_Click()
    voltmeter1.Range = 100
    voltmeter2.Range = 10
End Sub
Private Sub Command2_Click()
    voltmeter1.Range = 10
    voltmeter2.Range = 100
End Sub
Private Sub Command3_Click()
    Label1.Caption = voltmeter1.Measure
    Label2.Caption = voltmeter2.Measure
End Sub
Private Sub Form_Load()
    Set voltmeter1 = New Vtronix
    Set voltmeter2 = New HVsystems
End Sub
Private Sub Quit_Click()
    End
End Sub
Private Sub voltmeter1_overrange()
    MsgBox " Voltmeter 1 in overrange "
End Sub
Private Sub voltmeter2_overrange()
    MsgBox " Voltmeter 2 in overrange "
End Sub
```

The main form is a simple form with three buttons and two labels. Two of the buttons program ranges to the instruments. The third retrieves measurements from the machines.

While this is example is pure hypothetical, it shows clearly the use of classes to create objects. This is exactly how the printer object works. Depending on the printer you select, the object Printer is derived from another class. If you use the method Print, it will print your piece of text to the printer. It does not matter if this is a Laser, an inkjet or a Matrix printer. The code embedded in the class knows how to handle this low-level stuff. The user only needs to know that he can print using the Print method of the Printer object.

This kind of class usage is implemented in the GPIB system described later on in this book.

ClassWork is a library of transportable instrument classes. If you need access to a machine, you simply create an instance of this class by creating a new variable of the class.

```
Dim Voltmeter as new HP34401
Voltmeter.address=4
Voltmeter.Range VoltsDc
Debug.print Voltmeter.Measure
```

These simple commands will derive an instance 'voltmeter' from the HP34401 class, assign a GPIB address and select a range. The last command retrieves a measurement. If tomorrow that machines is not available, you can simply derive the object from a different class.

```
Dim Voltmeter as new FLUKE45
```

Later on, when we start dealing with GPIB and controlling actual hardware, I will explain in detail the concept of such a system, and how you can code this in Visual Basic.

Introduction to Part IV: Visual Basic and Hardware

Now that you have learned a big deal about the language, how to write and compile programs, talk to other programs and wrap them up for distribution, create objects, classes and controls and many, many, many more things, it is time to have a look at what Visual Basic can do in a technical environment.

A chemistry lab, an electronics lab, a physics lab, even an optics or medical lab. Forgive me if during this chapter, I would appear biased towards the electronics lab.

Typical lab work includes controlling a test setup, driving instruments and collecting and processing data. Processing data is something we can do offline with existing tools. Applying Visual Basic for Lab work mainly concentrates on the application of Visual Basic programs to help use control a test setup and acquire data for us. It can automate cyclic tasks, and collect data for us. This data can either be written disk or exposed using other means (a Telnet server for instance).

In order to build such setups we will need, besides the computer and Visual Basic, a plethora of equipment. This can go from simple switches to complex measurement equipment. Some of this equipment will be connected to the computer; some might be plugged into the computer.

To bring the task of automating a test setup or 'bench' to a good end, we need to know a bit more about the possibilities of our computer. After all, there is a hardware side involved and tying the knot between software and hardware requires a firm understanding of both sides.

Chapter 26 : The Computer

Before we start controlling hardware from our code, we need to have an idea how the machine and its associated parts function, and how they interact with the software. I am confident that you already know a great deal about the hardware but perhaps not from an electronics point of view.

26.1 : The PC: A Historical Overview

The PC was initially developed as 'a smart input terminal'. When Don Estridge and his team of 13 started this project, the goal was to make a small, intelligent terminal that could run some front-end input processing software. The idea was to unload the big Mainframe computers from the time consuming task of serving consoles and devote its time purely to number crunching. The viewpoint was to make the PC a pre-processor for data.

The project set up as an open-architecture low budget kind of thing. For the first time in its history, IBM allowed external companies to do most of the work. The original prototype was thrown together using a S100 bus computer board from Intel, a debug and Monitor program (that later would become the BIOS) previously written for a 6802 CPU from Motorola and a CP/M version for 8086.

Starting from this prototype a schematic was drafted, and the monitor program was extended to become, as we know it today, the BIOS. At this point, it became clear that CP/M was too limiting as an OS for the intentions of IBM. Engineers at IBM had seen a demonstration of an operating system called QDOS, developed by a small company called Seattle Computer products. One of the engineers at IBM approached Bill Gates, who was one of the external solution providers working on the PC program. It was agreed that Microsoft would port this QDOS to the PC's hardware platform, and port a Basic interpreter written by Bill Gates (for Tandy corporation) to run on it.

When the PC first introduced to the market in 1981, PC-DOS was its primary operating system. A Lot of market analysts pointed out that this was a doomed project, since no one would buy a computer that was not attached to a mainframe.

Well, almost 25 years later they are still banging their heads against the wall. The PC outnumbers any other computer platform in the world by a factor of at least 10,000. The mainframe has been moved to the museum a long time ago, except for those very specific applications that can only be solved using the horsepower of a Massively Parallel processor like a Cray. Today every home computer holds more computing power, and has more memory then the most powerful mainframe available in 1981.

Besides the software, the hardware has evolved substantially. Where the first machine ran PC DOS 1.0, today's machines run Windows 2000, XP, XP Media Center, 2003, UNIX, Solaris, Linux, FreeBSD, BeOs and every other possible operating system. Literally millions of applications have been developed, commercial as well as shareware / freeware. So called blade computers, which are complete Pc's in a small one unit high 19-inch rack configured in clusters of 1000 or more, and running a distributed operating system like BeoWulf Linux will outperform all but the most powerful mainframe.

This PC has done for the computer revolution, what the invention of the steam machine has done for the mechanical revolution.

26.2 : The PC: A Hardware Description

The original IBM-PC hardware merely consisted of some standard chips that Intel was selling at that time. The block schematic showed the following components:

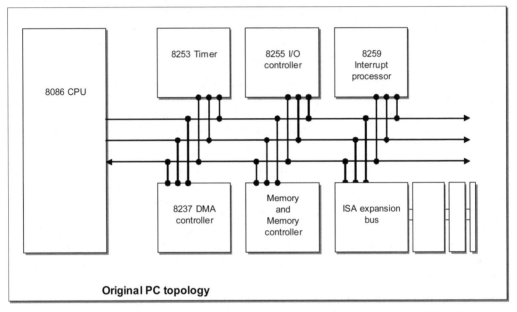

Original PC topology

Besides the CPU, memory and some chips to get the thing running there was nothing else in the machine. Every PC, whether it is an original IBM-5100 from 1979 or the latest state of the art beefed-up Dual Pentium-IV Xeon 3.8 GHz with 10 Gbyte of Rambus Memory, still adheres more or less to this topology.

You will still find an 8253 Triple timer, one or two 8259 interrupt controllers and a DMA controller of the 8237 type inside your computer. Maybe they are no longer visible as such but they are in there somewhere. The only things that have really changed in the PC are the speed and the width of the data and address bus and its interface buses.

The speed of all components and, markedly the speed of the CPU, have gone up tremendously. Where the original machine ran at a blazing 4.77 MHz, today's machines almost break the 4 GHz barrier. That is almost a 1000 fold performance!

This has led to the fact that new techniques had to be developed to cope with the new speed demons.

Things such as second level and third level cache have been developed, new internal buses emerged (VESA Local bus, PCI, AGP, PCI-Express), and new communication standards have been set forth (IRDA, PCI, Fire wire, USB). However, apart from this, the PC looks still the same.

A modern PC block diagram looks somewhat like this. The astonishing fact is, that you can translate this directly to a component schematic:

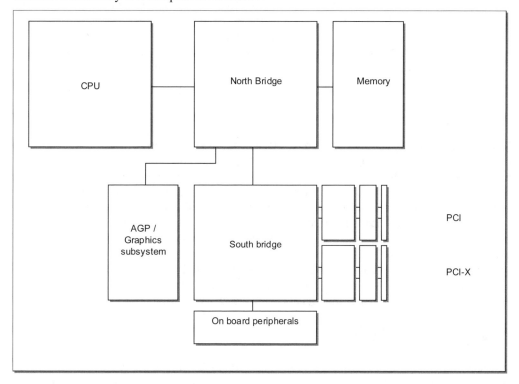

The entire PC has been scaled down to a mere three IC's. The CPU forms the main part. Today it interfaces with a so-called North bridge (although that designation is no longer correct) that contains all required electronics to interface the CPU to the memory and the PCI bus.

A third chip provides the interface between all off-board I/O and the PCI or PCI-express bus. Some additional chips like audio, Ethernet and maybe Firewire can be found as well on today's motherboards.

26.3 : The PC's Input and Output Components

So far, we have seen the parts that build a PC as we know it. All of these are located inside the box of the computer. In order to be able to connect it to the outside world, we need a means to interface the computer. And that is exactly what this chapter is all about.

26.3.1 : The Parallel port

The printer port is the standard parallel port that you normally use to connect a printer. This port is often referred to as a Centronics interface, although that is no longer correct. The Centronics interface was a 32-pin connector that happened to carry similar signals and protocol to what we today call the printer port. Over the years, the printer port has evolved far beyond the original Centronics specifications and the 32-pin connector has been abandoned altogether.

The PC has the capability to handle three printer ports. Event though it is possible to install more ports using the USB interface the number of ports available directly from the bios is still limited to three.

Whereas this port was mainly designed to attach printers and plotters, you can use it for many different tasks, and most people dealing with electronics and computers do. Over time, this port evolved as a parallel IO channel that can be used to control attached hardware. A number of professional machines use this interface to talk to the PC and the programs running on the computer. Items such as Device programmers (EPROM, Flash etc), Emulators for micro-processors to complete measuring systems are available off the shelf. The emergence of USB has pushed this port aside, to the point of almost extinction. Very few devices these days still use the parallel port and in the near future, the port will start disappearing altogether. Laptops often do not have one, and the new BTX form factor for motherboards specifies it as 'optional'. There are USB to parallel port adapters but these emulate a printer port from a printer's perspective. You cannot control individual pins like with a real printer port.

26.3.2 : The Serial port

The Serial port is the second standard port available on any computer. There are two different styles. You can have either the full-fledged 25-pin connector or the shrunken 9-pin connector. The port is controlled by a UART of the 8250 / 8251 or 165x0 types. The latter has more advanced features like transmit and receive FIFO's. However, from a programmer's point of view, these controllers all look the same.

Since a serial port holds many registers and is quite complicated to control at low level, I am not going to detail on that here and now. I will explain the things you need to know and how you can make an interface that works reliably all the time later on.

While the UART can be set to all sorts of different baud rates, parities, stop bits, modes and so on, the only one that is really important is 9600,n,8,1 mode. This is a typical communication mode, that is most widely used to talk to devices of all sorts.

I explained previously in detail the MsComm object that allows you to perform communication on this port. Later on in this section, I will discuss the hardware side of these channels. A standard PC can drive up to 4 serial ports. There are special plug in boards that give you access to more channels. However, these boards are costly and sometimes poorly supported. Anyhow, the chance that you will need more than two ports, is small.

The physical communication can take different forms. Most used is the so-called RS232 standard. For large systems, communicating over long distance, they use RS485. Like its cousin the printer port, this port is disappearing. Laptops drop this port in favor of the much faster and more versatile USB port, and motherboards have reduced the number of ports to one, if any. There are USB to serial converters that allow you to recreate the serial port but only from a serial port perspective. You can only use these to perform real serial communication and directly interfacing with the UART registers is not possible.

26.3.3 : The USB port.

This is the new standard in the PC interface domain. The reason for the development of this bus was the quest to diminish the vast amount of cables connected to a typical PC. Today's computers often require a bundle of different cables such as a PS2 keyboard, a PS@ or serial mouse, a parallel or serial printer, a serial modem, a network cable and a video cable. If you have a scanner, there is an additional cable required. An extra printer? Extra cable! In the end, you end up wit a terrible mess of all sorts of cables, and you never have the right one at hand.

USB tries to deliver the answer to this problem. By defining a universal bus that boasts fast communications in a Master to slave style you minimize the number of different cables to one. A software layer controls the transport of data from the host to the slaves. Just like in a network, you can 'split' the cable by inserting a hub. The driver inside the operating system handles all low-level tasks such as assigning the addresses and configuring the devices.

A couple of years after its introduction, USB had gained such popularity that it had become too slow to deal with all the devices hanging on the bus. Thus, a revised standard was created, dubbed USB 2.0, which boosted the maximum transfer rate from 12 to 480 megabit per second. The controllers are backward compatible and in fact, both USB1.1 and USB2.0 devices can live happily together on the same port. The controller will switch its behavior, depending on whom it is talking to.

26.3.4 : Fire Wire Channel

USB is a 'lightweight' bus, in the sense that it offers communication between a computer and its peripherals. USB is not a true network that can tie multiple computers and devices together. FireWire has a bigger capacity and additional capabilities. While the initial Firewire (an Apple trademark, Sony calls it iLink and its IEEE designation is 1394) bus had a throughput of 400 Megabit the revised 1394B standard pushes this beyond 3.2 gigabit per second.

Every device on a Firewire bus can be master or slave. While it is still true that a computer initiates a transfer, the actual dataflow can be controlled by a devices. It is possible to have two computers, a hard disk and a camcorder all interlinked using Firewire. Computer 1 talks to the hard disk, computer 2 talks to the hard disk and Computer 2 also initiated a transfer from the camera to the hard disk. All this happens simultaneously, bandwidth permitting of course. Data transport is classified according to priority and certain transfers can obtain a higher priority then others.

Firewire is commonly used for external storage and audio/video transport. The complexity of the bus, its hardware and the governing software are prohibiting all but the big developing houses to create new devices for this bus. Furthermore, a license is required to develop a Firewire device, and royalties need to be paid to Apple computers.

26.3.5 : Local Area Network (LAN) and Wide Area Network (Internet)

Most machines now either have access via a LAN board of some sort (Ethernet, Thin-net, Thick-Net, ATM, Token Ring etc...) to the premises network. This network links computers and peripherals together. Some machines, which are controlled by a computer, allow you to control them via these channels.

From a LAN to a WAN is only a small step. Controlling applications via LAN or internet is possible using the Winsock control, which has been described earlier. Since all these devices often share the same TCP/IP protocol this makes it an ideal candidate for communication. From a software perspective on the PC, this is the most universal and easiest communication. The drawback is the other side. If that is a computer then no problem. On the other hand, if it is a hardware device you are developing, then you are facing a number of problems. You need to implement the TCP/IP protocol, which requires a processor of some sort and appropriate software. Given the nature of TCP/IP transport, a relatively large buffer memory is required as well. Besides this you will also have to interface to your physical medium, whether this is 10 or 100 base-t , coax, WiFi, WiMax or optical.

26.3.6 : Field buses (CAN VAN etc)

Besides the above-mentioned communication systems, a number of dedicated automation buses have been set up. They are commonly used on factory floors and start finding their way to Lab environments. A number of instrument vendors already have equipment that can patch into these buses. The drawback of these buses, compared with the buses presented in previous points, is that you will need to buy an adapter card to plug into your pc.

The advantage is that these are very rugged buses that can withstand very harsh environments. They have no problem with noise and feature a fast data throughput and quasi real-time event handling.

26.3.7 : The GPIB Bus

Many consider this the 'golden-oldie' of all instrumentation buses. While this bus also requires a special adapter, this is possibly the most commonly used bus in instrumentation systems. While very old (end 60's), it is still regarded to as one of the most powerful buses around. The vast throughput (10MByte / second) and the well-documented bus (IEEE-488, IEEE488.2 and IEC625 standards) have lead to the huge success of this bus. Almost any data collecting equipment can be delivered off-factory with this interface on board. It allows you to connect up to 32 instruments directly onto one bus, has provisions for two masters, features interrupt capability and is overall very robust. The only prohibitive factor is its high cost. Expensive 24 pin connectors and specially shielded 24 conductor cables are required. The limited number of controller boards makes them expensive as well. The emergence of newer technologies such as USB and the now abundant presence of Ethernet based networks are slowly gaining preference over GPIB. More and more new machines feature, besides GPIB, USB or Ethernet as a communications medium, and it is expected for GPIB to disappear gradually over the next 10 to 15 years. Of course, given the long lifetime of professional test equipment, this bus still has a long life ahead of it.

26.3.8 : VXI / PXI / SCXI / etc..

These are not really connection channels to the pc, but channels amongst equipment. Typically, systems that support these buses have embedded computers. This means the PC is actually built into the same basic block that contains all the equipment. This emerging standard is still growing. A number of devices are available for these buses and these are used in factory automation projects. However, this application uses a different approach. Normally you connect your PC to a measurement setup. In these systems, you embed the computer in the system. Your PC actually becomes a fixed part of the setup. Where you normally plug acquisition board into the computer, here you plug the computer in the acquisition system. The anticipated big-boom has never happened and it looks like these buses will slowly die away in favor of other solutions.

26.3.9 : SCSI

SCSI (pronounced "skuzzy") is an acronym for the Small Computer System Interface. It grew out of a proprietary interface protocol, SASI, which was developed by Shugart Associates to connect computers to hard disk drives. Because of its origins, SCSI bus operations are oriented for efficient use by mass storage devices like hard disks, CD-ROMs, rewritable optical disk drives, and tape drives. SCSI came into widespread use around 1984 and is the standard way to connect workstations such as Sun computers to disk and tape drives. ANSI (American National Standards Institute) defines the definition of the SCSI bus, and how it should operate.

Since SCSI is used primarily as a connection to disk drives, you might wonder why we are discussing it in a chapter on data communications. The answer is that SCSI is a full-fledged peripheral bus that provides high-speed bulk communications between a host computer and slave device. Thus, although the protocols and the devices being interconnected are quite different, SCSI is very similar in function to GPIB and other data communications protocols. Over the years, SCSI has gone through a number of upgrades, each bringing a speed and feature boost. While very performant, it is virtually impossible to develop a SCSI slave device as the required hardware and software is rather complex. Besides that, the bus is specifically geared towards storage. There are external connections using specially shielded cables, but this is much more cumbersome than a USB, serial or even a printer port.

26.3.10 : Ps/2

PS/2 is the default keyboard, and mouse, interface that has replaced the old 5-pin din keyboard interface found on the original pc. Often overlooked as an interface this channel actually is fully bi-directional sporting a data and clock line and a 5-volt supply. The advantage of using this interface is that no driver software is required on the host (pc) side. Just read the input like you would read input from the keyboard. A number of peripherals such as barcode scanners actually use this interface to talk to the pc.

26.4 : The internal buses

Besides the already mentioned buses above, the PC has a number of internal buses as well. These are used to connect hardware directly. These buses are already used to interconnect the IO ports such as printer ports, video cards etcetera to the CPU and memory system. Over time, a number of buses have emerged and some have disappeared again.

26.4.1 : ISA Bus

The original PC as designed by IBM had an IO bus to plug in all sorts of components. At the same time the PC was introduced, IBM released a Technical manual describing the whole schematic of the computer and BIOS listings. From this, a number of third party developers started constructing their own add-on and plug in boards. Unfortunately IBM never specified the so called AT bus. To remedy this problem, Intel and a number of other important players started to specify timing and loading parameters. After some years, the interface bus gained the label ISA (Industry Standard Architecture) bus. While the bus was originally intended to put adapters such as video cards, printer ports, network etcetera in the computer, it also started to be used as IO bus for other boards. A number of companies provide digital I/O, AD-DA boards, relay cards and more.

Soon the bus was clogged up, because there are only a limited number of IO addresses, interrupts and DMA channels available. This and the cumbersome configuration of all the jumpers found on these early boards proved to be a big hassle and the bandwidth limitation proved critical as newer, faster processor came available.

While the original PC had an 8-bit data-bus, the introduction of the 286 called for a 16-bit bus. At that time, the designers decided to add more interrupts and DMA channels. This became known as the ISA-AT bus.

26.4.2 : EISA Bus

An attempt was made to extend the ISA bus even further while at the same time keeping it backward compatible with the ISA standard. A consortium lead by Intel and Compaq began developing what would become known as EISA (Extended Industry Standard Architecture). The main mechanical difference was a clever design for the connector slot. To support the faster and wider data and address buses many new control signals were added. Unfortunately, this caused such hardware overhead on the chipsets that the bus never caught on. Only a few machines ever used this bus and the concept was abandoned for the PCI bus.

26.4.3 : MICROCHANNEL Bus

Since the ISA bus started leading a life of it is own, IBM lost a big market share to third party developers, so they decided to reclaim their position by introducing a new IO concept. This bus featured very modern technologies such as bus mastering, interrupt sharing and other techniques that can be found in the PCI bus. Unfortunately, this bus faced the same problems as EISA. The hardware overhead made the overall implementation too expensive. Its lack of backward compatibility and the licensing fee required to develop such boards stalled the acceptance and eventually it was abandoned.

26.4.4 : VESA Bus

With the introduction of new GUI operating systems, the bandwidth to the video adapter became an important bottleneck. A consortium of Video Board manufacturers called VESA (Video Electronics Standards Association) was trying to emerge a new standard. To keep cost to a minimum, they decided to simply connect the video processor directly to the CPU's local address and data bus. The bus became widely used in the last days of the 486 processors. It managed to 'offload' the ISA bus for a number of bandwidth hungry tasks such as Video and hard disk access.

26.4.5 : PCI

The existing problems with all the internal buses mentioned before triggered Intel in 1992 to develop a new bus standard to interconnect peripheral components. The original idea was to create a standard for high-speed interconnections on a motherboard.

Since recent attempts to 'upgrade' the original ISA bus had failed, it was time to create a totally new bus architecture that could accommodate IO and perform operations in a more intelligent way. Given the fact that more and more peripherals had on-board intelligence, a mechanism was devised to allow boards to transfer data on their own. This was in essence a borrowed idea from the Micro Channel bus. In order to decouple the processor speed form the bus speed the decision was made to have a dedicate IO controller that handles all bus operation. The CPU simply creates a packet of information, stores it somewhere in memory and then tells the PCI controller where this has to go. The operation happens in parallel. This is in essence a DMA operation but PCI took it a step further. Intel started integrating this bus architecture in its motherboard chipsets and pretty soon card manufacturers started developing boards for PCI.

26.4.6 : PCI express

Over the years PCI evolved, culminating in today's PCI express. The ever-increasing requirement for bandwidth poses such a strain on the physical interconnections that it was no longer possible to send data parallel over a connector. The electrical load formed by all the connections, and the time sharing nature of a backplane bus prohibited further development. PCI express takes this problem away by first reducing the 60 something interface signals of normal PCI en replacing them with a serial data link, and secondly aborting the concept of a bus and make the communication links essentially point to point. On PCI express, boards no longer share the same electrical signals. Instead, they each have dedicated channels directly into the PCI express controller. PCI express is thus no longer a 'bus' structure.

PCI express, or PCIx for short, also offers the possibility to scale the speed of the interface.

26.4.7 : AGP port

Another step on the evolutionary ladder, the AGP bus tried to offload the bandwidth hungry video operations from the PCI bus. The PCI standard has a strict timing scheme that allows no one to stretch the limits of the bus. The AGP (Advanced Graphics Port) is not a real bus. It only supports one device and has no purpose other then feeding data to graphics boards. You can think of it as follows, 'AGP is to PCI what VESA was to ISA': a dedicated high-speed channel for Video applications.

26.4.8 : PCMCIA - PC Card - CardBus

Several years ago, when notebooks became popular a new problem had to be faced: How do we get add-on boards in such a tiny little box? Two consortia, one in Japan (JEIDA) and on in the USA (PCMCIA) started developing a new bus. In 1989, the PCMCIA consortium accepted the JEIDA developed connector standard and today these two consortia work together to promote this form factor. The official name for the bus has since then become 'PC-Card'. A special controller chip bridges the PCMCIA bus to the ISA or PCI bus and handles the interface. Cardbus is an extension of PCMCIA that allows it to actually bring a limited version of the PCI interface bus onto the same connector. The Cardbus controller figures out the type of board connected and will either emulate the ISA standard if an old style PCMCIA is detected, or connect the PCI bus to the device if a Cardbus compatible peripheral is detected.

The small form factor of these cards, originally devised for flash storage, has proven prohibitive to develop plug-in boards. Many interface cards require so called 'dongles' to attach the connectors to these cards.

26.4.9 : I2C Bus / SMbus

This bus was designed by Philips semiconductors in the early 80's as an easy way to interconnect integrated circuits. The Inter-Integrated Circuit (IIC or I2C) bus was designed to get rid of parallel address and data buses. It is a sort of serial communication bus that only requires two signals plus a ground. It features multi-master operations and collision detection in hardware. While it was originally intended to find its way in consumer electronics such as TV's, Video's and audio equipment, it now is found on computer motherboards as well. This bus is used for system monitoring and handles tasks such as battery control, temperature control, voltage and hardware monitoring etc. Typically, a small processor (the same CPU that handles keyboard and mouse) controls this bus and provides an interface to this I2C bus. In portable computers, this bus is also used for the touch-pad or stick that replaces the mouse.

SMBus, short for System Management Bus, is a modification of I2C in the sense that a hardware timeout has been added. If a transmission takes longer than a certain amount of time, or a line is stuck for longer than a given amount of time then all device on the bus reset themselves. This bus is commonly used to read the configuration parameters from the DDRAM memory boards.

26.4.10 : PC104

PC104 is not a bus in itself, but rather a computer form-factor standard. When the PC gained acceptance as an industrial control platform, it turned out that the big boards were cumbersome for many applications. Besides that, the card-edge connectors were to prone to bad contacts in industrial environments. A new form-factor emerged that was standardized as PC104. The ISA bus was adapted as interface between individual PC104 boards and a new connector was assigned. Later incorporations of PC104 include, besides the ISA interface the PCI interface as well, again adapted with an industrial connector.

26.4.11 : CompactPCI

CompactPCI is a small footprint version of the PCI interface. It features all of the PCI bus signals except the multiple IRQ and DMA signals, as it supports only one device. The connector is base don the SO-DIMM memory connectors often found in notebooks. Its usage is commonly for small footprint boards that are embedded somewhere in either a laptop or small form factor computer such as an industrial controller. Typical CompactPCI boards are wireless LAN transceivers and modems.

Chapter 27 : Controlling External PC ports

If you want to control a system attached to the computer you have a number of possibilities. You can either interface via a standard channel, such as the serial port or USB, or you can go the industrial way and use buses links like SCSI, GPIB and the likes. However, when building electronics, you do not always have the possibility to use these buses due to the hard and software overhead.

For the quick and dirty job, you only have two real options. Go serial (RS232) or bit-bang your stuff on a printer port. Each of these has a number of advantages and shortcomings. Given the availability of many USB solutions these days, this also becomes a viable option but required a bit more, albeit not much, work.

If these options do not fit the task at hand, you can invest some more time and use an off the shelf IO board plugged into your computer.

Your last option is to create a custom block of hardware from scratch and interface directly to the guts of the machine, bypassing the normal I/O ports found on the backside of a computer. This chapter will detail on these normal ports, while the next chapter will take a deeper look into the latter option.

27.1 : Finding the IO ports

Controlling PC I/O channels is very nice but before you can control them, you have to have an idea where to find them. You can apply a few rules of thumb.

As we have seen before, serial ports can be handled through the MsComm object. For these ports you do not need to know where exactly they reside in your system, as long as you know how many are present and where their connector is. You can use the system explorer in Windows to get a detailed listing of these devices.

Parallel ports can only reside on three possible addresses: 378, 278 and 3BC. However, most computers only have one and that is typically 378, although on notebooks and some computers it might be 0x3BC.

Custom I/O boards can only be mapped into specific regions of the IO address space of the PC.

You can either consult the manual for your particular I/O board or, in case of the printer ports, ask the computer where they reside. The only question remaining is how do I get the computer to tell me?

27.1.1 : The BIOS system area

During startup of the computer (even before the operating system boots), the BIOS program scans all hardware. The BIOS is a library with routines to perform I/O on your computer. It has simple routines to write text to the display, initialize the disk array etc. In other words, it makes your computer work. This BIOS performs a number of scans to detect the hardware present in the computer. It stores this information not only for the user but also for itself in the so-called BIOS data area. This is the portion of main memory on page 0 at offset 400.

This block of data exists even under Windows and Windows NT. The reason is simple: you cannot move this for risk of losing backward compatibility. A lot of older DOS style and 16-bit style programs access this page to retrieve such needed information. In other words, you can always retrieve data from it.

When the BIOS has completed its task and hands over control to the bootstrap loader, it leaves this data in memory. This data is sometimes called the System area or the 'System Metrics' Data. It is a block of 256 bytes that gives information about the machine.

A typical page dump looks like this

```
-d 0040:0000 ff
0040:0000  F8 03 F8 02 E8 03 E8 02-78 03 78 02 00 00 00 00    ........x.x.....
0040:0010  23 C8 00 80 02 00 30 A0-00 00 36 00 36 00 30 52    #.....0...6.6.0R
0040:0020  30 52 20 39 32 50 35 4C-35 4C 08 0E 08 0E 08 0E    0R 92P5L5L......
0040:0030  66 21 66 21 0D 1C 30 52-3A 34 30 52 30 52 01 00    f!f!..0R:40R0R..
0040:0040  04 00 20 00 00 00 00 00-00 03 50 00 40 20 00 00    ..........P.@..
0040:0050  00 17 00 00 00 00 00 00-00 00 00 00 00 00 00 00    ................
0040:0060  07 04 00 D4 03 29 30 76-07 87 1C FF 84 6F 13 00    .....)0v......o..
0040:0070  00 00 00 00 00 02 08 00-14 14 14 3C 01 01 01 01    ...........<....
0040:0080  1E 00 3E 00 31 08 00 60-09 11 0B 80 58 00 00 07    ..>.1..`....X...
0040:0090  87 07 00 00 00 00 00 10-12-A0 00 40 00 88 FD FF FF    ..........@.....
0040:00A0  00 00 00 00 00 00 00 00-2E 39 00 C0 00 00 00 00    .........9......
0040:00B0  00 00 00 00 00 00 00 00-00 00 00 00 00 00 00 00    ................
0040:00C0  00 00 00 00 00 00 00 00-00 00 00 00 00 00 00 00    ................
0040:00D0  00 00 00 00 00 00 00 00-00 00 00 01 00 00 00 30    ...............0
0040:00E0  00 00 00 00 00 00 00 00-00 00 00 00 00 00 00 00    ................
0040:00F0  00 00 00 00 00 00 00 00-00 00 00 00 00 00 00 00    ................
-
```

Most of this stuff is irrelevant for what we do, and can be overridden by the operating system anyway. However, some very interesting things can be found. Let us look at the very first line.

```
0040:0000  F8 03 F8 02 E8 03 E8 02-78 03 78 02 00 00 00 00    ........x.x.....
```

We are interested in this line, since it shows the available ports and the addresses they are located at. The first four words specify the serial ports and the next three words specify the parallel ports. The last word is undetermined. Some machines use it for a fourth printer port but in general, it is not in use.

Note	A port address is specified by 2 bytes in little-endian coding. This means that, in order to obtain the correct address, you have to swap the high and low byte. Example F8 03 becomes 0x03f8.

From left to right we find this 0x03f8 0x02f8 0x03e8 0x 02e8 for the serial ports and 0x0378 and 0x0278 for the parallel ports. This means on this particular machine, there are four serial ports and two parallel ports. If a port locator contains 0x0000 it means that this port does not exist. The BIOS functions (and most DOS programs and) use these tables to look up the address for their transactions. This means that, if you want to put a LPT port at a certain address, you can plug in the board and specify the address here yourself. Any printer routine will then be redirected to this new address.

Certain newer BIOS routines will fill all three ports by default. Two scenarios exist: one address is marked more than one time, in which the right most of the two is a redirected port to the left-most one in this table. The other scenario shows three different addresses but only one or two ports are physically present, in which case only the first or first two addresses are valid. This has to do with the way the BIOS is written. Some BIOS programs no longer probe for the existence of the card but simply copy the numbers as they have been set in the configuration screen by the user. The reason is that, given the fact that a BIOS becomes more complex, the memory space is limited and has become smallish in respect to what code needs to be put in there. Therefore, the non-essential routines such as these detecting schemes are the first to go.

27.1.2 : Using DEBUG to snoop around

Check the BIOS data area of your computer is easily done by using the DEBUG tool found on any computer. The DEBUG tools dates back from DOS 1.2. While this is a very powerful toolset, it is also potentially a very dangerous tool. If you have no clue what a certain DEBUG command do, then you should not try them without at least reading the help, or a book about machine language programming first. In the best case, you run the risk of crashing the computer, but in the worst case, you wipe out the partition data of the hard disk while doing it.

What I am going to describe now is harmless for your computer. The above doomsday scenario was just intended to warn you not to experiment with commands that are not explained here, unless you know what you are doing.

Debug can mostly be found in the DOS or WINDOWS\COMMAND directory and should normally be included in your search path by default.

Open a command box by clicking on START, go to RUN, type COMMAND and click OK. At the dos prompt simply type debug and hit enter.

```
C:\>debug
-
```

You will get the debug prompt "-".To display the commands at your disposal simply type? and press return.

```
C:\>debug
-?
assemble      A [address]
compare       C range address
dump          D [range]
enter         E address [list]
fill          F range list
go            G [=address] [addresses]
hex           H value1 value2
input         I port
load          L [address] [drive] [firstsector] [number]
move          M range address
name          N [pathname] [arglist]
output        O port byte
proceed       P [=address] [number]
quit          Q
register      R [register]
search        S range list
trace         T [=address] [value]
unassemble    U [range]
write         W [address] [drive] [firstsector] [number]
allocate expanded memory        XA [#pages]
deallocate expanded memory      XD [handle]
map expanded memory pages       XM [Lpage] [Ppage] [handle]
display expanded memory status  XS
-
```

As you can see, a wealth of instructions allows you to manipulate virtually everything on your computer.

Note Keep in mind that, when running debug under windows NT, 2000, XP or Server 2003, the input and output commands will cause a general protection failure. I/O access is restricted under these operating systems and even Debug has to comply with this.

27.1.2.1 : The Dump command

Probably one of the most important commands is the D (ump) command. It allows you to physically examine the contents of the memory.

```
-d 0040:0
0040:0000   F8 03 F8 02 E8 03 E8 02-78 03 78 02 00 00 00 00   ........x.x.....
0040:0010   23 C8 00 80 02 00 30 A0-00 00 1E 00 1E 00 75 16   #.....0.......u.
0040:0020   67 22 0D 1C 3F 32 0D 1C-0D 1C 0D 1C 64 20 20 39   g"..?2......d  9
0040:0030   30 52 30 52 34 4B 30 52-3A 34 30 52 0D 1C 01 00   0R0R4K0R:40R....
0040:0040   D6 00 20 00 00 00 00 00-00 03 50 00 40 20 00 00   ........P.@..
0040:0050   00 31 00 00 00 00 00 00-00 00 00 00 00 00 00 00   .1..............
0040:0060   07 04 00 D4 03 29 30 76-07 87 1C 04 E3 8C 10 00   .....)0v........
0040:0070   00 00 00 00 00 02 08 00-14 14 14 3C 01 01 01 01   ...........<....
-
```

If you simply type 'd 0040:0' and hit return, this command will show you the part of memory mentioned in the previous topic. Once you found what you need its time to leave DEBUG. This is done by simply hitting Q and pressing enter or return.

27.2 : Hardware Access

Now that we have decided what port to use, and we have found out the required information about its location, both physical and logical, it is time to look at how we can transmit information across. Any port inside the PC is accessible via a set of instructions residing in the microprocessor. The PC's processor has a separate IO space that is accessed using IN and OUT instructions. Hardware access is one of the things that Microsoft deliberately shields from the user. The entire base of Windows has a hardware abstraction layer that relies on so-called drivers to interface with the hardware. For the serial ports, USB ports, Ethernet ports and even printer ports, a whole range of drivers is available. Unfortunately, if no driver exists for our custom hardware, or we want to do something that the default windows driver does not provide, we will need access to the hardware.

Writing a driver is not an easy task, since it requires a great deal of knowledge of the internal workings of the operating system. Fortunately, there are plenty of IO engines available that can give you access to the most basic input and output commands. Win95IO is such an engine. This 32-bit DLL (see the topic on DLLs earlier in this book) was crafted in assembler and bypasses the operating system to read and write the registers directly.

There is, however, one more pitfall that even WIN95IO cannot circumvent. WindowsNT / 2000 / XP include an additional layer of software in the operating system that can detect such accesses. DLLs no longer run on the lowest level but on an abstraction level in these operating systems. Any attempt to access the hardware directly, will generate an exception and the program will terminate. On these operating systems, only a so-called system driver can create access.

Fortunately, here there is a solution too. The GiveIO system driver can restore the access to the lower levels. All that is required, is the installation of this system driver and the programs will work correctly. You can find GiveIO on the internet by simply using Google and searching for the word giveio.

Win95IO is explained in detail in the appendixes of this book.

Chapter 28 : The Printer port In Detail

This port (sometimes also called the Centronics port) dates from long before there was a PC. As the name indicates, it is a communication port mainly intended to control an attached printer. The Centronics designation comes from a company with the same name that has designed this kind of interface. Of course, we are not interested in its capabilities to drive a printer but more as a universal IO channel existing on any PC.

28.1 : Functional diagram

The schematic below shows the implementation of a standard printer port almost as it was found in the original IBM PC. The only elements lacking in this diagram, is the feedback patch from the data out to the input and the appropriate address decoding circuitry. Nevertheless, this diagram gives you a good overview of what is tied together and to what pins the signal are routed.

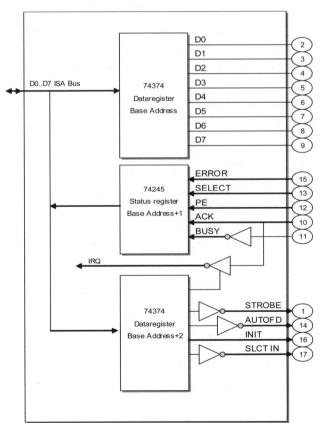

28.2 : Register level description

The table below shows an address map of any printer port. Besides the standard ports, there are today also ports known as EPP, ECP or bi-directional.

	D7	D6	D5	D4	D3	D2	D1	D0	
Base	D7	D6	D5	D4	D3	D2	D1	D0	Output Register
	9	8	7	6	5	4	3	2	
Base + 1	BS	AQ	OP	SL	ER	-	-	-	Status Register
	11	10	12	13	15	-	-	-	
Base + 2	-	-	-	IE	SI	IP	AF	ST	Control Register
	-	-	-	-	17	16	14	1	

A typical PC has at least one port (mostly on 0x378, sometimes on 0x3bc depending on where it resides). As explained in the previous chapter you can have up to three printer-ports in a PC. The numbers shown above correspond to the pin number of the 25-pole D-connector used for this kind of port.

The following table explains the meaning of the abbreviations used.

BS	Busy	Input
/A/Q	Acknowledge	Input
OP	Out of Paper	Input
SL	Select	Input
ER	Error	Input
IE	IRQ enable	Input
SI	Select input	Bidirectional
IP	Initialize Printer	Bidirectional
AF	Auto Feed	Bidirectional
ST	Strobe	Output

The Acknowledge pin is inverted inside the printer port hardware!

As you can see from the above, the printer port opens up many possibilities to control boards. In essence, you have 9 outputs and 6 inputs, not counting the bidirectional ones. However, since a printer port is part of the computer main board these days, care should be taken not to destroy it accidentally. The following schematic shows a typical interface that will protect the port under most circumstances. It also acts as a buffer to clean up the signals generated by the port.

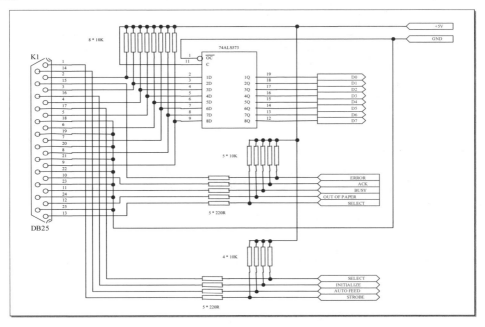

The pull-up resistors are required. Most people think that this is not the case. The deal is that the output channel of the Port is very strong in pulling lines low, but rather limited in pulling them back high. This tends to lead to not-so-clean edges for rising edge transients. Some attached electronics can have problems with this.

The above schematics also show how to make a 'safe' interface for all pins. In most cases, you will only use the D0 to D7 and four or five of the real input pins. Sometimes the Strobe pin is used as well. If you want to make systems that are transparent for printer information, you should use the Strobe pin as a disable pin. The printer accepts data when the strobe pin goes low. During that time, your hardware should not interfere with normal operations.

28.3 : Basic operations

If not used to drive a printer, a printer port can be used to control some external device such as an EPROM programmer, IO board or other piece of electronics. You will find that most often the port is used to create some pseudo serial interface. This 'emulation' is called bit banging and further on in this book.

To control the pins you need to make use of the INP and OUT commands of WIN95io. For people coming from a DOS basic: these operate in exactly the same way as under DOS basic. In the table below the mapping of the addresses is shown once again.

Base	D7	D6	D5	D4	D3	D2	D1	D0	Output Register
	9	8	7	6	5	4	3	2	
Base + 1	BS	AQ	OP	SL	ER	-	-	-	Status Register
	11	10	12	13	15	-	-	-	
Base + 2	-	-	-	IE	SI	IP	AF	ST	Control Register
	-	-	-	-	17	16	14	1	

Suppose you want to control the lines D0 to D7. The table shows that these are mapped onto the BASE address (which can be 378, 278 or 3BC). So, in order to send the byte '5A' simple do the following:

```
Const LPTport = &h378
Out LPTport, &h5a
```

The status register shows the status of the five input pins. To extract data, you simply execute an INP statement:

```
Const LPTport = &h3BC
X = INP (LPTport +1)
```

Note in the above examples that I define a constant to access the printer port. If you do this as a global in a module, it becomes easier to modify your program to run on different ports. You could also store the address for the printer port in a variable. That way you can dynamically change the address for the used port. You could then allow the user to redirect the IO to a different port (via an option or setup menu for instance).

Now that you have retrieved this information, you can use Boolean operations such as AND OR and NOT to isolate the bit or bits you want.

28.4 : Bit-Banging interfaces

As already explained, in most case the printer port will be used to emulate some kind of serial device interface. Typical uses are SPI, I2C, Micro Wire, and JTAG etc. They can even be proprietary interface such as test patterns for an integrated circuit.

Whereas there are several approaches to bit banging, only few are really interesting and transparent.

28.4.1 : Simple line control

When you simply need the printer port to act as a simple IO device the easiest approach is to make subroutines to control each line.

Suppose you have eight relays that must be controlled independently. The problem is that you can only write to the output. You cannot read from it (sometimes you can, but this depends on the printer port installed in the computer). Therefore, whatever information was present is overwritten and lost. The solution is to use an internal variable that holds the data to be sent out. The contents of this variable are modified at will and then written to the output port.

```
Dim portdata as integer
Const LPTport = &h378

Sub RelayOn(relay)
    Portdata = portdata or (2 ^ relay)
    Out LPTport,portdata
End sub

Sub RelayOff(relay)
    Portdata = portdata and (255-(2 ^ relay))
    Out LPTport,portdata
End Sub
```

The above routines simply calculate the binary value that corresponds with every output pin. In addition, depending on the routine set it using an OR function or reset it using an AND operation with the inverted pattern. Let us take a closer look:

Operation		Output status	Comment
Portdata = 82		01010010	Relays 7,5 and 2 are currently on
RelayOn (5)	$2^5 = 32$	00100000	we want to set relay 6 on as well
OR on the above numbers		01110010	The relays that were on are still on
RelayOff(5)		00100000	
Inversion of this mask (255-(2^r))		11011111	
ANDing the mask with the data		01010010	The relay is back off.

This piece of source shows you simple IO operations. However, there is more.

28.4.2 : Serial protocol emulation

Another example might use different pins for different purposes. Let us look at a simple shift register. This typically consists of a data input and a clock. There might also be a reset pin.

Suppose that reset is attached to D0, DATA is attached to pin D2 and CLOCK is attached to pin D5 of the printer port. The value of D0 = 1, D2 = 4 and D5 = 32.

Note	These values are simple binary conversions. You get the value of a pin from the following formula: value = 2 ^ number of the bit.

```
Dim LPTport,LPTdata
LPTport = &h3bc
LPTdata=0
Const RESETPIN = 1 ' these numbers are decimal representations
Const DATApin = 4  ' of the value of each pin. they are not the
Const CLOCKpin =32 ' pin numbers !!
```

The above is the initialization code. Now there are two ways to implement the actual code.

Example 1: Monolithic Code.

```
Sub transmit (pattern$)
    Out lptport,reset
    Out lptport,0
    For x = 1 to len (pattern$)
        If mid$(pattern$,x,1) = 1 then
            Out lptport,datapin
            Out lptport,datapin+clockpin
            Out lptport,datapin
            Out lptport,0
        Else
            Outlptport,0
            Out lptport,clockpin
            Out lptport,0
        End if
    Next x
End Sub
```

The above program is actually very simple for the person writing this, but to debug this, it gets a bit more complex. Moreover, for someone who is casting his eyes on this code for the first time it might look crazy. Now in this example it is still fairly easy but in most cases the program is more complicated. You might need to control some additional pins as well. The additions might look like this:

```
Out lptport,datapin+clockpin+chipselect+notreset
```

If you need to modify the protocol, you will most likely have to rewrite all of this code. The solution is to partition your code. The above routine is called a Monolithic piece of code. This is completely against all the concepts in Object oriented programming and should be avoided in all cases.

Example 2: Partitioned code.

```
Sub transmit (pattern$)
    ResetHi
    ResetLo
    For x = 1 to len (pattern$)
        If mid$(pattern$,x,1) = 1 then
            DataPinHI
        Else
            DataPinLo
        End if
    Next x
End Sub

Sub ResetHi()
    LPTdata = lptdata or resetpin
    Out LPTport,LPTdata
End Sub
Sub ResetLo()
    LPTdata = LPTdata and (255-ResetPin)
    Out LPTport,LPTdata
End Sub
Sub ClockHi()
    LPTdata = LPTdata or Clockpin
    Out LPTport,LPTdata
End Sub
Sub ClockLo()
    LPTdata = LPTdata AND (255-clockpin)
    Out LPTport,LPTdata
End sub
Sub DataHi()
    LPTdata = LPTdata OR datapin
    Out LPTport,LPTdata
End sub
Sub DataLo()
    LPTdata = LPTdata AND (255-datapin)
    Out LPTport,LPTdata
End sub
```

The above code is a lot longer to write but much easier to debug. You can nearly find the timing diagram implemented as code.

28.5 : Printer port Control Using ClassWork

Before we take a look at the actual code, a few words on Classwork. This is a library of routines I often use to control hardware and test equipment and that, over the years, has grown to include many devices. It is based entirely on classes, hence its name Classwork. Classes and their usage have been explained earlier in this book.

To use the printer port class, simply load the Printerport.cls file into your project.

```
Dim lptport as new Printerport.
LPTport.address = &h378
LPTport.D0 = True
LPTport.D5 = False
LPTport.dta = 123
If LPTport.BS = true then msgbox "Pin 11 is logic High"
```

This Class allows you to control all pins of the printer port independently. Assigning a new value to the DTA property can also change the output register.

Method or property	Function	Implementation	Type
D0. D7	Output pins D0 to D7 individually controllable	Sub	Boolean
Dta	The output pins D0 to D7 as a byte	Sub	Integer
BS,AQ,OP,SL,ER	The input pins individually	Function	Boolean
Nibble	The high 4 bits of status register scaled down	Function	integer

Note	The inversion in the printer port for the AQ pin is taken into account. If the result of function is TRUE then the corresponding pin is at logic High!

28.6 : Special printer port modes

28.6.1 : Bi-directional Parallel Ports

While I have shown you before how you can 'fake' a bi-directional port, this brings some problems in terms of software overhead and speed. Clever tricks allowed the standard parallel port design to be used for data input by making use of four of the five status register input lines to input data from an external device a nibble at a time. The fifth input line is used for handshake signals. A number of programs that allow you to transfer data between your desktop computer and your laptop machine by hooking their parallel ports together uses this technique. Software such as LapLink or even the interlink / intersvr program included in MS-DOS or the Direct-Cable connection used by Windows 95/98 use this mechanism.

Some people found out that the original implementation from IBM actually could be used in a full bidirectional mode, but that this feature had got lost in the course of time, due to an incorrect implementation and cost-savings. An additional drawback was that the output drivers could not be switched off, so you could only read back what you were writing to the port.

The increasing demand for a faster bi-directional port prompted the hardware vendors to draft up the Enhanced Parallel port. IBM enabled the parallel port for bi-directional operation by allowing the data register outputs to be tri-stated using bit 5 of the control register. At the same time, they devised a mechanism to allow high-speed bi-directional data transfers using DMA.

To make confusion even greater, Intel also introduced a Fast Mode parallel port that allowed higher speed data transfers.

Unfortunately, very few of the PC manufacturers adopted these ports due to either cost or licensing reasons.

28.6.2 : The IEEE 1284 Standard

Eventually the IEEE stepped in and decided to create some standardization in the parallel-port variations. IEEE Proposal 1284 defines five modes of parallel-port operation that allow parallel ports on PCs and peripheral devices (printers, scanners, modems, and so on) having differing capabilities to inter-operate with each other.

Compatibility Mode	This is the original mode of operation used by the PC parallel-port interface. It operates according to the Centronics Corporation Printer interface specification, with data being sent only from the PC to the external device. The signal definitions are described earlier in this section.
Nibble Mode	This mode uses the status line inputs of the original PC parallel interface to implement data transfers from the external device to the PC. Data bytes are transmitted over four of the status lines as two sequential 4-bit nibbles.
Byte Mode	This is the mode introduced by IBM on the PS/2. The improved parallel-port circuitry required to implement this mode allows data bytes to be transmitted over the data lines from an external device to the PC when the direction bit (bit 5) is set in the PC's control register.
EPP Mode.	The Enhanced Parallel Port Mode uses the parallel port data lines as an 8-bit bi-directional bus. Besides transmitting data, an addressing mechanism is available that for the first time allows the parallel port to operate as a bus.
ECP Mode.	The Extended Capabilities Port Mode is by far the most advanced and fastest interface but requires very complex parallel port circuitry. It allows a PC and an external device to freely communicate back and forth with each other. Enhanced parallel port circuitry allows a complete bypass of the original parallel-port control circuitry and it implements a completely new handshaking protocol.

The standard provides full backward compatibility by specifying the port to start up in Compatibility mode. Only when programs deliberately reprogram the port to any of the other modes will the interface controller switch over to the newer modes.

A mechanism was devised to allow detection of the capabilities of the connected peripheral. The computer sets the SLCT IN pin logic high and the AUTO FD pin to a logic low. If the attached device is 1284-compliant, it will respond by making the ERROR, SLCT, and PE pins high and pulling the ACK pin to ground.

This is a unique signature that will not be generated by a simple device. When this behavior is detected, the new modus-operandi can be programmed by setting the desired mode on the data lines and pulsing the strobe line. If this particular request is granted, the attached peripheral will set the SLCT pin high and pull the PE pin low. IF the requested mode is not supported both the SLCT and PE will go low. The one exception to this is Nibble Mode, for which the peripheral should respond with SLCT low and PE high.

Pin	Driven by	Centronics	Nibble	Byte	ECP	EPP
2-9	Host or peripheral	DO-D7	DO-D7	DO-D7	DO-D7	ADO AD7
1	Host	Strobe	HostClk	HostClk	HostClk	Write
14	Host	Auto FD	HostBusy	HostBusy	HostAck	DStrb
16	Host	Init	Init	Init	Reverse Request	Init
17	Host	Select In	1284 Active	1284 Active	1284 Active	AStrb
15	Peripheral	Error	DataAvail	DataAvail	Periph Request	User defined
13	Peripheral	Select	Xflag	Xflag	Xflag	User defined
12	Peripheral	Paper End	AckDataReq	AckDataReq	AckReverse	User defined
10	Peripheral	Ack	PtrClk	PtrClk	PeriphClk	Intr
11	Peripheral	Busy	PtrBusy	PtrBusy	PeriphAck	-Wait

28.7 : Enhanced Parallel Port

This port was developed in a co-partnership between Intel and Xircom and is the easiest to control, for the port hardware automatically creates all handshaking signals as opposed to require the software to do this, which was the case with the standard Centronics port.

Since the regular pin names are probably more familiar to the reader, I will use the normal signal names when explaining this mode. The real EPP names are mentioned between brackets.

In EPP Mode, the signals Paper End, Error, and Select are not used for communication. The driver software is free to control these bits to signal additional information to an attached device, but they play no role in the active data transport. An EPP device can request service by pulling the Acknowledge (interrupt) line low. The Init (init) pin the host to signal to all attached peripheral devices to terminate EPP Mode and return to Compatibility Mode.

An EPP device basically has two transport mechanisms: one for data and one for address. An EPP device is no longer a simple 8-bit port you write to, but can have many control registers that you can address. Imagine, for instance, a hard disk attached to an EPP port (these do exist). A normal hard disk has 16 registers that can be controlled. EPP has no problem in accommodating such devices as it can transmit a sub address.

The EPP mode has bus-oriented operations that provide some very significant benefits. Once a device register address has been selected, the EPP Mode port circuitry allows subsequent data bytes to be transferred using a single I/O instruction per byte. This results in very high burst rates to be achieved using string I/O instructions.

A typical EPP port can transfer 1.5-2 MBytes/sec transfer rates, which is 8 to 10 times greater than that of a simple Centronics parallel port and even outruns USB1.1. Since EPP is a bus structure, you can have multiple devices attached to one port.

The downside of all this extra capability in an EPP-compatible port is that the circuitry required to interface is far more complex than for a simple parallel port and the low-level driver software is correspondingly also more complex.

28.7.1 : Communication using the EPP protocol

28.7.1.1 : The EPP Handshake

Before data can be exchanged between the computer and an EPP device, both the port and the device must be switched to EPP mode. Since an EPP capable port requires a specific state on the pins before the port can actually be switched into EPP mode, we need to set this up. This is done by writing 00000100 to the control port (base+2).

To initiate an EPP transfer cycle, all you need to do is write information to the relevant EPP register.

28.7.1.2 : The EPP registers

The EPP Port also has a new set of registers. However, the base three registers have been inherited from the Standard Parallel Port. Below is a table showing the new and existing registers.

Address	Port Name	Read/Write
Base + 0	Data Port (SPP)	Write
Base + 1	Status Port (SPP)	Read
Base + 2	Control Port (SPP)	Write
Base + 3	Address Port (EPP)	Read/Write
Base + 4	Data Port (EPP)	Read/Write
Base + 5	MSB of 16bit transfer / SLSB of 32bit Transfers	
Base + 6	TLSB of a 32bit Transfers	
Base + 7	MSB of a 32 bit transfer	

The three first registers are identical of those of a standard printer port, so nothing new there. To use the EPP functionality you must use the additional registers. To send a byte to the slave, all you need to do is, write your data to base+4, and the controller board does the rest. Likewise, to change an address you place the address in base+3 and the rest is governed by the EPP circuitry. Both the data and address register are read/write so you can simply treat these as variables.

There is one slight modification to the Status port (base+1). The reserved bit (bit 0) now flags a time-out on the EPP port and is used to signal a loss of communication with the slave device. The timeout period is in the order of 10uS, and here is a first indication that you will need special hardware to respond in a timely fashion to EPP commands. If this bit is set, you have to clear it yourself and take appropriate action. Normally your communication driver should check and clear this bit before each read or write operation.

The last three registers, Base + 5, Base + 6 and Base + 7 can be used to perform direct 16 bit and 32 bit read/write operations. The data will automatically be split into bytes and transported sequentially under control of the EPP engine. However, not all implementations support these modes.

28.7.2 : Interfacing with an EPP system.

As the entire operation is hardware based, very little software is required. Actually, the only thing that needs to be done, is reading and writing to and from the EPP address and data registers and checking the timeout bit. During startup, it may be required to initialize the port in the correct mode.

Let us have a closer look at the individual operations,

28.7.2.1 : Write Data or Address to the target

When the PC wants to perform an EPP operation to write to the target device, it will pull the Write strobe low (1) and place an value on the data pins D0 to D7 (2).

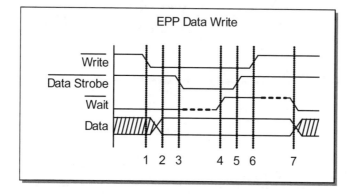

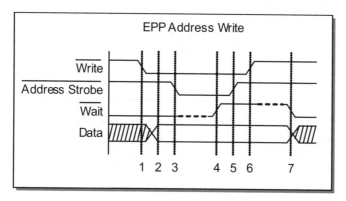

Next the computer will check for the WAIT line to be low and then drive the Data Strobe or Address strobe to a low level (3), depending on whether the operation is a data or address write operation.

The slave sees this high to low transition on the strobe and latches in the information from the data pins. When the slave has acquired the information, it will signal this to the host by making the WAIT line high (4). The host will then de-assert the Address or Data strobe (5) and de-assert the Write line (6). The bus is then free to perform more operations (7).

28.7.2.2 : Reading Data or Address from the target.

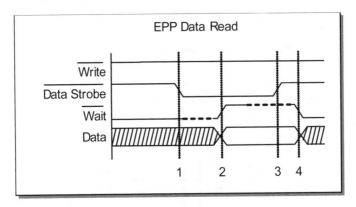

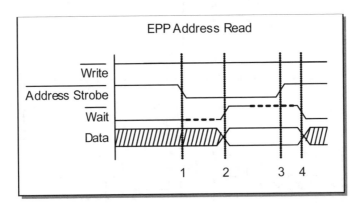

The read operations are similar in nature as the wrote operations except that this time the Write pin is not driven low and the Data bits D0 tot D7 are being driven from the slave side. The host drives the Data or Address strobe low and waits for the WAIT pin to become high. The host then samples the data available on the data bus and proceeds to de-assert the Strobe signal.

28.7.3 : Interface electronics

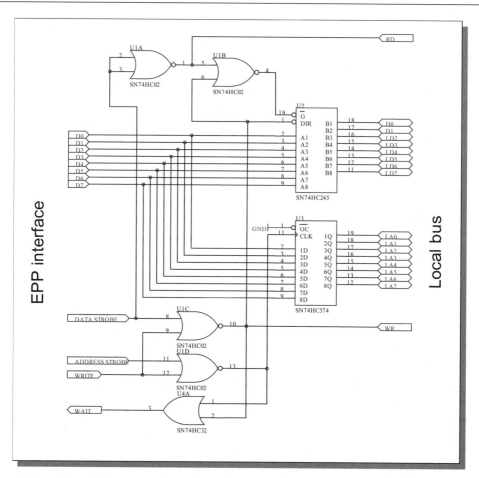

The above schematic shows a rudimentary EPP interface circuit. Note that it does not allow for reading back of the Address register though. The local bus behaves in a simple manner. Any Address write operation will put a new address value in the octal latch (74HC574). An EPP data write operation will put the data on the output of the octal bus transceiver (74HC245) and make the WR line logic high. It is up to your circuitry to sample this data.

During an EPP data read operation the bus transceiver (74HC245) is switched in reverse direction and a RD strobe is given. During this RD strobe, your circuitry must output the requested data onto LD0 to LD7.

A fully compliant interface circuit would require a bit more electronics and should actually have its own internal clock circuitry to latch on to the incoming data. The above gives you a simple circuit that allows you to experiment with the EPP transfer modes.

28.8 : Extended Capabilities Port

The Enhanced capabilities Port, or ECP for short, is by far the fastest and most powerful transport method over a printer port. Unfortunately, this comes at a price. The required hardware in the device is extensive, and not easy to create. The same goes for the software that drives communications through such a port. It involves writing a low-level driver that can interface with the ECP engine and provide the required memory for the DMA transfers that this port requires.

Because of the hardware complexities and associated software complexity this mode of operation is prohibitive for experimentation. In general, the circuitry is so complex it cannot be represented in schematic form but is coded in a synthesis language such as Verilog or VHDL and mapped into a custom chip or FPGA. Unfortunately, that is far beyond the scope of this book.

ECP uses a stream concept. After an initial setup phase between the computer and the device, two channels are created. One is called the Forward channel whereas the other is simply the Reverse Channel. Whenever the computer needs to send data to the attached device, the data is put into a FIFO transmit register. The ECP controller will see to it that this data gets to the other side. Software handshaking signals notify the software on the PC side what is the status of this transmit FIFO.

In a similar way, the device can assert the ReverseRequest. The ECP engine will then again completely autonomously fetch the data from the device transmit FIFO and transport them to the computers receive FIFO. Again, a software layer provides a status indication on what is going on in the FIFO's.

To speed up the transport between received and to be transmitted data and the application, a DMA transfer mechanism is available. This allows the ECP engine to directly write and read data to and from the main memory in the computer. The transport happens independently from the software on the computer. All the programmer needs to do is allocate memory for both buffers and provide the locations to the ECP control engine. To send a block of data the software informs the ECP controller that data is waiting in the allocated memory and tells it how many bytes need to be written. The controller then does the rest without further software interaction.

Chapter 29 : The Serial Port In Detail

The Serial port is somewhat the most standard communication channel for longer distances, and was in use long before the PC came along. The transport mechanism and physical layer make it an ideal choice to transmit data between devices of short to moderate distances.

When people talk about the serial port on a computer, they actually mean an RS232 serial port. There are numerous other serial ports around that are not necessarily compatible, neither on electrical nor protocol level.

29.1 : System description

Serial ports in a PC come in two flavors. You can have either the full-fledged 25-pin connector or the shrunken 9-pin connector. The port is controlled by a UART of the 8250 / 8251 or 165x0 types. The latter has more advanced features like transmit and receive FIFO's. However, from a programmer's point of view these controllers all look the same (except for the FIFO's that may require some additional code to handle).

Since the port holds many registers and is quite complicated to control low level, I am not going into detail on that here and now. I will explain the things you need to know and how you can make an interface that works reliable all the time. An in depth explanation on how the data is actually transported and how the UART works, will be given further on. For now it is sufficient to know that a UART takes a byte and sends it out one bit at a time at a given data rate. It can also take in bits at a given data rate and reassemble them into bytes.

The UART is in essence a parallel to serial and serial to parallel converter. It is smart enough to control the disassembling and reassembling of individual bytes and control the flow of data between itself and other UARTS interconnected to each other. It is possible to wire them up directly to each other but the fact is that the output signal of a UART is not really suited to be sent over a long cable susceptible to all sorts of interference. Therefore, the signal is typically level shifted. RS232 defines two signal levels. A so-called Mark and a Space. The Mark is a logical 1 and represented by a voltage between -3 and -12 volts in reference tot the ground. A Space is a logical 0 and defined as a +3 to +12 volts in reference to ground.

Additional information is sent in the dataflow to make sure that the UARTS remain synchronized with each other. A start bit always precedes 8 data bits and the transmission is terminated by one or more stop bits. In order to be able to trap errors, a parity bit can be inserted into the stream as well. In general, for every 8 bits of data about 2 to 3 bits of additional information are transmitted.

29.1.1 : Handshaking and flow control

To increase the reliability additional signals were created that could assist in the dataflow. Two signals are used between UARTs to signal that the device is ready for data. Ready to send (RTS) and Clear to Send (CTS) are used for that purpose. RTS signifies that an outgoing byte is available. As soon as the receiving side raises the CTS signal, the data traffic will start. These signals control the transmission of individual bytes.

Data terminal ready (DTR) and Data Set ready (DSR) perform this flow control on device level. They stem from the old days when mainframe computers were sending information to terminals. The terminal would signal that it was ready to receive a block of information. That could be a complete screen of text. The CTS/RTS would then control individual byte transfers. Once the mainframe had finished sending the page, it would turn of the DSR signal, signifying end of transmission. The terminal could then visualize the data. If the mainframe had new data, it would wait for the DTR signal to become active. This signifies the terminal was ready with whatever it needed to do and could receive further data. The mainframes often communicate with hundreds of terminals and use these signals to control the task switching. The DSR and DTR bits are NOT under control of the UART but are controllable by software. It is up to the user to set and check these bits. They have absolutely no impact on the operation of the UART. CTS/RTS on the other hand do have an impact on the dataflow. If the UART is switched to hardware handshaking then those are the lines being manipulated. Modern UART's have the possibility to control one or both, and actually, if both sides have a FIFO then those lines can be used to control packets of information.

29.1.2 : Software flow control

Since having to deal with all these extra cables was actually a bit a contradiction against the idea behind a UART (minimize the number of cables) they were disbanded to make way for software handshaking. Instead of playing with CTS/RTS and DTR/DSR, a number of reserved codes was introduced. Since data running over a serial link is typically text data and not binary data (at least it was in the old days) the ASCII code table actually defined a number of special functions. Some allowed control of the cursor; some could ring a bell, wipe the screen or even switch the dataflow on and off. Software handshaking is up to the user and is not controlled by the UART. The special codes look like any other byte to the UART and it is up to the software that generates and receives data to analyze the data and insert or extract these special codes and take appropriate action.

The most commonly used configuration of a serial port you are going to encounter, is the simple 3 wire setup of TX, RX and ground. Commonly 9600 baud is used with no parity bit, 8 data bits and 1 stop bit. (9600, n, 8, 1). Other commonly used settings are 4800 and 2400 baud with the above parity and start/stop bit settings.

29.1.3 : Which Flow Control Method Should I Use?

Like most simple questions, this one has no absolute answer. Both methods have advantages and disadvantages. Fortunately, MSCOMM has built-in support for both types of flow control.

The advantage to software flow control is that it requires no extra signals to operate. The disadvantage is that it requires software overhead to execute, so it can be slower and less reliable than hardware flow control. Another drawback to software flow control is that it can only be used in situations where the flow control characters do not interfere with the data and vice versa.

An advantage to hardware flow control is that it is fast, because the UARTs themselves interpret changes of state in the input signals and can generate an interrupt that COMM.DRV can react to immediately. Hardware flow control does not interfere with data, so it is inherently compatible with binary data but the extra control signals required need additional cabling an appropriate line drivers.

29.2 : Port interface

As explained before, a minimal serial interface needs only 3 wires: transmit (TX), receive (RX) and a reference (typically ground). More extended configurations will include additional handshaking signals and in case of a modem device, could also include the Ring signal and an on-hook / off-hook signal.

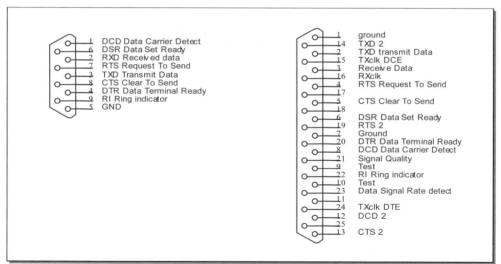

The diagrams above show the pin setting of a typical serial port as found on the back of a PC. Keep in mind that when communicating with the other side, you always need to connect a transmitter from one end to a receiver from the other end.

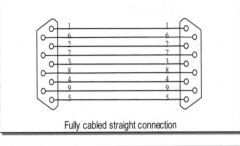

Fully cabled straight connection

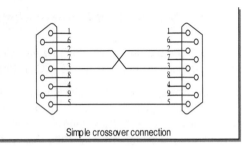

Simple crossover connection

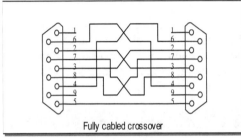

Fully cabled crossover

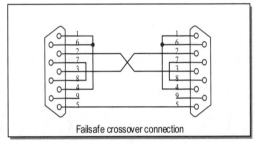

Failsafe crossover connection

The above images show the most commonly used cabling schemes. The Standard straight cable is used to interconnect a DTE to a DCE device. Perhaps the simplest cable to make but not the most commonly used. A more common connection is the top right schematic. It shows a simple interconnection between two devices. Unfortunately, you cannot always trust this to work as the handshaking signals may or may not be required. Therefore, the connection diagram shown in the bottom right corner is the most universal. By making this interconnection, you can fake the missing handshaking signals. If you have a device that requires the handshaking, you should use a fully cabled interconnection.

And last, but not least, the bottom left image shows a fully cabled crossover cable.

Note

If you are in doubt what the required interconnection scheme is, try the failsafe crossover connection first. As an additional safety measure, you can incorporate 100-ohm resistors in both the TX and RX line. Although the RS232 specification requires the circuitry to be short proof, it often is not. Adding 2 resistors does not outweigh having to replace the Io driver on one or both ends.

One of the nasty problems when dealing with serial ports is that most PCs have two. Moreover, you do not necessarily know which connector on the backplane corresponds to what logical port. The little circuit below acts as a full loop back plug. Fire up HyperTerminal or any other terminal program, select any settings and see if the terminal echoes what you are typing. If it does, you have just found the port, if it does not change the test plug over to the other port and see what happens.

29.2.1 : The electronics behind the connector

RS232 signals are specified between a maximum swing of +12 to -12 volts and a minimum swing of +3 to -3 volts. It is obvious that your piece of electronics will need the appropriate level translators to be able to accommodate this. Most of the circuits out there generate around +9 to -9 volts swing.

The original PC had a +12 and -12 volt supply and used a MC1488 and MC1489 driver/receiver circuit that was powered from these supplies. Newer ATX based machines use a different approach. The required RS232 voltage are generated from a single 5 volts or 3.3 volts power supply using a switching capacitor boost – inverter circuit. Popular circuits include Maxims Max232 (5 volt operation) and Max3232 (3.3 volt operation) circuits and derivatives.

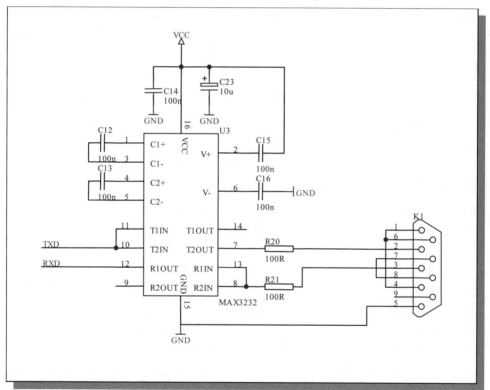

| Note | The above schematic uses a female 9 pin connector and can be plugged directly into the male connector as present on a PC motherboard. No need for a crossed cable. |

29.3 : The UART.

Let us take a closer look at how the UART works. Although this is not necessary to do serial communications, it helps in understanding and avoiding possible problems.

The UART is in essence nothing more than a shift register. Data goes in on one side and comes out the other side. The shift register can take in parallel data and serialize it, or take in serial data and parallelize it. Since a shift register works to the cadence of a clock, this is provided inside the UART as well. The so-called Baud generator creates the clock to which all shift operations take place. The problem is getting the sender and receiver to b in synchronization. After all, how do you find out where a bit begins and ends, and how far off your receive clock is from the transmit clock.

A simple but efficient mechanism was created: the start bit. This bit (a logic zero or positive level on the wire) takes the line out of sleep. The receiving UART will measure reset its clock generator on the rising edge of the signal. At that moment, the UART knows it is synchronous with the transmitter clock. Since both UARTs are set to identical baud rate, the transmission can now correctly take place.

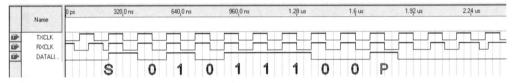

As you can see, in the above picture, initially the TXCLK and RXCLK are not aligned. The rising edge of the start bit triggers the RXCLK generator to restart. Since the baud rate is set to the same value on both sides, the clock will now be in sync. However, since there is no real synchronization, over time, the clocks will drift apart, but that will happen long after the byte is transferred. The data is sampled on the falling edge of the baud clock generator.

In modern UARTS the internal clock generator runs 8 or 16 times faster then the receive clock. An additional system monitors received information and can measure the length of one or more bits. If this length multiplied by this overclock value does end up being a fraction of the generated then the RXCLOCK can be adjusted in phase. That way it is absolutely guaranteed that the RXclock remains in step. In general any UART that can handle 115kBaud and faster employs this mechanism. Megabaud UARTs employ the 16-bit granularity.

29.4 : RS-232 and Other Serial Conventions

So far, we have only covered serial communication in general. Multiple standards out there all employ the same or similar mechanisms, but are different on the physical layer.

29.4.1 : RS232

RS-232 is one of the oldest standards and most commonly used for serial communications. It is a pure master/slave point-to-point connection. The voltage at the line has a swing from +12 to -12 volts with an allowable nominal of -3 to +3 volt. It is suitable for communication at moderate distances up to 33 meters.

In the course of time, the standard has been revised a number of times and it is now known as EIA232. There are extensions known to the RS232 standard that are specific to certain devices. For instance, Intel has created an addressable UART in which a ninth bit acts as a signal to switch between data and address. This UART is available on certain microcontrollers, but unfortunately, the PC cannot handle this format.

29.4.2 : RS422

This standard takes the same basic principle but uses a differential twisted-pair to carry the signals. While this doubles the number of wire required, it dramatically decreases the noise susceptibility. RS-422 can be used to drive lines as long as 1.2 kilometers without problems. Signal levels range from 12 volts all the way down to 200millivolts. In essence, it is not the signal itself that is important but the polarity of the signal on the twisted pair.

29.4.3 : RS-485

RS485 is an extension of RS422 but allows you to construct a network. It exists in two flavors: a two pair version (One TX and one RX pair) and a single pair. The single pair version can be used to interconnect up to 32 devices on a RS485 line. All devices share the same wires and they communicate in half duplex. While one is talking, the others are listening.

29.4.4 : Current Loop and Other Serial Standards

Current loop is a technique that dates back to the early telegraphy. At low data rates, current loop signals can go across a long distance. Loops of over 3,000 kilometers are possible and in fact, current loop was used in the early mores-code style telegraphs as used in the Wild Wild West.

Today they use UARTs to control the dataflow and speeds in excess of 9600 baud are possible. The only problem with current loop is the lack of a real standard, which sometimes makes it hard to be able to make two devices work together.

29.5 : Tips and tricks

There are a couple of tricks you can employ, if you have trouble finding out the pinning of an RS232 connector or are having trouble establishing communication.

If you are not entirely sure you have the correct port on the PC, simply launch HyperTerminal, or any other terminal program, select any baud rate, parity and data bit length but make sure that you select NO flow control. Using a paperclip, screwdriver, or short piece of wire, you short pins 2 and 3 together. It does not matter if it is a 25 pin or 9-pin connector. Whenever you type something on the terminal program, it should now appear on the screen, as you just made a crude echo device.

To find which pin of the port is output, just measure its voltage in respect to ground: The data out will have a negative voltage in respect to ground, while the input will have either zero or a slight positive voltage due to an internal weak pull-up in the receiver circuit.

In order to avoid problems with handshaking, it is wise to strap unused pins on the connector. RTS should be strapped to CTS and DTR should be strapped to DSR. You can find these wiring diagrams a bit earlier in this section on serial communication.

29.6 : Basic Serial Operations using MSCOMM

To program the serial interface you could control the UART directly, but that is doing things the hard way. Fortunately, Windows offers us help here under the form of MSCOMM.DLL. This standard component of the Windows Operating system handles all task related to serial communications. Besides initializing the UART, it also handles interrupts coming from one or more serial ports, and it implements a software FIFO as well.

On top of this engine is an object that allows you to interface directly to the MSCOMM.DLL library. How to use this, has already been explained in Part II of this manual

Chapter 30 : The ISA bus in detail

So far, we have only dealt with the externally accessible connectors of a computer. Besides the usage of these standard IO channels such as printer ports and serial ports, you can always construct your own adapter cards and plug them inside the computer.

30.1 : The ISA bus

In the previous chapter, I gave you an overview of the most common buses that are in existence today. The ISA bus is one of these buses. You can find a plethora of cards that host a variety of different functions. Besides standard computer functions such as Floppy and hard disk controllers, Serial ports, Printer ports, Video adapters and audio boards, there are indeed special boards for test and measurement functions.

These boards cover the whole spectra of T&M, from simple Digital IO, multiplexers, A/D-D/A converters to complete multi-meters and even oscilloscopes.

Complex boards such as multi-meters and oscilloscopes will again come with vendor supplied driver software. Simple cards mostly also have these drivers but not necessarily for all languages. And exactly for these boards, and the boards you might construct yourselves, this chapter is important.

The graphic below shows the pinning of the standard ISA bus. Many of these signals are not generally used for IO boards. Actually only very few signals are used for I/O.

62	GND	A0	31
61	14.3MHZ	A1	30
60	+5V	A2	29
59	ALE	A3	28
58	TC	A4	27
57	-DACK2	A5	26
56	IRQ3	A6	25
55	IRQ4	A7	24
54	IRQ5	A8	23
53	IRQ6	A9	22
52	IRQ7	A10	21
51	SYSCLK	A11	20
50	-REFSH	A12	19
49	DREQ1	A13	18
48	-DACK1	A14	17
47	DREQ3	A15	16
46	-DACK3	A16	15
45	-IOR	A17	14
44	-IOW	A18	13
43	-SMEMR	A19	12
42	-SMEMW	AEN	11
41	GND	IOCHRDY	10
40	+12V	D0	9
39	-0WS	D1	8
38	-12V	D2	7
37	DREQ2	D3	6
36	-5V	D4	5
35	IRQ9	D5	4
34	+5V	D6	3
33	RESDRV	D7	2
32	GND	-IOCHCK	1

CON AT62B

36	GND	SD15	18
35	-MASTER	SD14	17
34	+5V	SD13	16
33	DREQ7	SD12	15
32	-DACK7	SD11	14
31	DREQ6	SD10	13
30	-DACK6	SD9	12
29	DREQ5	SD8	11
28	-DACK5	-MEMW	10
27	DREQ0	-MEMR	9
26	-DACK0	SA17	8
25	IRQ14	SA18	7
24	IRQ15	SA19	6
23	IRQ12	SA20	5
22	IRQ11	SA21	4
21	IRQ10	SA22	3
20	-IOCS16	SA23	2
19	-MEMCS16	-SBHE	1

CON AT36B

The above picture shows a graphic representation of the ISA connectors and the signals present on each pin. For the purposes of pin identification on the 62-pin primary ISA connector, the front, or component side of the edge connector (the side of the board with components mounted on it) is called the A-side, and the backside is called the B-side. Similarly, for the 36-pin auxiliary connector, the front side of the edge connector is called the C-side and the other side the D-side.

Describing how to use each and every signal of this bus would go much too far for this book. However, the basics of this bus are very simple. Using the Address bus, the data bus, and the IOR and IOW lines a simple interface can be made. When the address of the decoder matches the address on the data-bus, the card is selected. Depending on IOR or IOW a read or write operation is going on. During the IOR pulse the card must can put data on the data-bus, and during the IOW pulse the card has to latch-in data from the data bus. Those are the basics of the operation.

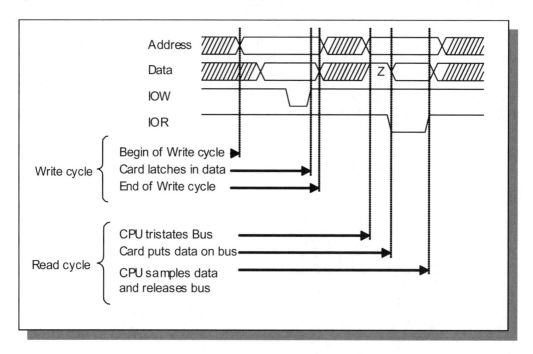

The image shows exactly what is going on during these read and write operations. The most important thing to remember is to sample in data on the rizing edge of IOW and to put data on the bus when IOR is going low and leave it there until IOR is going high again.

30.1.1 :   common interface chips

Before we start writing code, we will take a look at some common interface circuitry used on such cards. Understanding these will make it much easier to unravel the inner workings of the card and write a library for it.

30.1.1.1 :   8255

This is probably the most widely used interface circuit around. It offers a simple way to add 24 IO lines to a computer.

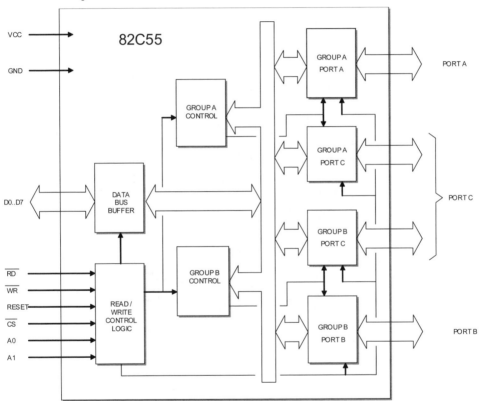

The image above shows you what is inside the 40 pin DIL or 44 pin PLCC package. The chip can be divided into three parts. Each part is a basic 8-bit IO channel that can be written to or read from.

The option exists to split the third channel into two parts and merge these parts with one of the two remaining ports, thus creating two 12-bit ports. In this mode, the extra four lines can be used as control lines to orchestrate data IO on the two other ports. Port A has also true bi-directional capabilities. The complete explanation of this chip can be found in the Datasheet appendix.

30.1.1.2 :   8253/8254

This is the most used complement to the 8255 on IO boards. This chip features three 16-bit counters/dividers. The figure below chows you the inner parts of this chip.

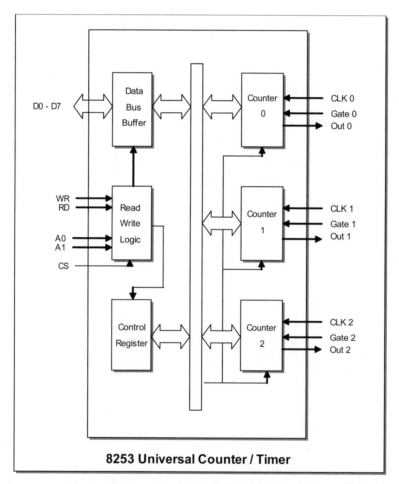

8253 Universal Counter / Timer

Just like with the 8255 a number of configurations are possible. Each counter can be used independently either as frequency generator, event counter or programmable divider. By cascading the counters, you can make a 32 or 48-bit counter/divider. The typical use for this component is measuring time intervals, frequencies or simply the number of times a certain event occurred. Programming this component is straightforward.

30.1.2 : Basic interface schematic using 8255 I/O controller

The images below show two possible ways of building an interface with an ISA bus. The first schematic uses the above described 8255 IO controller. This controller fits directly onto any Intel CPU architecture, so it is equally fit to connect with the PC's ISA bus.

An 8-bit cascadable comparator (74688) checks if the board is addressed. If address matches and the AEN line is low, the Chip is selected. The RD, WR and two lowest address bits go directly to the IO controller. Depending on the state of these signals, the controller decides what to do.

The address of the card is selected by strapping the address select inputs on the 74688 comparator to logic high or low.

Depending on the configuration sent to the IO controller various functions can be performed. See the chapter about the 8255 for more information or consult the datasheets in the appendixes.

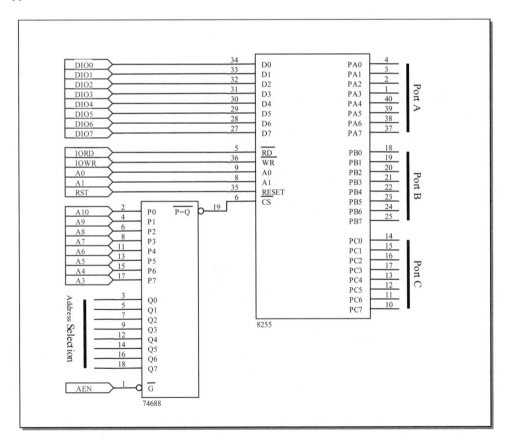

30.1.3 : Basic interface schematic using classic logic

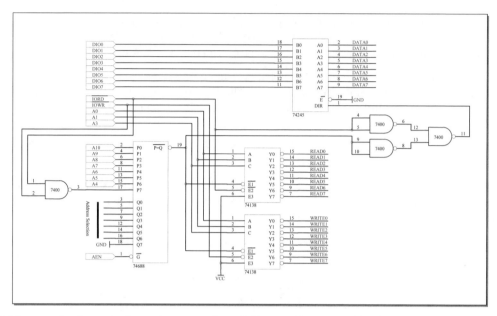

This second schematic shows how to make a full controller yourself. It has an address decoder similar to the one above to check the access to the card. However, since there is no smart IO controller we have to make the decoding logic ourselves. Two 74138 are used to decode the lowest three address bits into eight strobe lines that can be used in our circuitry. Besides the address lines, these chips take the Card select signal from the 74688 and the Read or Write line. By implementing the circuitry like this, one of the decoders reacts on write events and the other on read events. The 74245 buffer is put in the circuit to minimize the load on the bus. In the previous schematic the 8255 controller has this embedded in its system. Here we have to put it in ourselves.

Note

Take care about the connection of A and B buses of the 74245. It seems odd but this trick is implemented to save an additional component. If you switch A and B buses (like you would expect) you would need to invert the output of the last NAND gate, thus using an additional component.

The construction using the three NAND gates checks what kind of operation is being performed. In case of a READ operation, it combines this with the card select and switches the direction of the buffer, so the data flows from our circuitry to the computer. The computer can then access the data being put on the data lines. In case of a write, the buffer is set from computer to card.

There are numerous other possibilities to build interface circuitry for the ISA bus. It depends on what you want to do.

30.2 : Selecting an address for our card

The questions that rises now is: where can we map our board in the computer? Well there are a number of so-called experimenters' areas where you can safely do this. However, take care that nothing else is already there! Our board is not plug-and-play so Windows cannot detect it.

The safest area is the range 0x300 to 0x31F. It holds 32 possible addresses. This part of the IO range is clearly marked by both the IBM manuals and the official ISA spec as 'experimenters' area'.

Other unused regions in the IO map are set as 'undocumented'. They can be used but it depends on the machine.

You can check the availability of addresses by using the Windows System Setting panel.

Start – Settings – Control Panel and double-click on system.

A window will open that shows the settings of your computer. Click on the tab Device manager. This shows all devices in your computer.

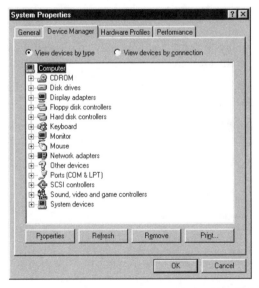

The devices are organized per functional group. You can double-click on each of the devices and look for the information you want but there are easier ways to accomplish this.

To get an overview of the used interrupts, IO ranges and DMA channels you simply have to double-click on Computer.

This opens a new window that shows the information we seek. Select one of the four options. In our case, we want to see the Input / Output (I/O) information.

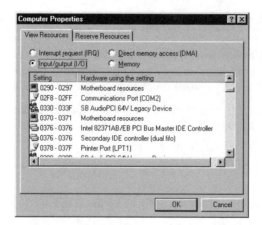

The above image shows part of the resources used in a computer. The experimental range in this particular machine could be used up to the address 0x330. However, do not count on it. You should check this when installing the board in a particular computer.

30.2.1 : Accessing our board

Now that we have built a plug-in board and hopefully configured it correctly, it is time to have a look at how to access it from software.

You can use the same techniques as described in the section about the printer port. After all, a printer port is an IO channel that resides on the ISA bus too.

In case of the 8255 controller, you can write a set of universal routines that handle the IO operations.

Example for 8255:

```
Const Ioboard = &h300
Sub WritePort(portnumber,databyte)
    Select case portnumber
    case 0,1,2,3
        out ioboard+portnumber,databyte
    case else
        msgbox "Error: you attempted to access an _
                illegal port in the 8255"
    End select
End Sub
Function Readport(portnumber)
    Select case portnumber
    case 0 to 3
        Readport = inp(ioboard+portnumber)
    case else
        msgbox "Error: you attempted to access an _
                illegal port in the 8255"
    End select
End Function
```

The above two routines allow you direct access to any of the registers in the IO board. Note that I use a select case construction to select the validity of the port number. Doing this makes the code much more readable than using a construction like:

```
if ((portnumber >0) and (portnumber <4)) then …
```

In addition, if you need to filter out address 1 separately you can simply add a *Case* statement.

```
Select case portnumber
      case 0,2,3
            Readport = inp(ioboard+portnumber)
      case 1
            ' accessing address 1
      case else
            msgbox "Error: you attempted to access an _
                  illegal port in the 8255"
End select
```

30.3 : PC104

PC104 is a standard that originated as a small form-factor computer board made by Ampro in 1987. The board was target for very small form factor computers and control applications. The entire motherboard was shrunk down as tight as possible and all non-essential interfaces and connectors were stripped. Over the years, more and more companies started building add-on boards as well as PC104 motherboards.

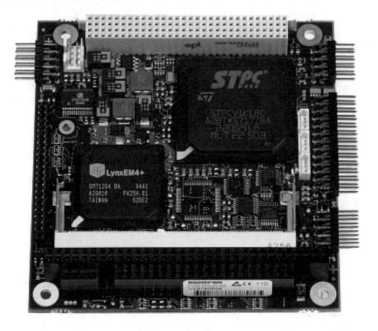

The Name PC104 is derived from the fact that it is indeed a PC and has an interface connector with 104 pins. The interface is in essence nothing else than the well-known ISA bus with a number of power supply lines added to it. Most boards are capable of running directly from 5volts only. On the image above the black connectors at the bottom form the original PC104 interface while the large white connector at the top forms the PCI interface.

In 1992, a consortium was created that drafted the first formal specification of PC104 and in 1997 ratified the PC104-plus specification as well.

PC104+ also accommodates a PCI connector that can host four devices directly, provided no embedded PCI devices are already on the motherboard.

Developing for PC104 is a matter of creating the correct board geometry and connector positioning. In all other respects, it is a full electrical equivalent of the ISA and PCI specifications.

Chapter 31 : USB

The USB bus was devised by a consortium lead by mayor hardware and software manufacturers and vendors such as Intel, Microsoft, Dell, IBM and Hewlett Packard. It found its roots in an earlier experiment called the Access bus. It originated as an idea to replace the myriad of different interface connectors found on a typical computer. The Access bus was originally intended to interconnect slow peripherals, such as mice, digitizers and keyboards, to a PC. When the big companies stepped in, the scope was broadened to include printers and other devices that required substantially more bandwidth.

Eventually the entire hardware concept was completely reworked and became known as USB1.0. Heavily pushed by chipset manufacturers, the bus finally caught on, as full support for it was included in the release of windows 98.

As devices evolved, they increased demand for bandwidth. External hard disks, high-resolution photo printers and other devices tend to move lots of data. Subsequent modifications have culminated in the release of USB2.0, which offers a 60-fold speed improvement.

The USB consortium www.usb.org closely governs the protocol and all pertaining standards to USB. Although it is possible for anyone to make a USB based product, it is not possible to start selling this product without the heads up of this consortium. The USB consortium evaluates each and every product, assigns it a unique vendor and product identification (called the VID and PID) and makes sure it passes all required electrical criteria, in order to guarantee compatibility.

31.1 : The USB port in detail

A so-called host controls the USB bus. This is typically a computer. There can only be one host on the USB bus. The specification does not provide facilities for a multi master environment. The USB On-The-Go does have such a provision but this is aimed at interconnecting host such as a pc and a handheld PDA.

The host initiates and controls all transactions and bandwidth allocation, and can handle up to 127 physical devices attached to it.

As USB has evolved from version 1.0 to version 2.0, a more refined terminology was called in existence. The current revision 2.0 specifies three modes of operation:

- High Speed - 480Mbits/s.
- Full Speed - 12Mbits/s.
- Low Speed - 1.5Mbits/s.

Communication is not happening at a constant speed. The connected devices share the available bandwidth on the bus, and a priority mechanism is governing the dataflow. USB has a number of different methods to transmit data, as well as a defined number of different messages that the bus can send and receive.

31.1.1 : USB Messages

Every block of information transmitted over the bus is using a predefined packet scheme, much like the IP packets over the Ethernet interface. Every packet contains a Packet Token, an optional payload and a status block.

The USB bus uses four types of packets. The Token packet, the Data packet, a Handshake packet and finally, a Start-of-Frame packet.

Every Packet has a synchronization block, SYNC, a Packet-Identification block, PID, as well as an End-Of-Packet, EOP, section.

31.1.1.1 : The Sync packet

The simplest packet is a handshake packet.

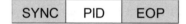

The synchronization packet controls the dataflow between a host and a slave. The message contained in the PID can be any of these three:

- ACK : the packet has been received and all is well.

- NAK: the device cannot send or receive data for the moment, or, in case of a slave sending a NAK, there simply is nothing to send.

- STALL: the slave needs servicing by the host. This message can handle, for instance, exception reporting.

31.1.1.2 : Token Packets

A token packet is used to control the data flow between a host and a slave device.

The token PID specifies the direction of dataflow or the setup information. The ADDRESS is the address of the slave device that is being accessed. Finally, the endpoint (EP) determines which physical endpoint the data is destined for. A USB device can have multiple so-called end-points. Take for instance a USB transceiver for a wireless keyboard and mouse. One endpoint could be allocated for the keyboard, while another endpoint is used for the mouse. In a similar fashion, a printer/scanner/fax can have more than two endpoints. The usage of endpoints allows for the creation of composite devices without having to sacrifice a USB address for each subsystem.

31.1.1.3 : Data Packets

The data packet contains the actual data being exchanged between host and slave. The actual payload can be between 0 and 1023 bytes long. As with all packets, a CRC is embedded to ensure the integrity of the data. Note however, that this CRC is of a different type than the CRC used in the other packets.

SYNC	PID	DATA	CRC	EOP

31.1.1.4 : Start Of frame packets

The Start of frame is in essence a sequence number that is being sent by the host roughly every one millisecond and is used for internal housekeeping of the packet sequences.

SYNC	PID	Frame Number	CRC	EOP

31.1.2 : USB transfers

Any communication between a host and a slave consists of multiple packets flying hence and forth between the host and the slave.

A typical communication between a host and slave could look like this:

Action	Packet	Direction	Operation
Setup token		H2S	Address and endpoint number
Data packet	SYNC PID DATA CRC EOP	H2S	Request a block of data
Handshake	SYNC PID EOP	S2H	Acknowledge command

The above would be the first transaction. The Host has sent a block of data to a certain device and endpoint in that device. The device will process the request and prepare the answer.

The next transaction could look like this:

Action	Packet						Direction	Operation
Setup token	SYNC	PID	ADDRESS	EP	CRC	EOP	H2S	Address and endpoint number
Data packet	SYNC	PID	DATA		CRC	EOP	S2H	The requested Data packet
Handshake	SYNC	PID	EOP				H2S	Acknowledge command

In this transaction, the host again initiates the transport, but this time the slave sends the data packet and the host acknowledges the reception of the packet.

31.1.3 : Transfer Types

USB distinguishes between four types of transfers on the bus.

A control transfer is used to exchange control and status information between a host and slave. They are heavily used during the enumeration of the device, and are short packets that are always initiated by the host.

An interrupt transfer is used if a slave wants to obtain attention from the host. However due to the master/slave nature of the USB bus, this transfer cannot be initiated by the slave. Contrary to what is common practice on microprocessors, the USB slave actually has to wait until it is being addressed by the host. However, once received, the slave will receive the undivided attention of the host.

An Isochronous transfer is used for data that needs to be transmitted within a certain predefined timeframe and which is continuous in nature. For instance, an audio or video stream is a typical example of an isochronous stream. The bandwidth is guaranteed but the stream is unidirectional in nature. There is no retry if an error is detected in the CRC code. Therefore, it is only useful in cases where a missing or corrupt packet will not be noticed, such as audio.

A Bulk transfer is used for large blocks of information that will require many packets, but where the timed delivery is not important. Here the error detection and re-transmission mechanism is in effect. This type of data is typically used for large data transport such as print jobs and file transport to and from external storage.

Much more can be said about the mechanism that governs the data flow but that, again, is beyond the scope of this book.

31.2 : USB from a hardware point of view.

USB uses a differential signal transmitted over a twisted pair (the D+ end D- lines). Although data is transported using a differential signal, the bus has a number of non-differential states (both lines high and both lines low) that are used to flag certain specific commands.

A device makes its presence known to the host by pulling either the D+ or the D- to a logic high level using a 1.5-kilo ohm resistor. If D+ is pulled-up, this means a High-Speed device is present. If D- is pulled high, a low speed device is present. A Full speed USB2.0 device uses the D+ pull-up but emits a special signal during reset, the so called 'chirp' that lets the host know it is full speed capable.

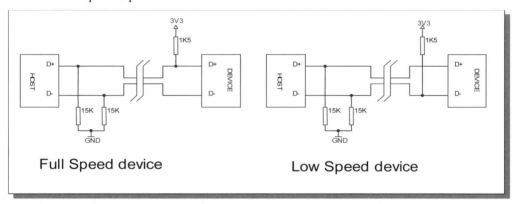

Besides the data lines, power is delivered as well. This power may or may not be used in the application. In case the supplied power is used, very stringent criteria are to be met. USB devices are classifies in three categories. Self-powered, Low power and High power. The Supply voltage coming out of the USB connector can be anywhere between 4.4 and 5.25 volts.

Under no circumstances is a USB device allowed to back feed power to the host. If a self-powered device detects a connection loss with the host, it should remove any signals from the D+ and D- lines as well.

A low current device can draw up to 100mA from the USB bus. A high current device can request 500mA but only after the initial setup and enumeration is done. Until the negotiation with the host is over it is not allowed to draw more than 500mA.

The tricky point is the standby current. As long as a device is in suspend mode, it is only allowed to draw a maximum of 500 microampere's. The leakage in the pull-up resistor alone drains 200 micro amps. Needless to say that this requires great care.

If you violate this, the bus will not fail but you will not be able to obtain the coveted USB logo certification. On the other hand, if you do fail the 100mA limit for a low power device or fail to draw less than 100mA as a high power device while enumerating, the host can cut off your power source completely.

31.2.1 : Building hardware

Designing you USB hardware is a matter of grabbing an appropriate chip and hooking it up to your application. There are a number of solutions possible. You can either find a microprocessor or microcontroller with a built in USB engine or go for a standalone chip that can be interfaced in a number of ways to either a microcontroller or a generic bus interface, or even a serial port.

31.2.1.1 : The USB connectors

USB connectors are available in three flavors. One A-type and two B-type connectors each available in both a male and female version. In order to avoid confusion on which end is connected to what, the USB consortium has opted to specify different connectors for both ends of the cable.

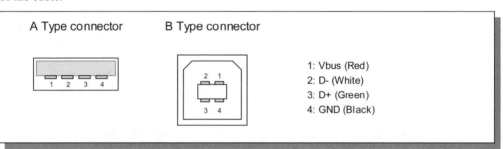

A Type connector   B Type connector

1: Vbus (Red)
2: D- (White)
3: D+ (Green)
4: GND (Black)

The A connector is exclusively used for the port that comes from a host, while the B connector is used for the port that goes to a slave. Any cable thus requires an A side and a B-side.

The B connector is available in a smaller version to accommodate for the ever-shrinking peripherals such as camcorders and digital cameras. The image below shows a Type B connector and a type A connector.

31.3 : AN USB to rs232 translator

Possibly the simplest solution, if you want to update an existing system to USB, is to build a USB to serial port translator. There are a number of chips out there that present a turnkey solution to this problem, including the required drivers. Future Technology Devices International (FTDI) of Glasgow Scotland makes one such device.

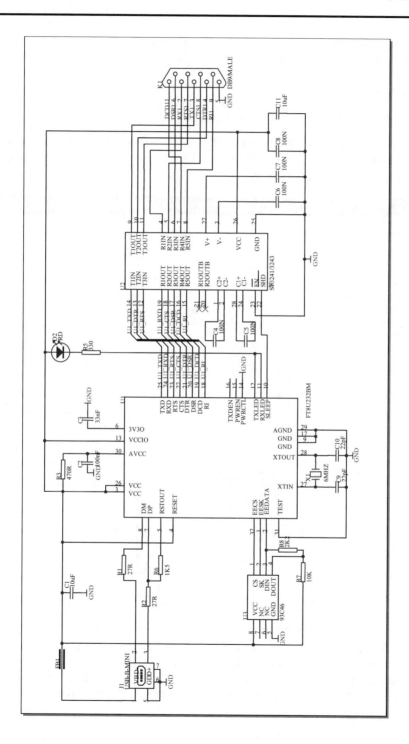

The FTDI232 integrates a complete USB Serial interface engine (SIE) and a UART into one 32 pin package. Drivers are available for almost any commonly used operating system in existence. The chip supports both bus-powered and self-powered operation and requires only minimal supporting electronics to perform its duties. In its most simple incarnation little more than a crystal, three capacitors and four resistors are needed. Of course, in order to make it a full-blown RS232 compliant translator, some additional components are required.

A level shifter, for instance, that translates the 5-volt I/O levels to their respective RS232 compliant levels, and an optional EEprom that allows customization of the Vendor ID and Product ID, as well as other parameters.

31.4 : An USB to GPIO translator using the FTDI245

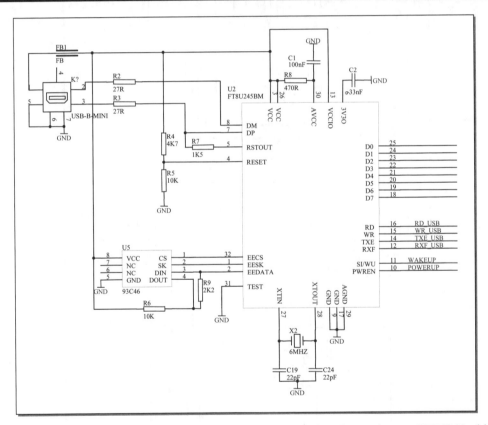

This schematic shows the basic circuitry to make a USB interface using an FTDI245 chip. From a programmers point of view the FTDI232 and FTDI245 are very much alike. From a hardware perspective the 245 offers direct access to the internal receive and transmit FIFO's using a data-bus and some handshake lines. The advantage is that you do not need a UART in your system.

You can still consider this entire system as a UART and by using the VCP driver from FTDI you can still access as such. The 245 also offers a special bit-banging mode that allows you to treat every pin on the data-bus as either an input, or an output. By installing the so-called direct-mode drivers, you can obtain full control over the 245 and emulate your own protocols. FTDI has a number of sample applications on their website.

Accessing the device in direct mode is a bit more elaborate then using a simple serial port emulation. The interface definition code and all the calls to the direct mode library themselves are a few pages of code. This code is available in the downloadable samples

A few routines are of interest.

Example:

```vb
Private Declare Function FT_Open Lib "FTD2XX.DLL" _
        (ByVal intDeviceNumber As Integer, _
        ByRef lngHandle As Long) As Long
Private Declare Function FT_EE_Read Lib "FTD2XX.DLL" _
        (ByVal lngHandle As Long, ByRef lpData As FT_PROGRAM_DATA) _
        As Long

Dim bManufacturer(32) As Byte
Dim bManufacturerID(16) As Byte
Dim bDescription(64) As Byte
Dim bSerialNumber(16) As Byte
Dim EEData As FT_PROGRAM_DATA
Private Type FT_PROGRAM_DATA
    VendorId As Integer
    ProductId As Integer
    Manufacturer As Long
    ManufacturerId As Long
    Description As Long
    SerialNumber As Long
    MaxPower As Integer
    PnP As Integer
    SelfPowered As Integer
    RemoteWakeup As Integer
    Rev4 As Boolean
    IsoIn As Boolean
    IsoOut As Boolean
    PullDownEnable As Boolean
    SerNumEnable As Boolean
    USBVersionEnable As Boolean
    USBVersion As Integer
End Type

Sub Probe_bus
    For x = 0 to 99 ' probe the first 100 devices
    If FT_Open(x,handle) =0 then ' device found
        EEData.Manufacturer = VarPtr(bManufacturer(0))
        EEData.ManufacturerId = VarPtr(bManufacturerID(0))
        EEData.Description = VarPtr(bDescription(0))
        EEData.SerialNumber = VarPtr(bSerialNumber(0))
        FT_EE_Read(handle,EEdata)
```

```
            strDescription = StrConv(bDescription, vbUnicode)
            msgbox "found :"&strDescription
        End if
    End sub
```

The **Probe_bus** routine scans the first 100 devices. If the **FT_open** function returns 0, then a device is found and a handle is returned in the variable 'handle'. In this case the EEdata variabele is initialized with the pointers to the correct variables and the FT_EE_read function is executed. Upon return from that function the EEdata variable holds all retrieved information.

The code may seem awkward at first but in essence, what is happening is the following: The FT_EE_read returns a block of data of the type FT_Program_data. In order to pass this data it needs to have pointers to the locations in memory where it can store this information. Using the VarPtr statement, we obtain the address of our variables and store them in the EEdata elements. The code in the FTDI supplied DLL takes these pointers, finds the memory space they point at an loads that memory with information. Upon return, all we need to do is read those variables.

By looking at the data returned, we can find if our device of interest is connected and, if so, take appropriate action.

The interesting bit is stored in the strSerialNumber. Every USB device should have a unique serial number. This allows you to talk to a specific device on the bus. If you find the device of interest, just copy the strSerialnumber in a local variable and off you go.

31.4.1 : Writing something to the output.

```
Sub find_me
    For x = 0 to 99 ' probe the first 100 devices
    If FT_Open(x,handle) =0 then ' device found
        EEData.Manufacturer = VarPtr(bManufacturer(0))
        EEData.ManufacturerId = VarPtr(bManufacturerID(0))
        EEData.Description = VarPtr(bDescription(0))
        EEData.SerialNumber = VarPtr(bSerialNumber(0))
        FT_EE_Read(handle,EEdata)
        strDescription = StrConv(bDescription, vbUnicode)
        if strDescription ="DEMO" then
            my_dev = strconv (bSerialNumber, vbUnicode)
        end if
    End if
End sub
Sub Write(something as integer)
    Dim longret  As Long
    Dim lngHandle As Long
    Dim lngBuffersize As Long
    Dim lngByteswritten As Long
    longret = FT_OpenEx(my_dev, FT_OPEN_BY_SERIAL_NUMBER,_
                        lngHandle)
```

```
         If longret = FT_OK Then
             longret = FT_ResetDevice(lngHandle)
             longret = FT_SetBitMode(lngHandle, &HFF, 1)
             longret = FT_Write(lngHandle,something, 1, lngByteswritten)
             longret = FT_Close(lngHandle)
         End If
     End sub
```

The above code consists of 2 routines. The first one probes the bus and attempts to find a device called 'DEMO1'. If found it copies the serial number to my_dev.

The second chunk of code allows writing a bit pattern to the device. Using FT_open and the serial number stored in **my_dev** we obtain a handle, reset the device using FT_resetDevice end write 1 byte. Finally, the device handle is closed again.

The entire direct mode DLL has a lot of routines. A detailed sample program is available that will find all devices , pick one and configure it for read and write.

31.5 : An USB to GPIO translator using the FTDI2232

A third device exists that offers a number of operation modes. The FTDI2232 has a programmable communication engine. Two independent channels can be configured to behave either as a ftdi232 or ftdi245 device. It is also possible to combine these channels and form a microcontroller like interfae with a 16 bit address bus, 8 bit databus and the necessary read and write strobes. Further special modes allow you to emulate directly certain protocols such as SPI and JTAG

This is an extensive device that offers a lot of possibilities. The configuration is simple using the supplied tools from FTDI and interfaceing from a programmers perspective is no more complicated than is the 232 or 245 device. FTDI has a couple if excellent application notes that describe in detail the use of this device in all the possible modes.

The schematic on the next page shows a 2 port RS232 solution based around the FTDI2232. Other connections diagrams are detailed in the FTDI2232 datasheet and application notes on FTDI;s website.

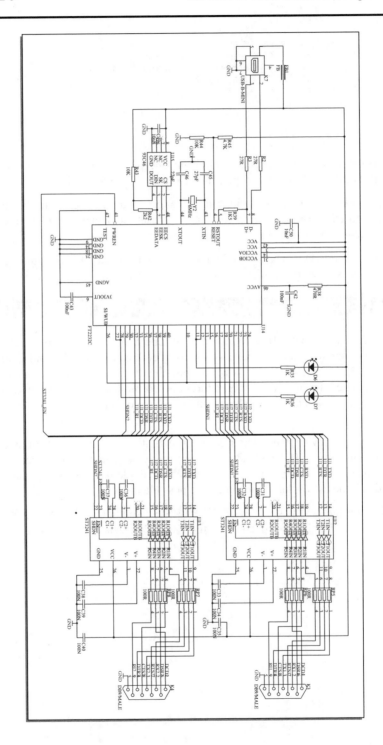

Chapter 32 : Ethernet

Visual basic has a number of provisions that make it really easy to communicate with en Ethernet base device. The problem is often in making such a device. In general, Ethernet transport requires extensive electronics and an elaborate piece of software, called an Ethernet stack, before a hardware device is capable of even the simplest operations on Ethernet. Fortunately, there are a number of turnkey solutions out there that make it a lot easier to tackle this problem. But first, let's take a look at cabling an Ethernet system and setting up a correct working network

32.1 : Wiring up a network

Modern networks most commonly use so called CAT-5 twisted pair cable. Older networks used coaxial cables. While you can buy ready made cables in multiple colors and lengths , sometimes you just need to make your own.

There are 2 basic cabling scemes around. One is a straight connection, the other is a so called cross-over connection.

32.1.1 : Straight Cables

The straight connection is the most ommonly used connection if you have a hub,router or switch on your network.

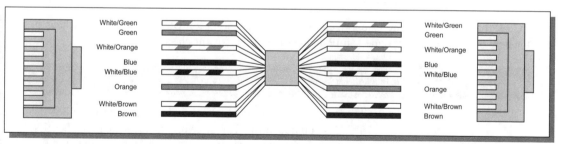

The pin numbers are assigned from top to bottom, top being number 1 and bottom being number eight. For a straight cable, both sides are cabled in exactly the same manner. The above diagram shows what goes where. This is a color scheme according to T568A. There exists a different color scheme, which is called T568B and swaps the orange/white-orange pair with the green/white-green pair.

32.1.2 : Crossover Cables

The crossover cable is most commonly used to interconnect 2 devices directly without a router, switch or hub. The wiring diagram is given below

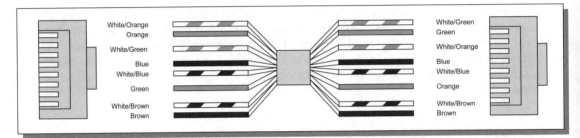

Most modern networking equipment is equipped with so-called Auto-MDX. This technology allows the network card to automatically detect how the other side is wired up and cross the signals automatically, thus removing the requirement for crossover cables. Most cables you buy ready made in the store are thus straight cables.

32.2 : Configuring the network

An Ethernet network running TCP/IP uses a logical map to find devices. Every device on an Ethernet has a MAC address, in the form of 6 Bytes. While low-level transport happens on MAC basis the TCP/IP engine adds its own addressing scheme on top of that in the form of a so called IP address. These 4 byte numbers have a defined meaning.

32.2.1 : The IP Address

TCP/IP based networks are categorized in classes. Depending on where your device resides in the network you will be assigned an IP address that reflects your class.

Class	Address Range	Details
A	1.0.0.1 to 126.255.255.254	Class A contains 126 top-level networks, each capable of hosting 16777214 unique host. The network is identified by the first number, the unique host ID is the last three numbers. For example an address of 67.14.12.33 would denote a host with unique address 14.12.33 belonging to network 67.
B	128.1.0.1 To 191.254.255.254	Class B has 16328 unique networks each capable of having 65534 hosts. For example IP address 144.12.55.210 would denote host 55.210 residing on network 144.12

C	192.0.1.1 to 223.255.254.254	Class C networks can support 254 each hosts on 2097150 possible networks. For example, 192.0.1.110 would denote host 110 of network 192.0.1.
D	224.0.0.0 to 239.255.255.254	This is a range reserved for multicasting. Multicasting groups are a block of devices that send messages with multiple destinations at a time.
E	240.0.0.0 to 254.255.255.254	Experimental.

A number of special addresses is in use. As you can see from the above table, none of the hosts has a value of 0 or 255 for the last byte of the IP address. These addresses are reserved for special functions. Typically a value of 0 for the last byte is used to address the entire network at once. This is used for data routing purposes. Typically that is where the routers and gateways in the network fabric reside.

A last byte setting of 255 is a broadcast address on your particular segment of the network. A packet sent to this address will be picked up by any device that resides in the same Class as the originator of the packet. These packets are used for Address resolving and to build routing tables for instances. Any new device that comes on the network will send a 'global call' and see who responds. Negotiations will then start to correctly configure and integrate the new device in the network.

32.2.2 : Subnet Mask

The subnet mask of a network allows you to further refine the network traffic. It allows you to further refine the network. The subnet mask allows you to identify what portion of the IP address is the network segment and what portion is the host segment.

Suppose that you have a network with 300 devices and you have two Class-C networks in use.

For example : 192.0.0.xx and 192.0.1.xx. In order for the devices on this network to know that there are two ranges you specify the subnet mask as 255.255.254.0

Let us have a look at how this works. The entire operation is nothing else then a binary AND operation. It all becomes clear when we write it out in binary form

255.255.252.0	1111.1111 – 1111.1111 – 1111.1110 – 0000.0000

This subnet mask identifies the first 23 bits as the Network address , while the last 9 bits are the device addresses. The Ethernet device knows by looking at its own address and the mask that any address in the range 192.0.0 or 192.0.1 are on its own segment, and that for any address not belonging to that range it needs to fall back to the gateway.

Subnet masks are thus used to split off the internal and external networks and allow the device to find out when to send information directly to another device (when the target IP falls within the netmask), and when to send it out.

32.3 : Basic networking housekeeping

A TCP/IP based network uses a number of internal housekeeping mechanisms. We have seen so far that IP addresses ending in 0 and 25 have a special meaning.

32.3.1 : Address Resolution Protocol

The ARP protocol sends a specially crafted packet to the broadcast address. By doing so a device makes its presence known on the network. All other devices will retrieve from the IP header the IP address of the originating device as well as the associated physical (MAC) address.

32.3.2 : Dynamic Host configuration Protocol

The newly connected device may send a DHCP request packet to the broadcast address. Its initial IP address will be set to 0.0.0.0. The DHCP server will respond to this request by sending a reply containing the IP address the requestor is to use from now on. When this packet is received by te device , it will change its IP address and perform an ARP so that all other machines are aware that there is a device at the newly assigned IP address. In order for this mechanism to work there must be a DHCP controller on the network segment. Typically in home networks the Internet gateway or router has this capability.

32.3.3 : Auto-IP

If no DHCP server is available then networked devices can fall back to AUTO-IP. This technique uses a specific range of addresses from 169.254.0.1 to 169.254.255.1. This mechanism will send an ARP packet on the network and see if a response is received. If a response is indeed received, this means that the address is taken. The device will change its IP address to the next in line and retry the operation. Once no response is received to the ARP it can safely be assumed that the address is free.

32.4 : Data transport sockets and ports

TCP/IP is not a protocol but a collection of protocols. So far we have seen that there are a number of different messages that can be sent over this network. ARP and DHCP are commonly used protocols from the TCP/IP group. There are a number of other ports that are very much of interest.

Any device has a specific set of protocols it MUST handle and can have an optional number of other protocols it may support. The Header of any TCP/IP packet includes a clear denotation of what protocol is used in coding the content of the packet. It also contains information on the endpoint of the message. This denotation is called the Port. You can see this Port number as an 'end station' inside a networked device. From a software perspective, we talk about sockets. Look at it this way. The Ethernet receiver is not a single line but rather a patch panel. Every protocol can have its own 'socket' on this patch panel. Whenever you want to listen to traffic according to a certain protocol, you need to plug into this 'socket'.

There is a defined list of ports that are used for specific purposes. Ports 0 to 1023 control elementary dataflow as well as dataflow and services on the TCP/IP network. Port numbers 1024 to 49151 can be used for whatever purposes you want. The base ports 0 to 23 are almost always used for specific protocols assigned to that port.

A number of such Ports are of interest to us

32.4.1 : Telnet

Telnet is a protocol that is used to exchange ascii data between two devices. It is commonly used to control remote terminals. This is an excellent candidate to emulate serial communication over Ethernet. The socket for telnet is number is 23

32.4.2 : ICMP

This control message protocol is typically used to inform the other side of a transmission problem. It can also be used to check if the other side is alive by transmitting a so-called 'Ping' packet.

32.4.3 : TFTP

The Trivial File Transfer Protocol is used to transfer files from one point to another.

32.4.4 : HTTP

Probaly the best know port (80) used to transport information targeted towards webbrowser applications. Whenever you surf the internet all traffic is coming through this port.

32.4.5 : SMTP

Simple Mail Transport Protocol. This is the port used to transport e-mail messages

32.5 : The Xport Device

The Xport is an integrated module manufactured by LanTronix. Inside the RJ45 connector body is all the electronics and software required to set up a complete TCP/IP networked devices. It contains , besides the ehternet transformer , a 80188 CPU , 256 Kilobytes Ram , 512 KiloBytes of flash memory , all power supply electronics and a complete Ethernet MAC and PHY.

Besides this Ethernet engine it also contains a serial port and 3 general purpose I/O pins.

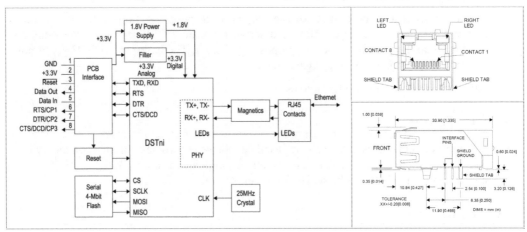

The module itself is barely larger then a RJ45 connector and contains all electronics including two LED's. The module operates directly off a 3.3-volt power supply and features 5-volt tolerant I/O pins. The serial port can be programmed with or without handshaking. The GPIO pins can fulfill multiple roles, and can be re-defined to become RTS, DTR, CTS or DCD of the serial port. The serial port UART can be programmed to any standard baud rate between 300 and 921600 bits per second. The number of data-bits can be 7 or 8 bit and 1 or 2 stop bits can be selected, while parity can be set to none, odd or even.

The embedded firmware supports all necessary management protocols as wel as TFTP to upload new firmware, HTTP as a web server and Telnet and UDP as general purpose transport mechanisms. You can set up the device to relay incoming data from the UDP TCP or Telnet port to the UART and back. You can also use the built in webserver to display custom webpages.

A complete toolkit is available free from lantronix web site at www.lantronix.com

32.6 : Sample System using the Xport

The schematic below shows a typical setup. I have added the MAX3232 level shifter in order to make the output fully RS232 compliant. An on board regulator makes the required 3.3 volts from a 5 volts supply.

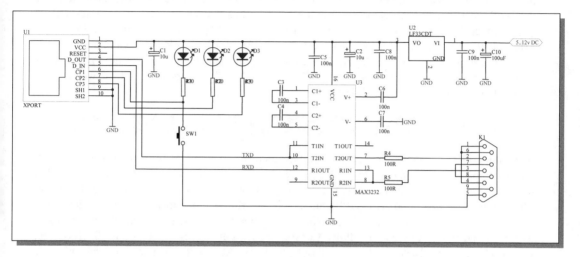

Once the device is configured using the Lantronix setup manager it can be contacted using the Winsock Custom control that has been explained in the section on networking.

Chapter 33 : GPIB.

In 1965, Hewlett-Packard, a major manufacturer of electronic test instruments, wanted to develop an interface to interconnect instruments, so that they could communicate and exchange data with each other. They came up with an interface bus that was to be known as the HP-IB bus (Hewlett-Packard Instrumentation Bus). This bus rapidly gained popularity, and in 1975 it was adopted by the IEEE as standard IEEE-488 and renamed to General Purpose Instrumentation Bus (GPIB). About 10 years later, the standard was revised to resolve a number of elements that were not very well defined in the original standard. This newer version of the standard is known as IEEE-488.2.

33.1 : The GPIB bus structure

Although GPIB is in fact a general-purpose bus, its primary goal is to interconnect one or more GPIB-compatible instruments to a PC. Several thousand of machines that have a GPIB interface are available on the market today. Even though newer interface such as USB and Ethernet have gained popularity, GPIB remains in use for test equipment. Fact is that the sheer speed of the bus still outruns all but the fastest networks. There is virtually no protocol overhead and the byte-wide bus allows transferring data at speeds in excess of 10MByte/sec, which outruns a 100Base-t network without problems. At any given time, one and only one device on the bus is in charge. This active controller coordinates all data transfers. A control passing mechanism allows other devices on the bus to take over this function. The active controller in most cases is a computer of some sort, but it can be an instrument talking to a storage unit or potter as well.

The controller determines who is a talker (devices that transmit data) or listener (devices that receive data) and makes sure that only one talker is active at any given point in time.

33.2 : IEEE488.2

The original IEEE-488 standard only defined the electrical properties and timing parameters of the bus. All messaging and commands were left completely up to the device manufacturers. This eventually got a bit out of hand and resulted in some compatibility problems between systems. In an attempt to eliminate these incompatibility problems, the IEEE-488.2 revision of the standard specified a data format and message protocols. In essence, a definition was made of a common command set that every IEEE-488.2 compliant device must follow.

Any data sent over the GPIB bus is byte wide information. However, in order to make the transport as easy to understand as possible, the commands were spelled out using the ASCII strings. Although rarely used, a provision to send binary data is in place as well.

33.2.1 : Common Command Set

The Common Command Set consists of 39 commands, and is defined by IEEE-488.2. Below is a table listing the commands and their functionality.

Command	Description
*CLS	Clear status command: Basically resets any errors
*ESE	Standard Events Status Enable
*ESE?	Standard Events Status Enable Query
*ESR?	Standard Events Status register Query
*IDN?	Identification Query
*OPC	Operation Complete Command
*OPC?	Operation Complete Query
*RST	Reset command
*SRE	Service request enable command
*SRE?	Service request enable query
*STB?	Read status byte query
*TST?	Self test query
*WAI?	Wait to continue command

33.3 : SCPI

At roughly the same time IEE488.2 was formalized, a proposal was made to further structurise the data traffic. This proposal outlined the Standard Commands for Programmable Instruments also known as SCPI. The SCPI set is a tree that has to be followed from a root command to an end function. Every node in the tree is defined by a colon. On the next page an image of a number of SCPI branches.

Each branch in the tree is preceded by a colon (:). To reduce the amount of traffic on the bus, only the four first characters of an instruction need to be sent. They are typically marked in capitals in the ser manuals of SCPI abiding instruments. Using the above tree, the following would be valid commands:

```
:SENSe:VOLTage:RANGe:AUTO<EOI>
:SENS:VOLT:RANG:AUTO<EOI>
:SENS:POWer:RANG:UPPer<EOI>
:TRIG:EXTernal:FALLING<EOI>
```

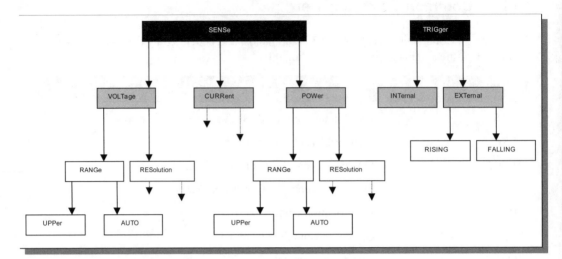

The following would be an illegal command:

: SENS : POWer : EXTernal : FALLING<EOI>

Since the command tree does not allow you to descend along this particular path.

The colon preceding the SCPI command forces the instrument to start at the root level. If you do not send a colon before a command, you remain at the same level as the last issued statement in the command.

: SENS : VOLT : RANG : AUTO<EOI>
UPPER<EOI>
AUTO<EOI>

The first command takes the instrument down to the range configuration for sensing volts and sets it to AUTO. The second command only sends the UPPER command. Since there is no preceding colon, the instrument stays at its current level in the branch of the command tree. Thus actually it will execute the command

: SENS : VOLT : RANG : UPPER<EOI>

Thanks to this flexibility, the amount of data that needs to be sent over GPIB can be reduced to a minimum if you apply clever code optimization.

Chapter 34 : Vision

This chapter will present a collection of routines, objects, controls and classes that together form the Visual Instrumentation Solution or Vision for short. The image below shows you how all parts of the Vision system fit together.

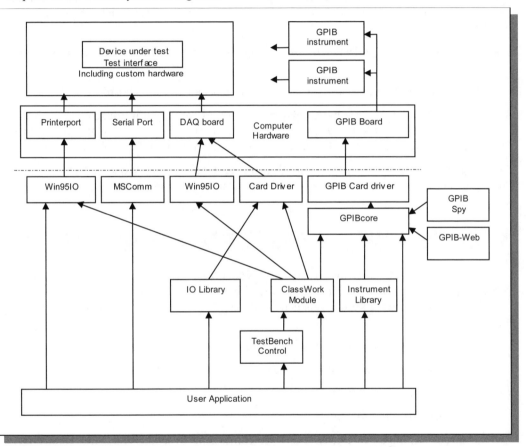

As you can see, the number of options at your disposal is rather high. All the low-level hardware interfacing is done using tools already described before: MsComm for Serial port IO and Win95io for Hardware access. Besides these two already known modules, a number of other modules exist.

GPIB card driver: This driver is supplied by the board maker. It offers an access path to the GPIB hardware.

Card Driver: A driver supplied by the board vendor of the IO or DAQ board.

GPIBcore: This library acts as the traffic controller for all GPIB operations. It manages all operations on the GPIB bus and offers error and status reporting via the standard debugging console of Visual Basic.

GPIBspy: Monitors all GPIB operations during runtime, and offers a debugging window to take control over GPIB operations when necessary

GPIBweb: Allows you to redirect GPIB operations via TCP/IP protocol to anywhere in the world. This can be used, not only to run, but as a monitor to control and debug test-setups remotely.

Instrument Library: A collection of instrument specific routines that ease the control of GPIB machines.

IO library: A collection of routines to control plug-in data-acquisition boards.

ClassWork Module: A Class holding all information to control an instrument or IO channel (Printer port, DAQ board etc). This exposes the hardware as an object to the programmer. Instruments and IO channels can be treated just like any other Visual Basic object.

TestBench Control: An ActiveX control that can interface to a ClassWork module. TestBench offers a rapid way of adding a GUI for your instruments or IO channels.

34.1 : GPIBcore

GPIBcore is a GPIB handler for Visual Basic written in Visual Basic. It handles basic GPIB operations in cooperation with the GPIB card driver provided with the board manufacturer. However, why not use the vendor-supplied driver directly? Well, a number of problems arise in doing that.

- The card drivers are board vendor specific.

- Initialization code is vendor dependent.

- Command set is different.

- Capabilities are different.

The command set might be extensive and sometimes hard to understand. Many card drivers contain so many routines that it becomes hard trying to understand what function you need and when you need it. Furthermore, you will need to understand the GPIB bus before you can talk to instruments. Not all machines respond in a uniform manner to GPIB operations.

This is where GPIBcore kicks in. It physically isolates the card-level operations from the programmer. At the same time, it takes care of all the low-level work related with device initialization and management. When different cards are to be used, or when the card driver changes completely, all you have to do is adapt the GPIBcore.

Note	GPIBcore relies on the GPIB32.DLL to access the GPIB bus. Any interface board that has followed this driver can thus be used without adaptation. Almost all GPIB boards in existence use this common GPIB32.DLL.

34.1.1 : GPIBcore features

GPIBcore sends a lot of debugging information to the standard debug console of Visual Basic. This should assist you in debugging your own instrument drivers. It is possible from the interactive window in visual basic to take control over the entire GPIB bus and interactively test operations. Besides GPIB functionality the GPIBcore also includes hardware IO functionality, binary data handling routines as well as some other missing instructions such as LOG10 calculations.

34.1.2 : Installing GPIBcore

All you need to do in order to use the GPIBcore, is simply load GPIBcore.BAS into your project, and call GPIBinit prior to executing any GPIB related command. It is strongly suggested NOT to modify GPIBcore in any way. Keep your own routines in your libraries. If an update should be made to GPIBcore, this will avoid backwards compatibility problems. Although it is possible that GPIBcore could contain programming errors, the core has been tested extensively and no known bugs are present.

34.2 : GPIBcore programming guide

The core can be divided in roughly 3 parts. The real GPIB related operations, The Hardware IO operations (via Win95io) and the supporting functions.

34.2.1 : GPIB functions

All GPIB management is handled by dedicated commands. All commands begin with GPIB and have meaningful variable declarations to facilitate programming.

34.2.2 : GPIBinit

Syntax:

```
GPIBinit
```

Description:

This function initializes the GPIB stream. It sets up communication with the card vendor specific driver. It resets the GPIB subsystem of the computer, and unlocks all attached devices on the bus. You can close the bus by executing a GPIBbye command. No GPIB commands can be executed before the call of this function. This function should be called during the startup of your program. Attempting to access the GPIB before this command has been executed will show warning messages on the immediate windows of Visual Basic. The program will neither stop nor crash, but none of the GPIB related operations will be executed.

34.2.3 : GPIBbye

Syntax and example:

```
GPIBbye
Bye
```

Description:

By issuing this command, you terminate the GPIB operations. The GPIB stream is released in an orderly manner. All devices are brought back to local state. Once the GPIB stream is closed all calls to GPIB functions other then GPIBinit will simple not be executed. (No error will be generated. They are simply ignored)

34.2.4 : GPIBopen

Syntax:

GPIBopen <address>,[descriptor]

Example:

```
GPIBopen 5
GPIBopen 5,"Multimeter"
```

Description:

This command opens a channel to the device at the specified address. This function places the machine in remote mode and initializes it as a Listener. You can specify your own name for the instrument in the optional descriptor variable. If you do not supply a name, then GPIBopen will interrogate the machine to find out its exact description. (Not all machines support this, in particular older non SCPI machines. Such machines will be listed as – unknown device –.)

When a device has been successfully opened, a brief report is generated on the immediate window of Visual Basic. The countering command is GPIBclose.

34.2.5 : GPIBclose

Syntax:

GPIBclose <address>

Example:

```
GPIBclose 5
```

Description:

This command will free a device from the GPIB bus. It places the machine back to Local mode. It is good practice to close all machines before exiting the program. However, starting with release 2.5 of GPIBcore all slaves are automatically closed upon program termination.

34.2.6 : GPIBtimeout

Syntax:

> GPIBtimeout <time in seconds>,[address]

Example:

```
GPIBtimeout 1
GPIBtimeout 30,2
```

Description:

This sets the timeout value for bus communications. If a machine does not respond within the selected timeframe, an error is generated. When setting a timeout value without specifying an address, you are setting the timeout level for the board level operations. If you want to control the instrument level timeouts, then you need to specify the address of the device as well.

34.2.7 : GPIBdefer

Syntax:

> GPIBdefer <state as Boolean>,[address]

Example:

```
GPIBdeferTrue
GPIBdefer false,22
```

Description:

This command defers the transport of GPIB calls. Any GPIB operations will be emulated when GPIBdefer is set to true. This means that the command is not sent to the bus but simply denied. The commands do show up in the console but are clearly labeled as deferred. This allows you to check syntax of the commands you are sending. You can also use this to write and debug code on a machine which doe not contain GPIB card.

A special case is the GPIBread function used when Deferring is switched on. The ib$ will contain the string "-VOID-". The value contained in IBret variable is a random number between 0 and 100. This allows you to check the functionality of your programs. If you specify an address then the DEFER state is altered for the specified address only. This is called a local defer, while a defer operation without specified address is a global defer. The local and global states are logically OR-ed together to decide whether there is access to a machine or not.

34.2.8 : GPIBsinglestep

Syntax:

> GPIBsinglestep <state as boolean>

Example:
```
GPIBsinglestep True
```

Description:

This function allows you to switch to single step mode for all GPIB operations. You can also change the mode using the console menus. This feature is useful for tracking GPIB timing problems. Whenever a GPIB command has been executed, a message box pops up to prompt you for further action. You can decide to take the next step, stop the program, or abort stepping and continue at normal speed.

34.2.9 : GPIBtroff

Syntax:

> GPIBtroff [address]

Example:
```
GPIBtroff
GPIBtroff 5
```

Description:

This command turns of tracing for all or one address at a time. Using this, you can eliminate the commands for the machines that you do not want to trace. By default, all addresses are traced.

34.2.10 : GPIBtron

Syntax:

> GPIBtron [address]

Example:
```
GPIBtron
GPIBtron 5
```

Description:

This command is the opposite for the GPIBtroff command: You can enable all or only selected addresses to be traced.

34.2.11 : GPIBwrite

Syntax:

> GPIBwrite <address>, <command as string>

Example:

```
GPIBwrite 5,"*RST"
GPIBwrite 10,":FUNCTION:SINE"
GPIBwrite 5,"H2"
```

Description:

This command transports commands to the machine at the designated address. The command should be formatted as a string. If you want to send numbers to the machine you should convert them using the str$ or sStr$ function.

```
GPIBwrite 5,"RANGE "+sstr$(x)
```

34.2.12 : GPIBread

Syntax:

> GPIBread address,[command]

Example:

```
GPIBread 5
GPIBread 5,"RESULT?"
```

Description:

This command allows you to read data from the GPIB stream. Data is returned in two global variables. IBret contains the numerical value of the returned information. IB$ contains the complete, unformatted string of data returned by the machines. Optionally, you can specify a command. This command is sent to the target before the read is attempted. Typically, you need to send some command to the device before it returns data. By specifying this command in the GPIBread function, you avoid having to issue a GPIBwrite first. It saves some lines of code in your program.

34.2.13 : GPIBfind

Syntax:

> X = GPIBfind <address>

Example:

```
X = GPIBfind(5)
```

Description:

This command checks the presence of a device at the specified address. If a device is found the functions returns TRUE, else it returns FALSE.

34.2.14 : GPIBFindAll

Syntax:

> GPIBfindall

Example:
```
GPIBfindAll
```

Description:

This command checks probes the entire bus for available devices. It does not attempt to open or identify them. It is merely checking their presence. A message box will pop up, showing the found devices.

34.2.15 : GPIBIdentifyAll

Syntax:

> GPIBIdentifyAll

Example:
```
GPIBIdentifyAll
```

Description:

This command checks probes the entire bus for available devices and takes temporary control over them. A message box will pop up, showing the found devices and their identification if they are SCPI compliant.

34.3 : GPIBcore I/O functions

The GPIBcore also provides means to interact with the PC's hardware on a low-level basis. Visual Basic provides access to disk, Com ports and printers in a standard way. However, if you want to use or 'abuse' these ports in a non-standard way, you will need a means of accessing the hardware registers. This functionality can be found in WIN95io.DLL.

This release of the core fully embeds this library into the GPIBcore.

34.3.1 : OUT

Syntax:

> OUT address, data

Example:

```
Out &h378,88
```

Description:

The out command allows you to write a data-byte to a specified IO address in the PC's IO space. This works in exactly the same way as in regular DOS based basic languages.

> **Note** Be very careful where you are writing. After all you could very quickly find yourself faced with the 'blue screen of death' if you are writing to certain addresses.

34.3.2 : INP

Syntax:

X = INP (address)

Example:

```
Result = inp(&h379)
```

Description:

The INP command allows you to read a data-byte from a specified IO address. This works in exactly the same way as in regular DOS based basic languages.

> **Note** Contrary to OUT and OUTW, you can read any location in the IO map without any problem.

34.4 : GPIBcore Miscellaneous support functions

34.4.1 : Delay

Syntax:

Delay <seconds>

Example:

```
Delay 5
```

Description:

This command relies on the internal system timer to provide for accurate timing sequences. It stops program execution until the specified number of seconds has elapsed.

34.4.2 : Microdelay

Syntax:

    Microdelay milliseconds

Example:
```
Microdelay 200
```

Description:

Same story as with the delay command, except this function counts milliseconds.

34.4.3 : SStr$

Syntax:

    string = sstr$ (value expression)

Example:
```
A$ = sstr$ (5)
```

Description:

This command is similar to the str$ function already present in Visual Basic. Except that, this flavor strips off the whitespace at the beginning and end of the returned string. Useful if you have a lot of

'x$ = trim$ (str$ (something)) style stuff in your code.

34.4.4 : Bin$

Syntax:

    String = bin$ (value expression)

Example:
```
X$ = bin$ (&h55)
X$ = bin$ (99)
```

Description:

This command will return a string containing zeros and ones that represents the binary notation of an integer number. The command can handle negative numbers. They are returned in standard two complements notation.

34.4.5 : vVal

Syntax:

String = bin$ (value expression)

Example:
```
x = vVal (&h55) ' x = 55h
x = vVal(&b10011001) ' x = 99h
```

This routine converts a string to a number. It operates in a similar manner as the Val command from Visual Basic, except that it can handle binary numbers as well.

34.4.6 : Logentry

Syntax:

Logentry string

Example:
```
Logentry "Hello world"
```

Description:

This is simply a command that allows you to write information to the console. This can be useful for debugging purposes.

34.4.7 : Log10

Syntax:

Xreturnvalue = Log10(value)

Example:
```
X = log10(y)
```

Description:

The Log10 function restores the base 10-logarithm capability of VB.

34.5 : ClassWork

ClassWork is a style of instrument drivers developed for use inside Vision. It builds on the concept of classes in Visual Basic to provide a uniform and easy access to instrument and hardware functions. Any existing instrument or interface, whether plug-in or GPIB based can be implemented as a ClassWork module.

34.5.1 : The ClassWork concept

A ClassWork module is the basic piece of code, consisting of procedures, functions and variables, which together form the interface to an instrument. This module is implemented as a class. By adhering to the concept set forth in this manual, you will easily construct your own modules and use existing modules.

The whole concept is constructed to provide a uniform and easy access channel to T&M (test and measurement) equipment from a programmer's point of view. While originally conceived for Visual Basic, you can imply this style on other languages as well.

The concept is such that it is taking away some of the particularities involved with each instrument. Not only is the way in which you gain control over a device standardized but also some of its basic functions. For instance, all power supplies have operators that allow you to program voltage and current. For any brand and model, this function has the same name. Because of this, I can immediately swap supplies with a different model and brand by simply redefining the class to which a particular instrument should belong.

Setup 1: Uses a machine from brand ABC model 12a. This machine has a command to set the voltage called SV. To set the voltage to 5 volts I would be required to send 'SV5' to the machine. The machine is set to respond to GPIB address 5.

Setup 2: Uses a supply from brand XYZ model 99z. This command to set the voltage is OUTPUT: VOLTS. In addition, the instrument has a dual output. To set this instrument to 5 volts you need to provide it with a string containing not only the voltage but also the channel. ': OUTPUT: VOLTS: CHANNEL1: 5V'. The machine is set to respond to GPIB address 22.

Suppose you have a program developed for case 1, and your supply malfunctions. You want to use the supply from setup 2. The following problems will arise:

-   The supply has a different command set, so you need to adapt you program.

-   It has multiple channels requiring additional information to be sent.

-   The GPIB addresses are different. Therefore, you need to fix these up as well.

This is where ClassWork comes in.

34.5.2 : The ClassWork solution

ClassWork defines a uniform set of commands to control these supplies. Both modules (one for each of the above-described supplies) contain a function to set the output voltage. This function will format the supplied data in a style that can be processed by the instrument. By doing this, you are abstracting the instruments.

ClassWork is breaking multi-channel devices into independent entities. Any device containing more than one channel is broken apart into single channel devices. Each of these single channels is controlled independently!

ClassWork still requires the address of the machine once and only once. During definition, you set the address and the required channel, and from then on, this item becomes a true standalone object you can use throughout your program.

A nice side-effect is that, while all of the above makes migration and maintenance easier, it also provides you with easier to understand code. In the past, you accessed machines using addresses.

Sure, you stored them in variables or constants, which in turn needed to be global. However, you still used to write things like:

```
Const supply=5
ABCvolts (supply, 5)
```

or
```
Const supply =22
XYZvolts (supply, 1, 5)
```

While solving this, ClassWork goes a step further. It treats your instrument as an object. Just as you have buttons and textboxes, you now have access to your instruments as objects.

You now simply define your supply and assign it an address and channel

```
Dim Supply as new ABC
Supply.address =5
Supply.assignto =1
```

If tomorrow your supply from ABC breaks down and you need to use brand XYZ, all you do is change a few words.

```
Dim Supply as new XYZ
Supply.address =22
Supply.assignto =1
```

ABC becomes XYZ and the 5 becomes a 22. Now, if in the unlikely event that channel 1 of this XYZ would be broken too and you were forced to use the second channel, you only change the assignto parameter and your program is running again.

```
Dim Supply as new XYZ
Supply.address =22
Supply.assignto =2
```

34.5.3 : Programming using ClassWork

Writing a program using ClassWork is just like writing any other program. The only thing that differs, is the way you approach instruments. Since ClassWork considers instruments as objects (a ClassWork instrument is logically an object derived from a Class), you can reference them just as you would do with a checkbox or a textbox.

Typically, you create a new project. The next thing you do is, add the GPIBcore module to your project. You need this module always, since ClassWork objects also use the same handler to perform GPIB I/O. So far, you have done nothing new (if you were already using the Vision system).

To load instrument libraries you now select Project - Add Class Module. The modules are located in the ClassWork directory of the Vision installation.

You still need to write your startup and shutdown code.

```
Private Sub Form_Load()
   GPIBinit
End Sub
Private Sub Quitprogram_Click()
   Bye
   End
End Sub
```

From now on things change. You need to derive instruments from the loaded classes. This is done by defining a new variable as a new <instrumentclass>.

```
Dim Voltmeter as new HP34401
Dim Supply as new HP6624
```

In your startup code you add a piece of code that sets the address and assignto parameters.

```
Private Sub Form_Load()
   GPIBinit
   Voltmeter.Address = 22
   Supply.Address =3
   Supply.AssignTo = 3
End Sub
```

Note For single channel instruments it is not required to use the assignto parameter. Per default, this parameter is set to 1.

You will notice that the Visual Basic environment will show you a list with possibilities you can select, just as if you were using any other control. That is exactly what is happening. Your instrument has been turned into an object.

34.5.4 : A Sample ClassWork program

The program below defines three instruments and performs a voltage sweep while plotting the voltage and current through a network.

```
' REM ClassWork testprogram
Dim Voltmeter As New HP34401
Dim Currentmeter As New HP34401
Dim Supply As New HP6624

Private Sub Form_Load()
    GPIBinit
    Voltmeter.Address = 22
    Currentmeter.Address = 23
    Supply.Address = 5
    Supply.Assignto = 3      ' we use channel 3 of the supply
End Sub
Private Sub Quitprog_Click()
    Bye
    End
End Sub
Private Sub sweep_Click()
    For x = Val(startvalue.Text) To Val(stopvalue.Text)
        Supply.voltage = x
        volts = Voltmeter.measure
        Current = Currentmeter.measure
        display.Text = display.Text & volts & ":" & Current &
                        _ vbclf
    Next x
End Sub
```

The initialization section is limited to establishing the GPIB link and assigning addresses to the instruments. From then on, you simply treat your instruments as any other control.

34.5.5 : Developing ClassWork Modules

Whilst ClassWork comes with a number of modules, you might need to write some yourself. In order to maintain the functionality of ClassWork, there are a number of rules to follow.

A ClassWork module is a piece of Visual Basic code that resides in a Class. Whatever functionality you want to implement, is up to you. However, in order for a Class to be a real ClassWork module, the following thing should be in place:

34.5.6 : Module Header

The ClassWork header should contain information about the library and the instrument covered by the library. A sample header can be found below. It marks clearly that it belongs to the ClassWork framework in the first two lines. Next it specifies that this library if for an HP34401 System multi-meter from Hewlett-Packard. The initial release of this particular piece of code was done on 15/11/1999, and some changes have been made on a later date. More detail could be given about exactly what and why but this is at the developer's discretion.

```
'************************************************************
' ClassWork Library
' Released under OpenSource Policy
'
' Instrument: HP34401 System multimeter
' Manufacturer: Hewlett Packard
'
' Initial release   15/11/1999      John.D.Designer
' Update            25/02/2000      John.D.Designer
'************************************************************
```

34.5.7 : Internal ClassWork variables.

The next thing to do, is to declare the two internal variables that are required by ClassWork. These can then be followed by the definition of the variables you might require. Since all derived objects run in their own memory space, they will each use their respective copy of the variable.

```
Private v_address   ' GPIB address for this device
Private v_entity    ' entity in multichannel devices
```

v_address:	is used as an internal placeholder for the GPIB address assigned to an object derived from the class.
v_entity:	is used to indicate which part of an instrument is targeted in case of a multimodule instrument. Multimodule instruments are defined as instruments that share the same physical GPIB port but have multiple in or output's all behaving in the same manner. For instance, a dual or triple channel power-supply or a 10-channel multi-meter.

34.5.8 : Initialize and Terminate events

Class_Initialize:

Whenever an instrument is derived from the class (this happens the moment the program executes), the initialize event will be fired. ClassWork uses this event only to notify the user that an object has been derived from this class. The message is being sent out using the standard Logentry command belonging to GPIBcore.

Besides this, you can implement whatever startup code might be required for your class.

Now what is the point of sending this comment? It informs the user how many instruments his program uses and of which type they are.

Example:

```
         Public Sub Class_Initialize ()
             Logentry "'ClassWork spawned a HP34401 instrument"
         End Sub
```

Class_Terminate:

The Class_Terminate is fired when the object derived from the class is destroyed. In case of a GPIB device, this event is used to close the GPIB channel and release the address.

Example:

```
         Private Sub Class_Terminate ()
             GPIBclose v_address
         End Sub
```

34.5.9 : Address assignment

In case of a GPIB device, the address property should be implemented. You are free to implement a 'get' statement, but this is not required.

Whenever the address is assigned (this can be during startup or it can also mean a change of address), this should cause the current address to be released, and the new address being assigned. The assigned address should be stored in the internal variable v_address. Throughout the rest of the code you must use this v_address when referring to your instrument.

```
         Public Property Let address (addr)
             GPIBclose v_address
             v_address = addr
             GPIBopen v_address
         End Property
```

34.5.10 : AssignTo assignment

This function might not always be applicable to your instrument but it MUST be implemented to maintain the highest possible level of compatibility. Simply store the number in the internal v_entity variable. Whenever you need to refer to a certain channel you use this v_entity variable. Again, here you are free to supply a 'get' command, but it is not required.

```
         Public Property Let Assignto (channel)
             v_entity = channel
         End Property
```

34.5.11 : Global Lead-in code overview

The complete picture looks like this:

```
'***********************************************************
' ClassWork Library
' Released under OpenSource Policy
'
' Instrument: HP34401 System multimeter
' Manufacturer: Hewlett Packard
'
' Initial release    15/11/1999      John.D.Designer
' Update             25/02/2000      John.D.Designer
'***********************************************************
Private v_address   ' GPIB address for this device
Private v_entity    ' entity in multichannel devices
Public Sub Class_Initialize ()
    Logentry "'ClassWork spawned a HP34401 instrument"
End Sub
Private Sub Class_Terminate ()
    GPIBclose v_address
End Sub
Public Property Let address (addr)
    GPIBclose v_address
    v_address = addr
    GPIBopen v_address
End Property
Public Property Let Assignto (channel)
    v_entity = channel
End Property
```

34.6 : General Rules for ClassWork module development

While the previous chapter described the required criteria to develop a ClassWork library, this section will describe an additional framework. It is advised to follow these guidelines to insure maximum compatibility. This chapter will try to show you when to use a property, method or event when creating module functions.

34.6.1 : Properties

RULE: If the item is not a real result of a primary function of the instrument, or the item is a setup parameter that configures the common (not directly measurement related) behavior, it should be implemented as a property (using Property Let). The data applied should be of the numerical type.

(Either a number or a Boolean). The data can also be contained in an array.

Examples:

A power supply is not a real 'measurement' device. It does not really 'measure' but it supplies you with power. Sure, you can read back the current it is actually delivering, but that was not the main goal of the instrument. Therefore, voltage and current are not real results of the instrument. To the supply, the Voltage and Current set are 'properties'. When retrieving the value of these properties, you can really read them values and return these as result of the action.

In a multi-meter, the number of digits used does not really determine the nature of the measurement. It has of course effect on the precision of the measurement but it has nothing to do with the physical quantity that needs to be measured. Selecting the physical quantity, deciding between voltages, current, resistance, is a different matter. Here you are changing the nature of the measurement and thus the measurement related behavior of the instrument.

34.6.2 : Methods (Sub)

RULE: A Subroutine is used whenever you change the instruments measurement related behavior of the measurement but do not perform an actual measurement. The functionality desired cannot be expressed using numbers.

Examples:

Selecting physical quantities like Voltage or Current for a multi-meter can be classified under this.

The same applies to selecting a function for a Waveform generator. Here you can implement Subroutines to specify the kind of waveform to be generated.

Of course, you could make a list with constants defining the Voltage = 1, Current =2 etc... However, this will cause problems. Not everybody will use the same conventions and this will then lead to code that is again not portable.

34.6.3 : Methods (Function)

RULE: A Function is used whenever you retrieve a primary measurement result. The result is a single number or Boolean value. The function can take arguments.

Examples:

The result of a measurement performed by a multi-meter. The multi-meter was previously set up with a number of digits (using a Property construction) and an indication of the nature of the measurement (VoltageDC using a Subroutine).

34.6.4 : Special Cases

Sometimes you will run into cases where you need to perform operations that cannot easily be catalogued as one of the above, or that return different kinds of information than those defined in the rules.

Example: Returning arrays:

This is a typical example. You retrieve a table with data representing a waveform from an oscilloscope.

Visual Basic does not allow you to return this type of data using a Function.

In this case, implement it as a Subroutine and change the content of the arguments from within the subroutine.

In all other cases, implement your functions as Subroutines (if not returning data) or as Functions (if returning single numbers).

34.6.5 : ClassWork implementation of the HP34401 driver

```
'*******************************************************
' ClassWork Library
' Released under OpenSource Policy
'
' Instrument: HP34401 System multimeter
' Manufacturer: Hewlett packard
'
' Initial release    15/11/1999      V.Himpe
'*******************************************************
Private v_address   ' GPIB address for this device
Private v_entity    ' entity in multichannel devices
Public Sub Class_Initialize()
    logentry "'Classwork spawned a HP34401 instrument"
End Sub
Public Property Let Address(addr)
    v_address = addr
    GPIBopen addr
End Property
Public Property Let Assignto(channel)
    v_entity = channel
End Property
Public Sub VoltsDc()
    GPIBwrite v_address, ":CONF:VOLT:DC"
End Sub
Public Sub VoltsAc()
    GPIBwrite v_address, ":CONF:VOLT:AC"
End Sub
Public Sub CurrentDC()
    GPIBwrite v_address, ":CONF:CURR:DC"
End Sub
Public Sub CurrentAC()
```

```
        GPIBwrite v_address, ":CONF:CURR:AC"
End Sub
Public Sub ohms4()
        GPIBwrite v_address, ":CONF:FRES"
End Sub
Public Sub Frequency()
        GPIBwrite v_address, ":CONF:FREQ"
End Sub
Public Sub Period()
        GPIBwrite v_address, ":CONF:PER"
End Sub
Public Sub ohms2()
        GPIBwrite v_address, ":CONF:RES"
End Sub
Public Sub Trigger(mode)
    Select Case mode
    Case 1      ' external (vanachteren)
        GPIBwrite v_address, "TRIG:SOUR:IMM"
    Case Else   ' internal
        GPIBwrite v_address, "TRIG:SOUR:EXT"
    End Select
End Sub
Public Function measure()
    GPIBwrite v_address, "INIT"
    GPIBread v_address, "FETCH?"
    measure = ibret
End Function
```

If you compare this block of code with the implementation as a standard module, you will find many similarities. Actually, it is very simple to convert a standard module to a ClassWork class. Just glue on the header, change some information and maybe clean up the code a bit. The hardest part will be deciding how to implement a certain function. Will it be a Method (Function, Sub), a property or an Event? If you follow the guidelines laid out before, this will not be that hard either.

34.7 : TestBench

TestBench is an add-on to ClassWork. It provides a simple way to build control panels for your instruments. TestBench objects are implemented as ActiveX controls and distributed in source-code format.

A TestBench control interacts directly with a ClassWork library. The following example shows how to link a TestBench control to an instrument. The name of the TestBench object is DVM1.

```
Dim MyVoltmeter as new HP34401
Set DVM1 = Myvoltmeter
```

TestBench controls implement a basic set of functions commonly found in the instruments they can be mapped to. A TestBench control works as a pass-thru channel for the instrument controls.

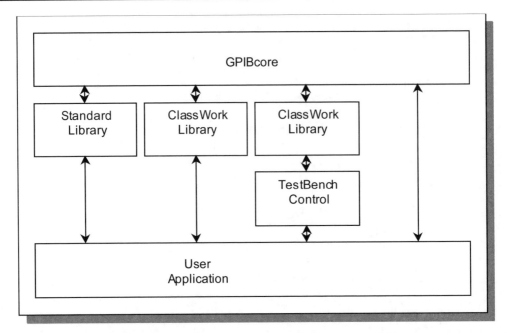

The above picture shows the implementation possibilities of all possible instrument control libraries. A program using TestBench can look like the image below.

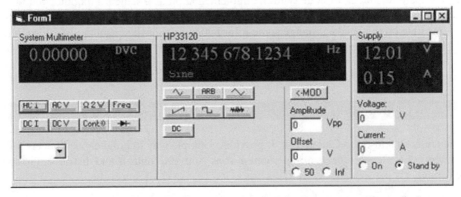

The TestBench controls feature a similar look and feel. Of course, you will not find any special features of the instruments here. The controls are written in such a way that they can interface with any ClassWork target.

It speaks for itself that you do not have to try to attach the Supply control to a multi-meter. This will immediately lead to errors. Having the TestBench control installed, and locked to a ClassWork target, does not mean that you lose access to the ClassWork library. You can still call special functions in the ClassWork library to set up items that the TestBench control does not handle for you.

Chapter 35 : Designing Test Programs

Writing a test program is not unlike writing an ordinary program. However there are some differences in the construction and programming style required. The most important thing to keep in mind is to write clean code. It does not hurt to write five extra lines of code, if it makes the program more readable. On the risk of becoming boring, I will repeat the most import standard programming techniques here.

35.1 : Clean code

Make simple code. Five simple commands are easier to understand, modify and support than one complex command.

35.1.1 : Modular programming.

Divide your program in functional subroutines and/or functions. Subroutines that must be accessible everywhere throughout the program, should be contained in separate modules. Give you subroutines and functions an understandable name. Also, when passing variables to and from subroutines, give them a meaningful name. Remember that the Visual Basic IDE will show you the variable names while you are writing code that calls the function or procedure. In addition, where possible you should typecast your variables.

Example:

```
Function FindBiggestInteger (value1 as integer,value2 as integer) as
integer
```

```
Function Fbi(v1,v2)
```

The first example shows a meaningful function name, a clean typecasting of the two expected variables, and a typecasting for the return value. The second line shows a crappy declaration for the same routine. While the name FBI (Find Biggest Integer) might mean something for the original programmer of the code, it might confuse someone who has to maintain or alter the code.

35.1.2 : Documenting code.

Wherever possible, write down some information about the code you are writing. In particular, this is important if you are doing mathematical or logical operations. It makes the code understandable for someone else or even for you. You might find yourself wondering how a certain piece of code works, even if you wrote it yourself just weeks before. Supporting an undocumented piece of code can be very hard. Writing documentation takes only a minimal

amount of time, it does not waste space in the final program and it does not take away
execution speed.

35.1.3 : Use indentation and CamelWriting.

This is improves the overall readability of the code. It becomes clearer which lines are
contained between decision blocks of code. Also, limit the number of commands to one per
line.

```
Function thisisanunreadableandlongfunctionname(x,y)
x=x+x:y=y+1:x=x/y:x=int(x/y)
thisisanunreadableandlongfunctionname=x+x/sin(x*y)
end function
```

The above could be rewritten as:

```
Function DoSomething (x,y)
    x = x+x
    y = y+1
    x = x/y
    x = int (x/y)
    DoSomething = x+x / sin (x*y)
End Function
```

Fortunately, the Visual Basic editor helps you out using different colors for variables,
commands, and comment. It also enforces CamelWriting for its internal function names.
Besides the above-mentioned items, there are some additional rules you might want to follow.

35.2 : Accessing instruments and hardware

In order to keep a modular program that can be maintained for a long time, you should divide it
into functional units.

35.2.1 : Accessing instruments

Whenever you access instruments, try to use the provided function libraries (standard libraries
or ClassWork objects). If you find yourself in the situation when there is no ready made
solution, then build a library of your own. Do not write low-level code to access an instrument
anywhere I your program. Instead, build the library. In future programs it might be useful, and
it makes the program far more readable.

35.2.2 : Accessing hardware in the computer

The same rules as for accessing instruments can be applied here. Try to shield the real program for the low-level work by using intermediate layers.

35.3 : Collecting data versus Analyzing

The first aim of a test and measurement program is to collect data, not analyze it. To analyze collected data, there are far more powerful tools available (Excel, MathCAD, Mathlab etc). Therefore, you should concentrate your programming effort on just that. Store the retrieved data in log-files and post process them later.

35.4 : Creating log files

When you are writing a program to collect data, you will need a means to off-load this data. Saving measurement data especially happens in so call 'log-files'. Besides the measurement data, it might be interesting to store additional information as well:

The name of the tester: This can prove helpful. In case of any problems, you can always contact this person for more information.

The date and time: To do some kind of version control on test reports, and to improve traceability of the report and item under test.

The number of the sample: In case you find bizarre results, you might want to re-test this particular device.

The temperature at which it was tested: All electrical parameters drift over temperature. Therefore, it is wise to know this. Furthermore, some tests require temperature sweeps.

All initial conditions of the test: In case you find crazy data, this can prove helpful to reproduce the exact conditions of the test. This information can be of utmost importance to recreate a certain effect in a component.

In the next chapter some special programming techniques will be described. Amongst them is the generation of CSV files. This is a format particularly useful to create log files. It can be read by almost any data processing program like Excel MathCAD etc.

35.5 : Anatomy of a well structured test-program

A well-structured program looks like an onion. You can peel it away layer by layer until you reach the core: the component under test.

Layer 1: At the outmost layer are the user interface and the data storage handlers. Depending on the actions of the user and/or files (scripts!), messages will be passed to certain measurement algorithms (U/I sweeps, level detection, ADC measurement etc) and to the functional control routines that control the behavior of the chip. The returned data will be displayed on the user interface or stored to disk.

Layer 2: Measurement Algorithms will talk to either the instrument drivers, to collect data or setup instruments, or the control drivers to configure the chip and or test-board. The Functional control routines will implement the operations required to transport information to and from the chip (serial buses, SPI etc, test-pins). Retrieved information is delivered to the Measurement algorithms and functional control algorithms.

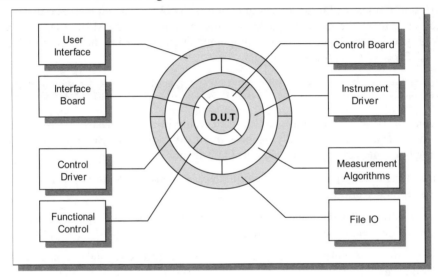

Layer 3: The instrument driver will control instruments and make them apply the correct voltages, currents and signals to the component. The control driver will orchestrate the operation of all hardware on the test-board and the interface to the computer.

Layer 4: The interface board will switch these signals to the appropriate pins of the component. The control board (Printer port or Data acquisition system) will apply digital stimuli to our chip directly from the computer. All this happens under total control of the instrument drivers and the control drivers.

Core: Here we find our component under test. This little critter will take all of the stimuli delivered to it, process them and return us with some information that then can be offloaded and presented to the user and stored for later evaluation.

Every module in any layer should be constructed in such a fashion that it takes information from above and passes it down below. Anything coming back from the layer below is processed and passed on to the layer above. However, you must avoid at all times to 'skip' layers. The program loses modularity and portability. Every subroutine must have an unambiguous task. By following these rules, you will have a program that has a lowest level the hardware interface. The moment something changes there, you can update the entire project by patching that and only that layer.

Chapter 36 : Special Programming techniques

During the development of test programs, you will encounter some specific problems. Most of these problems can be tackled using some logic thinking. However, some problems can be hard to find a solution for. This chapter will attempt to clarify some of the specific problems you might struggle with when developing your program.

36.1 : Stream Interpreting

What is stream interpreting? Simply said, it is the generation of a data-stream to a target. This stream can be accompanied by a number of control signals such as a select line and a clock or strobe line. When the output of the stream generator is fed to an output port, we are talking about a bit-banged interface. You are in fact manipulating bits to 'emulate' one interface onto another interface.

36.1.1 : Monolithic Program

Let us take an example with a shift register.

A shift register has a clock input a reset line and a data input. We will connect this shift register on a standard parallel port (In this case the Printer port, but it could be an IO port of the 8255 controller on our home-built IO board as well).

The reset line will be connected to bit D0, the clock line will be attached to Bit D1 and the data in of the shift register will be connected to D2 of the I/O port.

Thus, we can already define some constants.

```
Const Shift_RST = 1
Const Shift_CLK=2
Const Shift_DIN=4 ' bit 2 is worth the decimal value 4
```

The first thing we should do, is to build our stream from the supplied data. The easiest way to do this is, represent the data as a string containing 1's and 0's. Fortunately the GPIBcore contains the Bin$ function.

The stream could also come from a graphical user interface for that matter. Anyhow, for the moment the origin of the stream is of no importance.

To interprete the stream, we have to make some sort of scanning algorithm that checks the value of a certain character in the string and sets the output bits accordingly.

```
Sub SendStream(stream$)
    for x = 1 to len(stream$)
        if mid$(stream$,x,1)="1" then
```

```
            out Ioport,shift_din
            outIOPort,Shift_Din+Shift_CLK
            out Ioport,Shift_Din
        else
            out Ioport,0
            outIOPort,Shift_CLK
            out Ioport,0
        end if
    next x
End Sub
```

The above block of code will send scan the stream independent of its length, and send out the appropriate bit. A clock pulse is generated after the update of the Din pin as well. To reset the shift register, we can simply put two more commands before we start scanning the string.

The final code would look like this:

```
Sub SendStream(stream$)
    out Ioport,Shift_RST
    out Ioport,0
    for x = 1 to len(stream$)
        if mid$(stream$,x,1)="1" then
            out Ioport,shift_din
            outIOPort,Shift_Din+Shift_CLK
            out Ioport,Shift_Din
        else
            out Ioport,0
            outIOPort,Shift_CLK
            out Ioport,0
        end if
    next x
End Sub
```

36.1.2 : Modular program

The disadvantage of the above program is, that it is one block of monolithic code that is hard to port to different hardware. Of course, you can change the pin definition by altering the definition of the three constants involved, but that is not real portability. What if you need a number of instructions control a certain pin?

Therefore, you need to make your program modular. If you rewrite the above example in the following way, you will get a truly portable program. Besides the fact that it is better portable, it is also better readable. Even someone who never programmed before or does not understand the BASIC language (I cannot image they exist), can understand this code.

```
Sub SendStream(stream$)
    RSThi
    RSTlo
    for x = 1 to len(stream$)
        if mid$(stream$,x,1)="1" then
            DINhi
```

```
                    CLKHI
                    CLKLO
              else
                    DINlo
                    CLKhi
                    CLKlo
              end if
          next x
      End Sub
```

Now all we have to do, is define the routines that hook our operations to the hardware.

```
          Dim mask as integer

          Sub RSThi
              Out Ioport+1,128
          End Sub

          Sub RSTlo
              Out Ioport+1,0
          End Sub

          Sub CLKhi
              mask = mask or 1
          End Sub

          Sub CLKlo
              mask = mask and (255-1)
          End Sub

          Sub DINhi
              out ioport+2,(inp(ioport+2) or 8)
          End Sub

          Sub DINlo
              out ioport+2,(inp(ioport+2) and (255-8))
          End Sub
```

The above code shows that the code to handle the RST pin is changing a bit in a certain register. The other 2 bits physically reside in another register.

The CLK pin is a physical pin on a parallel port. However, we are not allowed to change that status of the other pins, and we cannot read from the port. Therefore, we need to declare a variable that holds the status of our IO port. Therefore the declared variable *mask*. Other routines in our program may use this Mask bit as well.

The DIN pin belongs to a port that can be read back. There I used code that retrieves the current setting and alter them. This is called a read-modify-write operation.

As you can see this code is truly portable and adaptable to any situation possible. It is sufficient to adapt the layer below the stream interpreter to port it.

36.1.3 : Creating the stream

So far, I have made the interpreter and the I/O routines. However, where do we get the stream? There are a number of options: you create it by converting a value to a binary stream using the BIN$ function in the GPIBcore. Alternatively, you can ask the user to type the stream. On the other hand, maybe you can provide him with a graphical user interface. And the latter is exactly what I am about to do here.

Remember the arrays of objects described in one of the very first parts of this book? Well, that is what I am going to use. Simply make an array of checkboxes. Each checkbox represents one bit in the stream. If you order them logically then the element 0 will represent bit 0, element 2 represents bit 1 and so on.

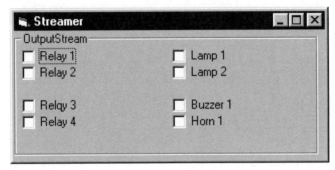

The creation of the stream is then attached to the Click event of the array of controls.

```
Sub Bitstream_Click(index as integer)
    stream$=""
    for x = 0 to number_of_elements
        if Bitstream(x).value =1 then
            stream$="1"+stream$
        else
            stream$="0"+stream$
        end if
    next x
    sendstream(stream$)
End Sub
```

And there you have it: a graphical interface to our stream interpreter. If you now assign a meaningful name to every checkbox, you have a very user-friendly program.

Chapter 37 : Building user interfaces.

An important point of concern is building a user interface for your test program. Designing an intuitive easy-to-use program is not an easy job. Too many programs are simply 'kludged' together into a working state and then used 'as-is'.

This should not be the case for your programs. By the time you have reached this chapter, you should already know a lot about the BASIC language, about designing Windows programs, controlling instruments, writing structured and expandable programs. And it is exactly all the above knowledge you will need to create a friendly and easy-to-use interface for your program.

37.1 : Build a splash screen and design a logo and icon.

No kidding! No time to be modest now. It is okay to brag a bit about the program. Design a catchy icon (16*16 and 32*32 bit in 16 colors) to put on the title bar of your program. Make the same icon in a bigger format to put on a splash screen.

The splash screen should contain at least the name of the program, copyright information, and a version number. You can also put some info about the company or person who wrote it. Moreover, a nice graphic does not hurt. As an example, you can take a look at splash screen from Word or Excel or even Visual Basic itself.

The Splash screen is at the same time a good spot to start allocating the memory you need, loading any data you need and initializing any instruments you need. You can do this most easily by loading the sub-forms of your program into memory without showing them. This will effectively allocate whatever resources are needed.

If you have clean partitioned code, you can write a subroutines that initializes the hardware you will use, like GPIB or printer ports, to a known state as well. When all this is done, you simply pass control to the main form of the program and unload the splash screen.

```
Sub Splash_load()
      DoEvents ' Make sure we are being shown !
      load frm_MainForm
      ' update a statusbox here
      label1.caption ="Loading forms …"
      DoEvents
      load frm_Setup
      DoEvents
      load frm_ExtraForm1
      DoEvents
      load frm_EveryOtherForm
      label1.caption ="Initializing system"
      DoEvents
      InitializeSystem
      DoEvents
      mainform.show
      DoEvents
      Me.hide
End Sub
```

The above block of code does all of this and shows some status information to the user as well. Make sure you do not forget the DoEvents statement between every load command. This allows Windows the necessary time to handle its internal management. Some of this time is used to manage the just loaded form.

Besides giving your program a professional look, it also speeds up the perceived speed of your program.

37.2 : Constructing the Main form.

The main form is the most important piece of your program. You should think about the way you want to organize it. After all, this is the place that the user will be looking at most.

37.2.1 : The Workplace of your program

A good main form is designed as a switchboard. You have all the things you use most in front of you. All extra information is hidden in additional screens. Remove any superfluous information from the screen and into sub-forms.

Depending on the time, you have to write the program you could implement 'dockable' toolbars and other fancy stuff but this is not necessary for a good program. Sometimes too many gizmos' can be annoying too. After all a test program is bound to be used by technical minded people, and they do not care about funky colors (well … most of them that is).

A nice thing to have thing is a status bar. Show the date and time and a single line of info. This gives your program that little 'extra' touch and does not cost much. The info-line can be used to tell the user something about what he is doing or going to do.

37.2.2 : Construct a Decent Menu

A decent menu should have a clean layout. Sort the items on a mane per category. File operations should be put under the File menu, Tools under a Tools menu and Help under a Help menu. The golden rule here is: Keep it logical. Wherever possible, try to assign hotkeys. It makes the program friendlier and it does not cost you a single line of code. The Visual Basic compiler takes care of the hotkeys. Look at standard windows programs to add hotkeys to your menus.

Images on menus can look cool but take too much time to implement. It is better to construct a separate toolbar than embedding the icons in the menu itself.

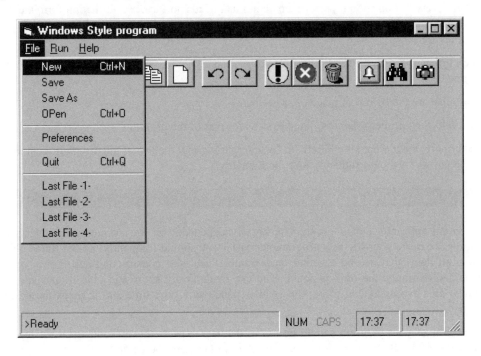

37.2.3 : Tooltips

Try to put some meaningful information in the ToolTipText property of the controls on the screen. It is not a lot of work but can provide that extra bit of information to the user when he needs it. This can literally save you a bunch of calls for support from your user. In addition, it does not require you writing any code.

37.2.4 : Toolbars

A toolbar can be a very handy thing. A single icon might mean more than a thousand words. However, a superfluous toolbar will scare the user as well. Put only the real tools on the toolbar, and provide additional information using the ToolTipText property of the toolbar control. The icons on the toolbar should have a clear meaning. Do not put the symbol for Cut (scissors), if you are going to use it to paste text. Sounds pretty obvious? Yes, in this case. However, what about things like Print and Print setup? The answer is simple:

A toolbar contains only single-action objects. A printer setup button is out of place on a toolbar. Every button should perform an action that needs no further information form the user. No pop-up boxes or fly-outs. Just plain and simple one-click does it all actions. Typical examples are:

Save current file, Print current file, Cut, Copy, Paste, Undo, Redo, Help, Run, Stop, Break, Continue etc.

Things that are totally out of place on, a toolbar:

Color selectors, printer selectors, setup screens for part of the program.

Furthermore, the toolbar should remain constant throughout the use of the program. That means that no parts of it should suddenly lose functionality.

37.3 : Organizing Objects and controls.

The visual appearance of a program is heavily dependant on the arranging of objects and controls. To make your life as a programmer easier you should frequently use the frame object. Group all items that belong together on a frame. Then start constructing sub frames on this frame and rearrange the objects again. You can dynamically show and hide frames and sub-frames. This avoids having to pop-up smaller windows all the time and it keeps the desktop orderly.

Other parts of your program should be where the user expects those: Toolbars at the top, just below the menu, Status bars at the bottom. And in-between the central working area of your program. Try to keep your layout style as consistent as possible with what is commonly used in any Windows-based program.

37.4 : Configuration and tool forms

Whenever you want to provide extra forms to allow the setup of several parameters, try to be as specific as possible. Do not make one huge form. Break it down into small chunks of information, but at the same time avoid 500 different setup forms. The best way is to make a separate setup form that contains a tab-strip. Depending on the actual stuff the user wants to configure, he can click on one of the tabs and then perform the setup for that section. A typical example would be the following:

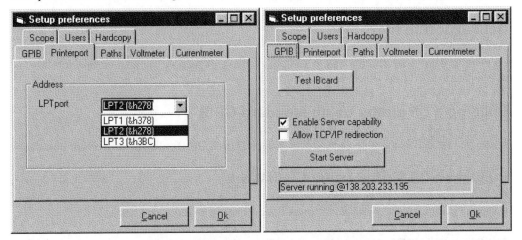

37.5 : Help files

Whenever possible, construct a help file for your program. This involves writing some text in a specified format and running it through a so-called Help-Compiler. The details about this process are a bit too extensive for this manual but can be found in the on-line help of Visual Basic.

For most of the test programs developed, the use of ToolTipText is far more useful. When you feel additional help is required, then you always have a pop-up box display some more text.

Chapter 38 : And yet more case studies

SPI stack on LPT

This sample shows a practical implementation of stream generation on a printer port. It shows both methods, one functional and on graphical.

Data export to file

Formatting data in an orderly way is not always easy. A sample application that formats and writes data to CSV files (Excel format).

Building a U/I plotter using standard GPIB

A sample that builds a simple curve-tracer using standard GPIB calls and instrument libraries.

Building a U/I Plotter using ClassWork

A sample that builds the same curve-tracer but now using ClassWork libraries.

Building a U/I Plotter using TestBench

The same sample all over again, but now using a TestBench front panel for ClassWork.

38.1 : Case Study 11: SPI stack on LPT

A typical operation you might perform is to shift data in and out of a component. Most likely, you will use a printer port for this purpose, since it is standard property on any computer. You could as well implement this stack for a custom IO board or ready-made IO board. The only layer you would have to adapt is the hardware access.

If we follow the rules of a good structured program, we will begin by writing the low-level interface code that will glue all routines to our hardware.

The SPI bus defines four pins:

- SCK: Serial Clock

- CS: Chip Select

- DO: data to the chip

- DI: data from the chip.

The SPI bus uses a strict sequencing diagram that tells us that, in order to talk to a component, we should have the clock line low and then take the chip select line low.

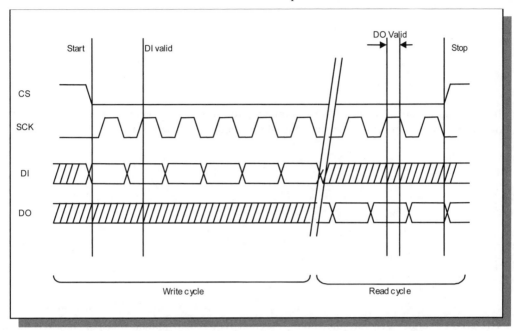

The above diagram shows us the timing information of the SPI bus on every consecutive clock pulse (1 rising and one falling edge) the chip will take in or send out data. Data is taken in and sent out on the rising edge. The outgoing data remains valid during the time that the SCK pin is HI. To terminate a transaction, you leave the SCK line low and then make CS high.

In our example, we will use bits D0 to D2 as output and the BS bit as input. There are a number of ways you can implement the transport routines. In this example, I will use the ClassWork library that controls printer ports.

```
Dim LPT1 as New PrinterPort
LPT1.port= &h378

Sub SCKhi
    lpt1.D0 = True
End Sub
Sub SCKlo
    lpt1.D0 = False
End Sub
Sub Cshi
    lpt1.D1 = True
End Sub
Sub Cslo
    lpt1.D1 = False
End Sub
```

```
Sub Dohi
    lpt1.D2 = True
End Sub
Sub Dolo
    lpt1.D2 = False
End Sub

Function SampleDI
    sampledi = LPT1.BS
End function
```

In case you do not want to use this approach, you always 'bit-bang' using 'AND' and 'OR' operations. Next step is to create some high-level routines that perform simple tasks.

```
Sub OpensPI
    Cshi
    SCKlo
    Dolo
    CSlo
End Sub

Sub CloseSPI
    SCKlo
    Dolo
    CShi
End Sub
```

The above routines generate the timing diagram required to initiate transport and terminate transport. Now, all we need are the effective transport routines. Since our routines can be used on several data-lengths, we might want to make them adaptive.

```
Sub SendData (dta$)
    For x = 1 to len(dta$)
        if mid$(dta$,x,1)="1" then
            DOhi
        else
            DOlo
        end if
        SCKhi    ' clockpulse generation
        SCKlo
    Next x
End Sub
```

The above routine will always transit an amount of bits equal to the number of characters in the DTA$. The final routine is the one retrieving data from the SPI bus. It accepts the number of bits desired.

```
Sub ReceiveData(number_of_bits)
    y$=""
    for x = 1 to number_fo_bits
        if SampleSPI=true then
            y$=y$+"1"
```

```
                    else
                          Y$=y$+"0"
                    End if
              next x
         End Sub
```

The final functions will implement the entire SPI frame now. Our final chip could accept a 5-bit address and 8 bit data stream and would then return 4 bits of status information.

```
         Function SPI(address$,dta$)
                  OpenSPI
                  senddata address$
                  senddata dta$
                  SPI = receivedata (4)
                  closeSPI
         End Sub
```

The above function would effectively accomplish this entire data exchange protocol. Furthermore, thanks to the layered architecture of our library, it can be maintained and adapted very easily to different hardware platforms. The only things that need to be changed are the routines that glue the SPI stack to the hardware. If we do not want to use the ClassWork library, we simply call other functions from somewhere else, or we implement our own logic there. The entire stack is expandable in all directions: to the user level, to the hardware level and in the functionality level.

The next step might be the construction of a graphical control of the bits you are sending. The easiest way is to create an array of objects that can be set to one or zero. Best would be to simply put a number of checkboxes on the screen. When you create these as an array then you can assign the element 0 to bit 0, element 1 to bit 1 etc. Need more bits? Put more check boxes. Since all checkboxes will fire the same piece of code, the construction of the transport mechanism is simple.

```
         Sub SPIcheckbox_click(index as integer)
              tmp$=""
              for x = 0 to 7 ' amount of checkboxes
                  if SPIcheckbox(x).value=1 then
                       tmp$=tmp$+"1"
                  else
                       tmp$=tmp$+"0"
                  end if
              next x

              OpenSPI
              Senddata(tmp$)
              CloseSPI

         End Sub
```

And presto ! Instant user access to the entire SPI stream, without limiting the adaptability of the code.

38.2 : Case Study 12: Data export to file

Most test programs will collect data and have the need to store it somewhere. You can of course develop your own file format but it might become more interesting, if you could use some standard format supported by many programs. Question is, what format?

There is one format recognized by almost any data processing program that is even readable for humans: the CSV format or Comma Separated Values format. If you give the filename the extension CSV, then these programs will know exactly how to treat these files, and import them in a consistent way into their internal format. Nice side effect is, that the file remains readable by your programs as well as by any text viewer too. You could even edit it manually if you would.

Structure of CSV files:

```
<entry>,<entry>,<entry>,<entry>,<entry>[CR LF]
<entry>[CR LF]
<entry>,<entry>,<entry>,<entry>,<entry>[CR LF]
<entry>,<entry>,<entry>,<entry>[CR LF]
<entry>,<entry>,[CR LF]
<entry>,<entry>,,<entry>[CR LF]
```

The above syntax shows you immediately all you need to know. Every line contains a number of entries separated by a comma and terminated with a [CR LF] (carriage return-line feed &h13 &h10) pair. The CR-LF you will get automatically if you simply use the print command without terminator (, or ;) to write to a file. Therefore, there are no pitfalls there. It is even allowed to have a comma without and entry followed by CR-LF or even two commas without anything in between. Note that for maximum compatibility it is wise to put at least a space in between.

To the CSV import filter, the comma means nothing else as 'go to the next column. The data contained in an entry field can be numeric, alpha or alphanumeric. If an entry contains a valid number (1, 1.2 1.2E+122, -1.12e-99) and nothing else than this, then it will be correctly imported as a number. If there is any other information in the entry then it will be interpreted as text.

This means that the following CSV file:

```
10.2 Volts, 3.12 Amps [CR LF]
11.5 Volts, 12.7 Amps [CR LF]
```

will be read as

10.2 Volts	3.12 Amps
11.5 Volts	12.7 Amps

Lets look at an example files:

```
This, Is, A, Text [CR LF]
This,is,a,text,too, [CR LF]
```

```
This,,is, , also,, valid,,[CR LF]
1,2,1.23,a,b,c[CR LF]
```

When imported, this will look like the following:

This	Is	A	Text			
This	is	a	text	too		
This		is		also		valid
1	2	1.23	a	b	c	

Note that trailing commas without text will be stripped from the import.

38.3 : Generating CSV files.

The following piece of code might make life very easy for you:

A CSV file, which is short for Comma Separated Value, is a format that is recognized by programs such as Excel. In short, it is a format that assists in post processing data. There is nothing special about the format. When coding an io handler to dump data to a CSV file you will need to process each individual parameter you want to send to the file. The code below makes life easier.

The functions CSVtext and CSVnumber allow you to send data directly to the file. The required comma as separator is added automatically. The CSVnewline function creates a new line in the output file.

```
Dim CSVfilename$ ` holder for the filename

Sub CSVtext (txt$)
     x = freefile
     Open CSVfilename$ for append as #x
          print #1,txt$ +",";
     Close c
End sub

Sub CSVnumber (number)
     x = freefile
     Open CSVfilename$ for append as #x
          print #1,str$(number) +"," ;
     Close c
End sub

Sub CSVnewline
     x = freefile
     Open CSVfilename$ for append as #x
          print #1,""
     Close c
End Sub
```

You simply put the target filename in the variable CSVfilename$. The file will be accessed in append mode automatically, so no data is overwritten.

38.4 : Case 13: A U/I plotter using GPIBcore operations

This little program will perform a voltage sweep and measure the current through a load. The resulting data will be stored in an array for later processing.

The first thing we need to do is find out the addresses of our instruments and store them int the program. Next thing is to write the GPIB code to initialize the bus and open the instruments. It is a good practice to close the GPIB bus upon exit, so a small blurb of code will be attached to a menu entry as well.

```
Const PSU =5
Const DVM =22

Sub Form_load()
     GPIBinit
     GPIBopen PSU
     GPIBopen DVM
End Sub

Sub Quitprogram
     bye
     end
End sub
```

The next thing we need to do, is create a form that holds entry fields for the start, stop and step value of the voltage sweep. The textboxes will be called respectively **STARTval**, **STOPval** and **STEPval**. In addition, a textbox called **report** will be used to output the logged data. Finally, we need a button to trigger all of this action.

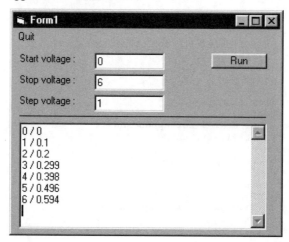

Now we need to know the commands to set the voltage of the supply. Note that these commands are instrument dependent and need to be looked up in the user manual of the instrument.

Powersupply: "VSET <channel>: <V.vvv>"

Multimeter: "RANGE:CURRENT DC" and "MEASURE?"

In our case, we are going to use channel 1 of the power supply so we need to send it the string 'VSET 1:' followed by the desired voltage. Now that we have this information, we can write the main loop of the program.

```
Sub Sweep_click()
      gpibwrite DVM,"RANGE:CURRENT DC"
      for x = val(startval.text) to val(stopval.text) _
            step val(stepval.text)
          gpibwrite PSU,"VSET 1:"+str$(x)
          GPIBread DVM,"MEASURE?"
          report.text=report.text +str$(x)+" / "+str$(ibret)
      next x
End Sub
```

The net result is a program that plots exactly what we want to a textbox. Now, it is up to you to write file IO or even a graphic charter using an Mschart object, or even your own charter using graphics operations.

Of course, in the above example we could have used some of the modules existing for those instruments. Suppose we have a module for a multi-meter (say a HP34401) loaded. The sweep routine could then look like this:

```
Sub Sweep_click()
      HP34401CurrentDC dvm
      for x = val(startval.text) to val(stopval.text) _
            step val(stepval.text)
          gpibwrite PSU,"VSET 1:"+str$(x)
          HP34401Measure
          report.text=report.text +str$(x)+" / "+str$(ibret)
      next x
End Sub
```

As you can see, the dedicate calls have been replaced by calls to functions and subroutines in the Library for the instrument.

38.5 : Case 13: A U/I plotter using ClassWork operations

This little program will perform exactly the same function as the previous example, except that this time it will use the ClassWork libraries to handle the instruments.

The User interface looks exactly the same but most of the code changes. Let us take a look at the system startup code:

```
        Dim PSU as new HP6624 ' Create an object of class HP6624
        Dim DVM as new HP34401 ' Create object from HP34401 class

        Sub Form_load()
            GPIBinit
            PSU.address = 5   ' address of the supply
            PSU.Assignto = 1  ' use first channel of this supply
            DVM.address = 22  ' address of the DVM
            DVM.CurrentDC     ' select Current DC range
        End Sub

        Sub Quitprogram
            bye
            end
        End sub
```

As you can see the initialization block looks a bit different. All of the settings for the instrument are done here. The address has been assigned, the appropriate channel for the supply has been selected and the range for the multi-meter has been specified.

Now it is time to have a look at our sweep function:

```
        Sub Sweep_click()
            for x = val(startval.text) to val(stopval.text) _
                    step val(stepval.text)
                PSU.Voltage x
                value = DVM.Measure
                report.text=report.text +str$(x)+" / "+str$(value)
            next x
        End Sub
```

You can see that the way to approach the instruments, is exactly like you approach any other object in your program. That is the idea behind ClassWork: it exposes the instruments as objects to your program.

38.6 : Case 13: A U/I plotter using TestBench operations

This last example shows you how to add TestBench controls to your program. The code is the same as the previous example, with a minor difference in the startup section. However, let us look at the screen first:

The controls for our program have been moved to a small panel. So nothing special there. In fact, it is not necessary to move them to a panel but it looks more consistent with the TestBench controls. Next to the panel are the two inserted TestBench controls: One for the power supply and one for the multi-meter. The power supply has been named PSU and the multi-meter has got the name DVM.

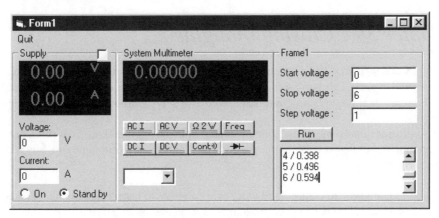

Of course, now we have to use different names for our supply and multi-meter when we derive them from ClassWork objects.

```
Dim MyPSU as new HP6624 ' Create an object of class HP6624
Dim MyDVM as new HP34401 ' Create object from HP34401 class

Sub Form_load()
    GPIBinit
    MyPSU.address = 5    ' address of the supply
    MyPSU.Assignto = 1   ' use first channel of this supply
    MyDVM.address = 22   ' address of the DVM
    MyDVM.CurrentDC      ' select Current DC range

    Set DVM.Target = MyDVM ' TestBench link to ClassWork
    Set PSU.Target = MyPSU ' TestBench link to ClassWork
End Sub

Sub Quitprogram
    bye
    end
End sub
```

The reason I changed the name of the ClassWork objects is to avoid having to rename anything else in my project. All calls will now be done to the TestBench controls which in turn will pass them to the ClassWork object, that will talk to GPIBcore, which will perform the GPIB I/O until all returning data has been handed back to TestBench.

Sounds complicated? No, it is simple logic applied to a very modular program, using lots of modern concepts and the awesome power of Visual Basic, Object Oriented Programming and Rapid Application Development.

Chapter 39 : Closing thoughts

Many books about Visual Basic, or any other language for that matter, deal with programming techniques and syntax. This book was written from a different perspective, namely that of a non-programmer that requires programming in order to solve a problem.

I make no illusions that some of the code presented in this book could not be written better by a real programmer, but that was never the goal. If you want to learn programming, buy a book on programming techniques.

If you want to learn how to control hardware, using an easy to learn language like Visual Basic, buy this book, even if you have never programmed in Visual basic before.